STRUCTURE
AND PROPERTIES
OF
ORGANIC COMPOUNDS

A BRIEF SURVEY

CARL R. NOLLER

Robert

Professor of Chemistry, Stanford University

W. B. SAUNDERS COMPANY

Philadelphia, London   1962

547
N79t

PREFACE

Some knowledge of organic chemistry is necessary or desirable for many college and university students. Those who major in chemistry or who expect to become involved in essentially chemical research in one of the biological sciences cannot be trained too thoroughly in organic chemistry. Others, however, need only be conversant with the field. The requirements of the latter group usually are met by the short course, and it is for such courses that the present text is written.

The author of any text is faced with the problem of what to leave out. The shorter the text, the greater this problem becomes. Nevertheless, short courses should not be diluted courses. The purpose of such courses should not be to give the student a smattering of all phases of the subject; rather, they should provide him with material that is most likely to be useful to him in his occupation and that will be part of his reservoir of knowledge as an educated person.

With these objectives in mind, the emphasis in this text has been placed on bonding and structure, and on those physical and chemical properties of materials that the student is most apt to encounter in his daily experiences. What is the constitution of a substance? What is its source? What are the physical and chemical properties of a compound in terms of the ordinary contacts the student will have with it? These are the questions that this text tries to answer for premedical and predental students, for nurses, for majors in home economics and in agriculture, and for students of the various divisions of biology.

The usual listing of the numerous methods of synthesis and of the reactions of compounds have been omitted. Only those syntheses are given that are used in the production of common chemicals, and only those reactions that the student is likely to encounter as he uses individual compounds or makes qualitative or quantitative analyses for them.

Theory also is for the most part omitted. Considerable attention is given to bonding and to the attractive forces between molecules as they affect physical properties, but there is little discussion of mechanism. Where some explanation of a reaction seems desirable, an arbitrary statement may be made without elaboration. If the student asks the question "Why?", he can be referred to a larger text, such as the author's *Chemistry of Organic Compounds*.

The present book has been organized as a so-called "integrated text," because some time is saved by avoiding the division into aliphatic, aromatic, and heterocyclic chemistry. Moreover, in a short course, the discussion of compounds with functional groups is introduced soon enough to avoid boring the student (and the instructor) with the properties of hydrocarbons.

In the interest of saving space, equations frequently are omitted if the preparation of some compound involves a general reaction. Thus the statement "acetophenone and benzophenone can be made from benzene by the Friedel-Crafts reaction" is not followed by equations. The instructor may wish to ask his students for such equations as an exercise, or he may tell them to write equations for the reactions while they study the text. Likewise, the text has not been profusely illustrated. It is assumed that the student's daily exposure to the advertisements in current popular magazines will provide him with sufficient illustrations of manufacturing facilities and products.

Side headings within the text have been omitted, but the content and organization of the text are emphasized by marginal notations. The summary material at the end of each chapter usually is given in a form somewhat different from that in the text, with the object of encouraging the student to think about what he has read. A limited number of exercises is provided. Despite the small size of the book, sufficient material is provided to enable the instructor to choose that which fits his particular needs.

CARL R. NOLLER

Stanford University

CONTENTS

v

CHAPTER 1

INTRODUCTION

Organic chemistry is the chemistry of common things. Food, clothing, and fuels are composed of organic compounds. Protective coatings, plastics, dyes, and medicinals also belong to the realm of organic chemistry, whether they are produced by nature or by man. Some of these compounds are quite simple. For example the chief component of natural gas is methane, whose molecules are made up of one atom of carbon and four atoms of hydrogen. On the other hand each molecule of influenza virus contains millions of atoms. However, despite the large *number* of atoms in some molecules, there usually are only a few *kinds* of atoms present. Thus, although the molecules of a simple protein may contain thousands of atoms, the only kinds of atoms present are carbon, hydrogen, oxygen, and nitrogen. Other proteins may contain sulfur also, and the conjugated proteins may contain phosphorus or very small percentages of other elements such as iron, copper, zinc, cobalt, or magnesium. Likewise molecules of other organic compounds may contain almost any element, but most organic compounds contain only carbon and one or more of the elements hydrogen, oxygen, and nitrogen.

Scope of organic chemistry

It should be noted that the one element all organic compounds contain is carbon, and organic chemistry could be called more exactly the *chemistry of the compounds of carbon*. The designation *organic* originally was given to this branch of chemistry because compounds that have the properties now associated with carbon compounds were isolated from materials of biological origin, whereas compounds isolated from nonliving matter had different properties and were called *inorganic*. As chemical knowledge increased, it became recognized that compounds containing carbon could be made by other than biological processes, but the term *organic chemistry* has persisted.

Definition

The organic chemist is concerned with the physical and chemical properties of organic compounds and with reactions by which organic compounds can be made. Organic materials, as they occur in nature, usually are complex mixtures of different kinds of organic compounds which in themselves may be of varying degrees of complexity. One of the tasks of the organic chemist is the separation of these mixtures into their components and the purification of the individual substances until they contain essentially molecules of only one kind. Next the pure compounds are analyzed to determine what elements are present and to determine their rela-

Purification and analysis of compounds

tive amounts. From these results and from the atomic weights of the elements, it is possible to calculate the relative number of the different kinds of atoms in the molecule, which is expressed by the **empirical formula.** For example, in formaldehyde the atomic ratio of carbon to hydrogen to oxygen is $1:2:1$, which is expressed by the empirical formula, CH_2O. However, analysis of acetic acid also indicates an empirical formula, CH_2O, as does analysis of glucose, a sugar. Determinations of the relative molecular weights by the vapor density method, elevation of the boiling point or lowering of the freezing point, show that, although the gram molecular weight[1] of formaldehyde is 30 and hence corresponds to CH_2O, that of acetic acid is 60, corresponding to $C_2H_4O_2$, and that of glucose is 180, corresponding to $C_6H_{12}O_6$.[2] The latter formulas, which indicate not merely the ratio of the atoms but also the actual number of atoms in the molecule, are called **molecular formulas.**

Necessity for molecular weight determinations

Usually even the determination of the molecular formula of an organic compound is not sufficient to characterize it uniquely, because several different compounds may have the same molecular formula. Thus ethyl alcohol and methyl ether both have the molecular formula, C_4H_6O. One is a gas, b.p. $-24°$, and the other a liquid, b.p. $78°$. They differ in the *order* in which the atoms are linked together. In ethyl alcohol, one carbon atom is bonded to three hydrogens and the second carbon; the second carbon is bonded to the first carbon, to two hydrogen atoms, and to oxygen; and the oxygen is bonded to the second carbon and one hydrogen. In methyl ether, oxygen is bonded to the two carbon atoms, and each carbon atom is bonded to the oxygen and to three hydrogens. The order of linkage of atoms in a molecule is called the *structure* of the molecule and is represented by **structural formulas** such as those given in I and II. Hence, after the molecular

Determination of structure

Ethyl alcohol   Methyl ether
I   II

formula of a new compound is known, its structure must be determined. Usually the structure is established by carrying out reactions that break a molecule down into smaller fragments in the hope that products of known structure will be obtained. Identification of these products may enable one, with the aid of the rules of valence or bonding and a knowledge of the types of reaction that can occur, to postulate a structure that could have yielded the derived molecules.

Synthesis

Finally the organic chemist must synthesize the compound for which a structure has been postulated. By *synthesis* is meant the building of the molecule from smaller molecules of known structure by reactions known to produce the desired types of linkage or bonds and the order of arrangement of the atoms in the proposed structure. If the product synthesized has

---

[1] Hereafter the term *molecular weight* always will mean the *gram molecular weight*.

[2] Students who do not recall the procedures for arriving at empirical and molecular formulas should review this portion of their course in general chemistry.

all of the properties of the original compound, the chemist is reasonably sure that the postulated structure is correct. In addition to its use in proof of structure, synthesis may be of importance as a means of producing a valuable compound, such as a vitamin or a hormone, more readily than it can be isolated from a natural source. Of still more importance is the synthesis of many compounds that do not occur in nature, such as medicinals, or dyes, or intermediates for the production of plastics.

The isolation of organic compounds, the determination of their structure, and their synthesis are of concern primarily to the organic chemist or to those intending to undertake research in borderline fields of organic chemistry such as medicine, physiology, biology, and agriculture. On the other hand, those who do not intend to do research in these fields, and others who come in contact with organic compounds in their work or everyday life, will be interested chiefly in the nature of organic compounds and in their physical and chemical properties. They will want to know whether different organic compounds are related to each other, and in what way; to be able to predict from the structure of an organic compound whether one would expect it to be a gas, liquid, or solid, whether soluble or insoluble in water or in an organic liquid such as a cleaning fluid, whether flammable or nonflammable, whether tough and flexible or hard and brittle, whether colored or colorless. It is these aspects of organic chemistry with which this book primarily is concerned.

Emphasis different for different students

SUMMARY

1. Organic compounds all contain carbon.
2. The number of atoms in an organic molecule may be only a few or very many; that is, gram molecular weights may range from 16 to several million.
3. The number of kinds of atoms in a molecule usually is small. Besides carbon, the elements most frequently present are hydrogen, oxygen, and nitrogen, although any other elements of the periodic table may be present.
4. Frequently different organic compounds have the same elements present in the same proportions but differ in the total number of atoms in the molecule. Hence the determination of molecular weights is more important in organic chemistry than in inorganic chemistry.
5. Formulas that express only the kinds and relative numbers of atoms in the molecule, e.g., CH_2O, are called empirical formulas; those that express also the total number of atoms present, e.g., $C_2H_4O_2$, or $C_6H_{12}O_6$, are called molecular formulas.
6. Several organic compounds may have the same molecular formula but differ in the order of attachment of the atoms. This order of attachment is called the structure of the molecule and is represented by structural formulas.
7. Organic chemistry is concerned with the isolation and purification of organic compounds, with the determination of their molecular formulas and structure, and with their synthesis.

EXERCISES

1. For each of the compounds having the following empirical formulas, the approximate molecular weight is given. What is the molecular formula of each compound? (a) C_3H_4N, 100; (b) C_2HNO_2, 220; (c) CHBr, 435; (d) C_4H_8N, 285; (e) C_3H_9As, 124.

2. Calculate the percentage of each of the elements in compounds having the following molecular formulas: (a) C_5H_{12}; (b) C_3H_8O; (c) $C_2H_3ClO_2$; (d) C_2H_5NO; (e) C_2H_5ClHg; (f) C_2H_5I; (g) $C_2H_6O_2S$; (h) C_3H_9P; (i) CBr_4; (j) CH_3Cl_3Si.

3. What is the minimum molecular weight of a compound that contains (a) 59.2 per cent chlorine; (b) 35.6 per cent sulfur; (c) 11.6 per cent nitrogen; (d) 9.9 per cent iodine?

4. What is the volume at standard temperature and pressure (S.T.P. = 0°C and 760 mm. Hg) of (a) 16 g. of methane, CH_4; (b) 3 g. of methane, CH_4; (c) 8 g. of methyl ether, C_2H_6O; (d) 5 g. of methylamine, CH_5N?

CHAPTER 2

VALENCE AND STRUCTURE IN CHEMISTRY

It was stated in Chapter 1 that organic compóunds first were differentiated from inorganic compounds because of differences in their origin and in their physical and chemical properties. No rigid differentiation may be made on these bases, and, as has been stated, a better differentiation is whether or not a compound contains carbon. Even so, a few carbon compounds, such as the oxides of carbon and the carbonates, ordinarily are classed with the inorganic group. Nevertheless most organic compounds melt at temperatures below 300°, whereas salts, the chief class of inorganic compounds, ordinarily do not melt until temperatures above 1000° are reached. Usually an organic compound dissolves in several organic liquids, whereas inorganic compounds usually are insoluble in organic liquids. Molten salts and aqueous solutions of salts conduct an electric current, but organic liquids and aqueous solutions of most organic compounds do not. Finally, the reactions between different organic compounds usually are slow and frequently do not go to completion, whereas inorganic reactions commonly take place so rapidly that it is difficult to measure the rate of the reaction.

Organic and inorganic compounds

The cause of these differences lies in the differences in the origin of the forces holding the atoms together, which in turn may be explained by the electron theory of valence. All matter is composed of positive, negative, and neutral particles, and all forces are electrical. Positively charged particles repel each other, as do negative particles; but particles with unlike charges attract each other. Chemistry usually is concerned only with the positively charged nuclei of atoms and with the negatively charged electrons that surround them. The hydrogen atom, with a nuclear charge of $+1$, has one negative electron about the nucleus; helium, with a charge of $+2$, has two negative electrons; and lithium, with a charge of $+3$, has three electrons. The electrons are not distributed randomly about the nucleus but are to be found in predictable regions of space known as *orbitals*.

Electrical nature of matter

Orbitals are divided into shells and subshells, which successively are farther and farther away from the nucleus. Thus the first shell, or K shell, is closest to the nucleus and consists of only one orbital, called the $1s$ orbital.

Electron shells and subshells

The second, or L shell, has four orbitals, which are divided into two subshells. The first subshell consists of the $2s$ orbital; the other of three $2p$ orbitals. The third, or M shell, has nine orbitals, which are divided among three subshells. One $3s$ orbital constitutes the first subshell, three $3p$ orbitals constitute the second subshell, and five $3d$ orbitals make up the third subshell. All of the orbitals of any one subshell are of the same energy state; that is, an electron has the same tendency to occupy any one of the orbitals in a given subshell as any other. Each orbital may contain a maximum of two electrons, provided they are spinning in opposite directions. The fact that each orbital may contain only two electrons is called the *Pauli exclusion principle*.

Negative electrons tend to approach the positive nucleus as closely as possible, and hence fill the lower orbitals first. Atoms that have all of their electrons as close as possible to the nucleus are in their most stable state, called the *ground state* of the atom. If an electron is in a higher orbital, that is, one farther from the nucleus than when in the ground state, the atom is said to be in an *excited state*, because energy is required to promote an electron from a lower orbital to a higher orbital.

Electronic structure of atoms

In Table 1, orbitals are represented by circles and electrons by dots within the circles. The electrons of hydrogen and helium are in the $1s$ orbital. Lithium has two electrons in the $1s$ orbital and one in the $2s$ orbital; beryllium two and two; boron two, two, and one; carbon two, two, one, and one; nitrogen two, two, one, one, and one. It will be noted that for carbon and nitrogen the electrons in the p orbitals are not paired but distribute themselves among the available orbitals. The reason is that the three p orbitals are all of equal energy; that is, an atom is equally stable with an electron in one p orbital as in another p orbital. Because electrons are negative charges of electricity, they repel each other, and if more than one electron is in the p level, the electrons tend to distribute themselves in different orbitals (*Hund rule*). The only reason electrons pair in a given orbital is that the atom is energetically more stable when its electrons are paired in a lower orbital (provided the electrons have opposite spin) than when the electrons are unpaired in higher orbitals which are farther away from the positive nucleus. Hence oxygen, with eight electrons, has two

Electrons occupy different orbitals if possible

TABLE 1.   GROUND STATES OF ATOMS OF THE FIRST TWO PERIODS

PERIOD	ATOM	ORBITAL				
		1s	2s	2p$_x$	2p$_y$	2p$_z$
First	H	⊙	○	○	○	○
Second	He	⊙	○	○	○	○
	Li	⊙	⊙	○	○	○
	Be	⊙	⊙	○	○	○
	B	⊙	⊙	⊙	○	○
	C	⊙	⊙	⊙	⊙	○
	N	⊙	⊙	⊙	⊙	⊙
	O	⊙	⊙	⊙	⊙	⊙
	F	⊙	⊙	⊙	⊙	⊙
	Ne	⊙	⊙	⊙	⊙	⊙

paired and two unpaired in the *p* orbitals; fluorine has three paired and one unpaired; neon has all electrons paired, and its second shell is completely filled.

The rare gas atoms all have filled shells and are very stable and unreactive, whereas atoms with incompletely filled shells are reactive. Thus the filling of shells leads to greater stability. It is this tendency to approach an energetically more stable state that leads to compound formation between atoms. The filling of shells may be accomplished in two ways. One way is by the *transfer of electrons* from one atom to another. Thus lithium can revert to the helium structure by loss of one electron, and fluorine can attain the neon structure by gaining one electron. Transfer of an electron from lithium to fluorine accomplishes both, and a large amount of energy is liberated with the formation of the salt, lithium fluoride. Similarly, transfer of an electron from a sodium atom to a chlorine atom gives sodium chloride, in which sodium has the neon structure and chlorine the argon structure. It will be remembered from courses in general chemistry that only electrons in the outermost shell are involved in bond formation because, with the exception of the transition elements, the inner shells are filled.

Compound formation by electron transfer

The atoms involved in these processes originally were electrically neutral; that is, the number of electrons equalled the number of positive charges on the nucleus. In the salts that are formed, the metallic atoms have lost an electron and become positively charged while the halogens have gained an electron and become negatively charged. These charged particles are called *ions,* and the attractive forces between ions of opposite charge are called **ionic bonds** (Fig. 1).

Transfer of electrons leads to ionic bonds

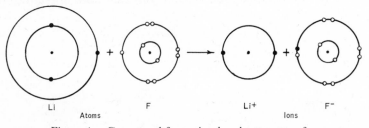

Figure 1.   Compound formation by electron transfer.

In these representations of electronic structures, the nucleus, because of its small size, is indicated by a dot at the center. Surrounding the nucleus are the electron shells, which are represented by large circles on which are superposed small dots or circles to indicate the electrons within the shells. The number of electrons is equal to the number of positive charges on the nuclei. The different symbols for electrons do not mean that electrons of one atom differ from those of another. They are used merely to help keep track of the total number of electrons and to indicate the original source of the electrons. Because their charges are distributed equally about the ions, oppositely charged particles attract each other equally in all directions. The result is a crystal lattice in which the arrangement is governed chiefly by the sizes of the ions and by the number of charges on them. In lithium fluoride and in sodium chloride, each metal ion is surrounded by

Representation of electronic structures

Ionic bonds lead
to crystal lattice

six halogen ions and each halogen ion by six metal ions giving a crystalline solid belonging to the cubic system. The attractive forces between the ions of unlike charge are so great that the compound must be heated to a high temperature before it melts. When the compound is in the molten state or in solution, the ions are free to move, and a current flows through the liquid if two electrodes are introduced and an electromotive force is applied. The negative ions migrate to the positive pole, where they are discharged by giving up an electron; while the positive ions move to the negative pole, where they are discharged by acquiring an electron. Thus electrolysis of molten sodium chloride gives metallic sodium at the cathode and gaseous chlorine at the anode.

Carbon has little
tendency to gain or
lose four electrons

As the center of the periodic table is approached, it becomes more and more difficult for the atoms to gain or lose a sufficient number of electrons to attain the rare gas structure. Beryllium must lose two electrons, but after one is lost the resulting positive charge holds the second electron more strongly. Oxygen must gain two electrons, but having gained one, the negative charge makes it more difficult to acquire a second electron. By the time carbon is reached, at the center of the table, it is practically impossible for it either to gain or lose four electrons.

Nevertheless it is known that even like atoms, for which the tendency to gain or lose electrons should be the same, undergo compound formation. For example the hydrogen molecule containing two atoms of hydrogen, and the halogen molecules containing two atoms of halogen, are more stable than the same elements in the atomic state. Obviously a method other than electron transfer can lead to compound formation. This method is the

Molecules formed
by atoms that share
electrons

sharing of electrons, in which each atom shares one of its electrons with the other atom, thereby filling the electron shells of both atoms and liberating energy

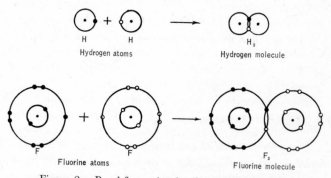

Figure 2.   Bond formation by sharing of electrons.

(Fig. 2). The water molecule is formed by the sharing of one electron from each of two hydrogen atoms with the two unpaired electrons of an oxygen atom; the ammonia molecule by the sharing of three electrons from three hydrogen atoms with the three unpaired electrons of a nitrogen atom (Fig. 3).

In the first way of completing electron shells, electron transfer, the particles are charged and the charge is distributed evenly over the whole particle, which attracts oppositely charged particles equally in all directions. In the second way the shared pair of negative electrons is relatively

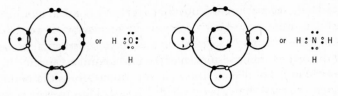

Figure 3.   Electronic representations of the water and the ammonia molecule.

localized between two positive nuclei and holds only these two nuclei together; that is, a true bond exists between the two atoms. The first type of bonding is called an **electrovalence,** or an **electrovalent** or **ionic bond;** the second is called a **covalence,** or covalent or **electron-pair bond.** Both types are electrostatic in nature, but in one the positively or negatively charged particles attract particles of opposite charge in all directions, whereas in the other a single pair of electrons attracts only two positive nuclei. In the first case, although the number of positive charges equals the number of negative charges, thus preserving the law of multiple proportions, no true molecules exist but only an ordered arrangement of ions that gives rise to crystals of indefinite size. Only empirical formulas can be given for such compounds. For example the formula NaCl does not represent a true molecule consisting of one sodium ion and one chlorine ion. The result of electron sharing, however, is a real molecule which is uncharged because each atom gives up as much negative charge as it receives. Hence, although the attractive forces or bonds between the atoms within the molecule are strong, there is relatively little attraction between the different molecules. For this reason most compounds containing only covalent bonds are gases, liquids, or low-melting solids. Moreover, since the molecules are uncharged, the liquids and molten solids do not conduct the electric current.

Covalence is a true bond

Covalent bonds give rise to true molecules

Other facts should be noted about molecules that have covalent bonds. Instead of being two dimensional or flat, as indicated in Figure 3, molecules occupy space. The oxygen and nitrogen atoms may be considered as spheres with the four pairs of electrons in the outer shells separated as far as possible from each other on the surface of the sphere, leading to an arrangement in which each pair is at the corner of a regular tetrahedron, as indicated in Figure 4a. Accordingly the bonds to other atoms make an angle of 109°28′ with each other, which is called the tetrahedral angle (Fig. 4b, c, d).

Molecules are three dimensional

This explanation of the spatial distribution of bonds is an oversimplification. Bond angles of 109°28′ exist only when atoms are tetracovalent and when all four groups attached to the central atom are alike, as in

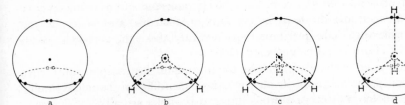

Figure 4.   Arrangement of bonds in polyatomic molecules.

Bond angles not rigid

methane, CH_4, or the ammonium ion, $[NH_4]^+$. Bond angles are rather "soft," and mutual attraction or repulsion of nearby atoms or groups within the molecule may cause an expansion or contraction of the bond angles with corresponding distortion of the tetrahedral arrangement. Moreover if an atom is bonded to less than four other atoms the bond angles may be greater or less than the tetrahedral angle. Thus the size of the bond angles in benzene is 120°, and the measured bond angles of the water molecule and the ammonia molecule are 105° and 107° respectively.

Representations of molecules

Molecules are represented by spatial or extended structures only if there is some special reason for doing so. Usually some condensed symbolism is used, as in Figure 5.

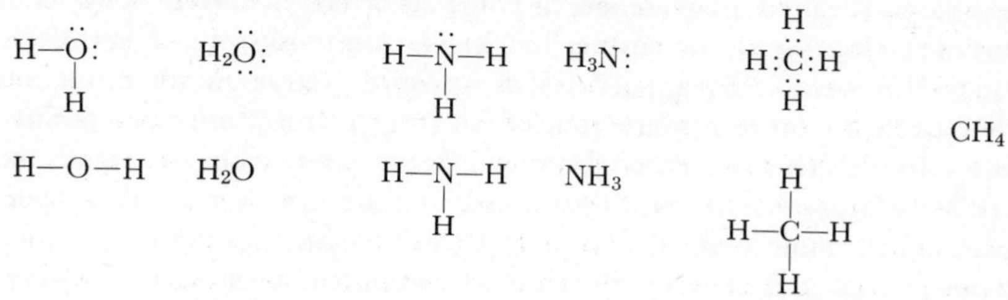

Figure. 5. Various representations of covalent molecules.

Ordinarily the electron-pair bond is indicated by a long dash joining the symbols involved. Even the bonds may be omitted where the structure is obvious. It is important to remember that tricovalent nitrogen and dicovalent oxygen always have one and two unshared pairs of electrons in the valence shell, even though they may be omitted from formulas containing nitrogen or oxygen. They play an important part in determining the physical and chemical properties of oxygen and nitrogen compounds. Electrovalent bonding may be left unexpressed, as in the formula NaCl, or indicated by superscript charges, as in Na^+Cl^-.

Hybrid orbitals

Thus far little has been said about carbon. In the ground state, the carbon atom has two paired electrons in the $2s$ orbital and two unpaired electrons in two $2p$ orbitals. However, instead of bonding with only two hydrogen atoms, it bonds with four to give methane, CH_4. The reason for this is that, by making use of the electrons in the $2s$ orbital as well as those in the p orbitals, all four orbitals are filled, giving rise to a closed shell; whereas, if only two electrons were shared, one orbital would remain empty. The energy evolved on bond formation is more than sufficient to promote the four valence electrons into four equivalent *hybrid orbitals*, permitting each electron to pair with that of a hydrogen atom. Hence the CH_4 molecule is more stable, that is, the total energy is less, than a $:CH_2$ molecule and two hydrogen atoms or even than a $:CH_2$ molecule and a hydrogen molecule. In methane the four shared pairs of electrons, and hence the four hydrogen nuclei, are distributed tetrahedrally about the carbon atom, the H—C—H angles all being exactly 109°28′.

Polarized bonds

Although all bonds formed by the sharing of electrons are called covalent bonds, the degree of covalence varies depending on the relative ability of the nuclei to attract electrons. If the two nuclei are alike, as is true for the hydrogen or chlorine molecule, the mean position of the bonding pair is of necessity half way between the two nuclei. If the two nuclei are different, the mean position may be closer to one or the other nucleus. Consider, for example, the hydride of carbon, CH_4, of nitrogen, NH_3, of oxygen, H_2O, and of fluorine, HF. The positive charge on the nucleus of carbon, nitrogen, oxygen, and fluorine is 6, 7, 8, and 9, respectively. With increasing charge on the nucleus the $1s$ shell of electrons is pulled closer and closer to the nucleus; but, if the $1s$ shell is closer, the $2s$ shell will approach more closely, and so on for succeeding shells. In the carbon-hydrogen bond, the effect of the greater nuclear charge of carbon is just about balanced by the fact that the $1s$ orbital of hydrogen is closer to the nucleus than the hybrid orbitals of carbon made up of one $2s$ orbital and three $2p$ orbitals (*sp³ hybrids*). The result is that the attraction of the carbon nucleus and of the hydrogen nucleus for the shared pair of electrons is just about equal. However, with increasing atomic number in the same row of the periodic table, the increasing nuclear charge prevails, pulling the shared pairs closer and closer to the larger nucleus and away from hydrogen. The result is that the hydrogen becomes somewhat positively charged with respect to the other element, and the bond is said to be *polarized*. The effect of this polarization is reflected in the increasing ease with which hydrogen is removed as a proton from the molecule, that is, by the increasing acidity in going from methane to ammonia to water to hydrogen fluoride. In the absence of electron-attracting groups on carbon, hydrogen attached to carbon is less readily removed as a proton, $[H^+]$, or as a hydride ion, $[H:^-]$, than when attached to any other element.

Increasing charge on nucleus pulls electrons closer

The unique position of carbon at the center of the second period accounts also for the fact that the number of its compounds is at least ten times that of all the compounds that do not contain carbon. In this position it is equally difficult either to lose or to gain electrons, and hence, after hydrogen, carbon is the element that forms the strongest covalent bond with itself. One measure of bond strength is the energy required to break a bond, that is, the change in energy for the following reaction.

Uniqueness of carbon

$$R:R' \rightarrow R\cdot + \cdot R'$$

The accompanying table lists the approximate **bond strengths** in kilocalories per mole for a number of bonds. These figures are only averages, the

APPROXIMATE BOND STRENGTHS OF SOME SINGLE BONDS

BOND	KCAL./MOLE	BOND	KCAL./MOLE	BOND	KCAL./MOLE
H—H	104	O—O	35	N—N	39
C—H	99	O—H	111	N—H	93
C—C	83	O—C	86	N—C	73

individual bond strength being affected by the nature of the rest of the molecule. However, they show why, although a maximum of three oxygen atoms can be united to each other in known compounds, and ten of nitrogen, carbon can be bonded with itself indefinitely. Moreover, being at the center of the row, it has four electrons to share, which give rise to four bonds to other elements tetrahedrally distributed about the carbon; hence highly branched

Carbon-carbon bonds are strong

Basic principles of
organic chemistry

and cyclic structures are possible. The principles that *carbon has a valence of four* and that *carbon atoms can combine with each other indefinitely* were promulgated by Kekulé, a German chemist (1829–1896), in the middle of the nineteenth century, long before the advent of the electronic theory of valence. They form the basis of the theory of structural organic chemistry.

SUMMARY

1. Compounds formed by the transfer of electrons from one element to another are said to contain electrovalent bonds, whereas those formed by the sharing of electrons between elements are said to contain covalent bonds.

2. Most inorganic compounds contain electrovalent bonds; most organic compounds contain only covalent bonds.

3. Electrovalent bonds cause a compound to be a solid that melts at a high temperature, is insoluble in organic liquids, and conducts the electric current when molten or in solution. Compounds having only covalent bonds usually are gases, liquids, or low-melting solids, are soluble in organic liquids, and are nonconducting in the liquid state or in solution.

4. The carbon atom normally is tetracovalent. When carbon is bonded to four other atoms, the bonds are directed to the corners of a regular or distorted tetrahedron, the carbon atom being at the center.

5. There are different degrees of electrovalence or covalence, varying from almost purely electrovalent to purely covalent. Bonds between like atoms, e.g., that in the hydrogen molecule or in the chlorine molecule, are purely covalent, and the carbon-hydrogen bond is practically so. On the other hand in the bonds of oxygen or nitrogen with hydrogen or carbon, the bonding pair of electrons is drawn closer to the oxygen or nitrogen nucleus than to the hydrogen or carbon nucleus, giving rise to a slight difference in charge between the bonded atoms.

6. Because of the high carbon-carbon bond strength, that is, the large amount of energy required to unpair the shared pair of electrons (so-called breaking of the bond), carbon atoms can bond with each other indefinitely to yield molecules that are stable at ordinary temperatures. Because the four bonds are tetrahedrally distributed, complicated spatial structures can exist.

EXERCISES

1. Using different symbols for the electrons to indicate their source, write electronic formulas for: (a) magnesium chloride (ionic bonds); (b) carbon tetrachloride, CCl_4 (covalent bonds); (c) hydrogen sulfide (covalent bonds); (d) ammonium chloride (covalent and ionic bonds).
2. Arrange the following groups in the order of increasing polarity of the bond between the two atoms: (a) H—F, C—H, O—H, N—H, C—C; (b) C—O, C—N, C—H, C—C, C—F.
3. Compounds are known that have the following molecular formulas: (a) CH_4O; (b) C_2H_6; (c) CH_5N; (d) CH_3Cl; (e) $SiCl_4$. Write a structural formula for each compound, using a dash to indicate a shared pair of electrons.

CHAPTER 3

SATURATED
HYDROCARBONS

The simplest organic compounds contain only hydrogen and carbon and are called *hydrocarbons.* Because they are simple and because they form the basis of systematic nomenclature, it is desirable to consider them first. Hydrocarbons may be divided according to the following classification.

A. Saturated Hydrocarbons. Those having the maximum number of hydrogen atoms for a particular carbon skeleton.

1. ALKANES OR PARAFFINS. Acyclic or open chain compounds, i.e., those in which carbon atoms are linked consecutively or branched from each other.

2. CYCLANES, CYCLOPARAFFINS, NAPHTHENES OR HYDROAROMATICS. Compounds in which the carbon atoms are joined to form a closed ring.

B. Unsaturated Hydrocarbons. Those having less than the maximum number of hydrogens for a particular carbon skeleton.

1. ALKENES OR OLEFINS. Acyclic compounds having two fewer hydrogen atoms than the corresponding alkanes (one double bond).

2. CYCLENES. Cyclic compounds having two fewer hydrogen atoms than the corresponding cyclanes (one double bond).

3. DIENES. Acyclic or cyclic compounds having two double bonds.

4. ALKYNES OR ACETYLENES. Acyclic compounds having four fewer hydrogen atoms than the alkanes (one triple bond).

C. Aromatic Hydrocarbons. Cyclic compounds having at least six fewer hydrogen atoms than cyclanes (a special type of unsaturation).

Classification of hydro-carbons into saturated, unsaturated and aromatic

ALKANES

Methane, the chief component of natural gas, which comes from wells driven into natural reservoirs in the earth's crust, has the molecular formula CH_4. It boils at $-161°$. Its structure has been discussed on p. 10. A second gas, usually present in natural gas in smaller amounts, is **ethane,** b.p. $-89°$. It has the molecular formula C_2H_6. Because hydrogen has only one electron to share, it can combine with only one other element and hence cannot act as a link between the two carbon atoms. Therefore the two carbon atoms in ethane must be bonded to each other, leaving three un-

Structural formulas show order of attach-ment of atoms

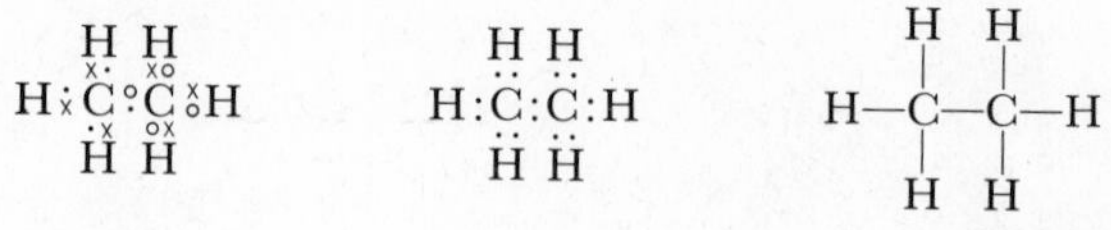

$$
\begin{array}{ccc}
\text{H H} & \text{H H} & \text{H H} \\
\text{H} \overset{\text{x}}{\times} \text{C} \overset{\text{xo}}{\circ} \text{C} \overset{\text{x}}{\times} \text{H} & \text{H:C:C:H} & \text{H—C—C—H} \\
\text{H H} & \text{H H} & \text{H H} \\
(a) & (b) & (c)
\end{array}
$$

Figure 6. Representations of the structure of ethane.

paired electrons on each carbon atom. These six electrons are able to pair with the electrons of six hydrogen atoms, thus accounting for the molecular formula. The structure of ethane may be written electronically, as in Figure 6a, which uses different marks to indicate the source of the electrons, or as in b, where no differentiation is made because all electrons are identical. The former procedure frequently is useful in writing electronic structures for more complicated molecules in order to keep track of the total number of electrons. Usually it is simplest to use the long dash for a shared electron pair, as in c.

Molecular models show spatial arrangement of atoms

Spatial arrangements can be shown more clearly by ball and stick models, as in Figure 7. Models constructed so as to give the proper inter-

Methane   Ethane

Figure 7. Ball and stick molecular models.

atomic distances and distances of closest approach between molecules are shown in Figure 8 and are known as Stuart, Fisher-Hirschfelder, or Briegleb models.

Methane   Ethane

Figure 8. Stuart, Fischer-Hirschfelder, or Briegleb models.

A third hydrocarbon in natural gas is **propane,** C_3H_8, which boils at $-42°$. Here three carbon atoms are joined to each other, leaving eight electrons for bonding to hydrogen and giving rise to the structural formula

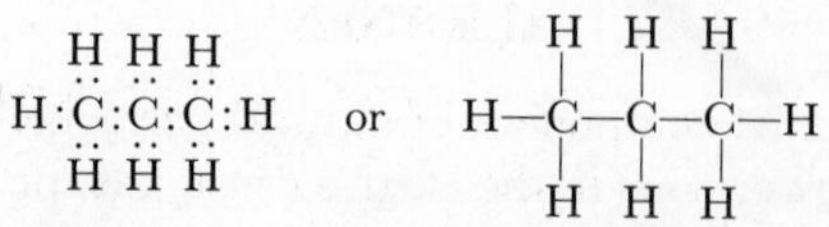

$$
\begin{array}{ccc}
\text{H H H} & & \text{H H H} \\
\text{H:C:C:C:H} & \text{or} & \text{H—C—C—C—H} \\
\text{H H H} & & \text{H H H}
\end{array}
$$

It should be remembered at all times that these molecules are not planar as they appear to be in the usual representations on the printed page or chalk board, but that the four bonds to any carbon atom always are tetrahedrally distributed. Hence the following formulas for propane become identical in the space model, and only one propane is known.

$$\begin{array}{cccc}
\text{H} & \text{CH}_3 & \text{H} & \text{CH}_3 \\
| & | & | & | \\
\text{H}_3\text{C}-\text{C}-\text{CH}_3 & \text{H}_3\text{C}-\text{C}-\text{H} & \text{H}-\text{C}-\text{CH}_3 & \text{H}-\text{C}-\text{H} \\
| & | & | & | \\
\text{H} & \text{H} & \text{CH}_3 & \text{CH}_3
\end{array}$$

It can be seen that the alkanes belong to a family of compounds having the general formula C_nH_{2n+2} in which each member contains one more carbon atom and two more hydrogen atoms than its predecessor. Any such family of compounds is known as a **homologous series,** and the members of the series are called **homologs** (Gr. *homos,* same, and *logos,* speech; that is, related or similar). Obviously the next member of the alkanes should have the molecular formula C_4H_{10}. Actually *two compounds having this same molecular formula are known.* Both occur in natural gas or are dissolved in petroleum; one boils at $-0.5°$ and the other at $-12°$. Structural theory can explain the two compounds, because the carbon atoms may be linked consecutively as shown below in *a*, or one carbon may branch from the middle of a three-carbon chain as in *b*. Because the atoms are arranged

Homologs and homologous series

$$\begin{array}{cc}
\begin{array}{cccc}
\text{H} & \text{H} & \text{H} & \text{H} \\
| & | & | & | \\
\text{H}-\text{C}-\text{C}-\text{C}-\text{C}-\text{H} \\
| & | & | & | \\
\text{H} & \text{H} & \text{H} & \text{H}
\end{array}
&
\begin{array}{ccc}
\text{H} & \text{H} & \text{H} \\
| & | & | \\
\text{H}-\text{C}-\text{C}-\text{C}-\text{H} \\
| & | & | \\
\text{H} & | & \text{H} \\
 & \text{H}-\text{C}-\text{H} \\
 & | \\
 & \text{H}
\end{array}
\\
(a) & (b)
\end{array}$$

differently in the two molecules it is not surprising that they have different chemical and physical properties. Compounds that have the same molecular formula but differ in properties were called **isomers** (Gr. *isos,* equal, and *meros,* part) by the Swedish chemist, Berzelius (1779–1848), and the phenomenon is known as **isomerism.** Several types of isomerism are known. The type exhibited here, which depends on the order of attachment of the atoms, is known as **structural isomerism.**

Isomers and isomerism

The four-carbon hydrocarbons are called **butanes.** To distinguish between them, the one with four carbon atoms in a chain is called **normal butane** or **n-butane,** and the one with a branched chain is **isobutane** or *i*-butane. The former has the higher boiling point. Beginning with alkanes having five carbon atoms, systematic names are used in which a Greek or Latin prefix, indicating the number of carbon atoms in the molecule, is attached to the ending *ane* to denote a member of the alkane family.

Names for higher hydrocarbons

C_5	pentanes	C_{16}–C_{19}	etc.
C_6	hexanes	C_{20}	eicosanes
C_7	heptanes	C_{21}	heneicosanes
C_8	octanes	C_{22}	docosanes
C_9	nonanes	C_{23}	tricosanes
C_{10}	decanes	C_{24}–C_{29}	etc.
C_{11}	undecanes	C_{30}	triacontanes
C_{12}	dodecanes	C_{31}	hentriacontanes
C_{13}	tridecanes	C_{32}–C_{39}	etc.
C_{14}	tetradecanes	C_{40}	tetracontanes
C_{15}	pentadecanes		etc.

Three pentanes would be expected, because three arrangements of the carbon atoms, called *carbon skeletons,* are possible.

$$C—C—C—C—C \qquad\qquad \begin{matrix} C—C—C—C \\ | \\ C \end{matrix} \qquad\qquad \begin{matrix} C \\ | \\ C—C—C \\ | \\ C \end{matrix}$$

They give rise to three alkanes.

$$\begin{matrix} H & H & H & H & H \\ | & | & | & | & | \\ H—C—C—C—C—C—H \\ | & | & | & | & | \\ H & H & H & H & H \end{matrix}$$

$$\begin{matrix} H & H & & H & & H \\ | & | & & | & & | \\ H—C—C—&—C—&—C—H \\ | & | & H—C—H & | \\ H & H & | & H \\ & & H \end{matrix}$$

$$\begin{matrix} & & H \\ & & | \\ & H & H—C—H & H \\ & | & | & | \\ H—C—&—C—&—C—H \\ & | & | & | \\ & H & H—C—H & H \\ & & | \\ & & H \end{matrix}$$

n-Pentane   *i*-Pentane   Neopentane

Actually three and only three compounds having the molecular formula C_5H_{12} are known. The compound to which the first structure has been assigned boils at 36° and is called **normal pentane;** that having the second structure boils at 28° and is called **isopentane;** and that having the third structure boils at 9.5° and is called **neopentane** (Gr. *neos,* new).

The above formulas are known as *extended structural formulas.* In order to
Condensed structural formulas   conserve space and time in writing, they usually are replaced by *condensed structural formulas,* for example, $CH_3(CH_2)_3CH_3$, $CH_3CH_2CH(CH_3)_2$ or $C_2H_5CH(CH_3)_2$, and $C(CH_3)_4$.

For compounds of more than three carbon atoms, the tetrahedral distribution of the valences might be thought capable of giving isomeric compounds even for normal hydrocarbons. A five-carbon chain might be expected to exist in numerous conformations. In the examples illustrated in Figure 9, only the carbon skeleton is indicated. Actually no isomers corresponding to these different arrangements have been detected. It is believed

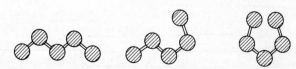

Figure 9.   Some possible conformations of a five-carbon chain.

Rotation about single bonds limits number of isomers.   that all of the above arrangements and an infinite number of others exist in gases and liquids, but that, because of essentially free rotation about a single bond, the various forms interconvert rapidly at room temperature.

Five structurally isomeric hexanes are expected, and only five are known. As the number of carbon atoms increases, the number of structural isomers possible soon reaches astronomical proportions as shown by the following figures which were arrived at by rather complicated mathematical formulas.

C_7 —9	C_{15}—4347
C_8 —18	C_{20}—366,319
C_9 —35	C_{30}—4,111,846,763
C_{10}—75	C_{40}—6.25 × 10^{13}

Obviously each organic compound must have a name. The development of nomenclature in organic chemistry always has followed the same pattern. When only a few compounds of a particular type are known and before their structures have been determined, they are given names usually indicative of their source. These names are called *common* names. As more compounds of a series become known, an attempt is made to develop a more systematic nomenclature which shows the relation of the new compounds to the older ones. Finally an attempt is made to develop a truly rational system. In the meantime, however, the older names have become established, and it is difficult to replace them by new ones, with the result that the simpler compounds usually have two or three names. Because all of these names are in more or less general use, it is necessary to become familiar with them and to be able to use them interchangeably. *Common names*

When a second butane was found it was called *isobutane,* and the third pentane became *neopentane,* but new prefixes, if coined indefinitely, would become difficult to remember. The term *iso* still is retained for all compounds having a single carbon atom branch at the end of a straight chain. Thus isohexane is $(CH_3)_2CH(CH_2)_2CH_3$ and isononane is $(CH_3)_2CH(CH_2)_5CH_3$. The term *neo* is used in this series only for neopentane and neohexane.

The necessity for devising a system that could be used for a larger number of isomers led to naming compounds as derivatives of a simple compound. Thus any alkane can be considered as derived from methane by replacing the hydrogen atoms by other groups of atoms. In isobutane three hydrogens of methane have been replaced by three CH_3 groups, and in isopentane by two CH_3 groups and one C_2H_5 group. In neopentane four hydrogens have been replaced by four CH_3 groups. If these groups are given names, the compounds can be named as derivatives of methane. The groups themselves are hydrocarbons less one hydrogen atom and are called *alkyl* groups. They are named by dropping the *ane* of the alkane having the same number of carbon atoms and adding *yl*. CH_3 is *methyl* and C_2H_5 is *ethyl*. Isobutane then becomes trimethylmethane, isopentane becomes dimethylethylmethane, and neopentane is tetramethylmethane. The prefix always is attached directly to the name to give one word. *As derivatives of methane*

Names for alkyl groups

It is customary to make use also of groups containing three and four carbon atoms in order to name more complicated compounds. Because there are *two kinds of hydrogen*[1] in propane, there are two propyl groups, $CH_3CH_2CH_2-$ and $CH_3\overset{|}{C}HCH_3$. In order to indicate more clearly the carbon atom which lacks a hydrogen atom, it is customary to attach a long dash. In a molecule the group must be bonded to some other atom or group of atoms at this point. To distinguish between the two propyl groups by name, they are called *normal propyl* or *n-propyl,* and *isopropyl* or *i-propyl,* respectively. Two groups each can be derived from *n*-butane and isobutane.

---

[1] This expression arises from the fact that the properties of an atom in a molecule depend not only on the atom itself but also on the atom or atoms to which it is bonded. Thus it is possible to distinguish a hydrogen atom bonded to carbon from one bonded to oxygen or nitrogen. Likewise a hydrogen atom bonded to a carbon atom that in turn is joined to one carbon atom and two other hydrogen atoms is different from a hydrogen atom bonded to a carbon atom joined to two carbon atoms and one other hydrogen atom.

Primary, secondary, and
tertiary carbon atoms

n-Butane gives rise to the *n-butyl* group, $CH_3(CH_2)_2CH_2$—, and a group, $CH_3CH_2CHCH_3$, which is called *secondary butyl* or *s-butyl* because the carbon atom which lacks a hydrogen atom is united directly to two other carbon atoms. Such a carbon atom is known as a *secondary carbon atom.* Isobutane gives rise to the *isobutyl* or *i-butyl* group, $(CH_3)_2CHCH_2$—, and to the group $(CH_3)_3C$—. The latter is known as *tertiary butyl* or *t-butyl,* because the carbon atom lacking a hydrogen atom is a *tertiary carbon atom;* that is, it is united to three other carbon atoms. These eight groups form the basis for the systematic naming of a large number of compounds. Their names and their structures must be memorized. Once this has been done, the nomenclature of most organic compounds is remarkably simple. For convenience these groups and their names are collected in Table 2.

Most highly branched
carbon is starting point

It is customary to name only branched alkanes as derivatives of methane. In general the most highly branched carbon atom is considered to be the methane carbon, unless a less highly branched atom permits naming

TABLE 2.   ALKYL GROUPS CONTAINING UP TO FOUR CARBON ATOMS

STRUCTURE OF GROUP	COMMON NAME	GENEVA NAME*
CH_3—	methyl	methyl
CH_3CH_2— or C_2H_5—	ethyl	ethyl
$CH_3CH_2CH_2$—	*n*-propyl	propyl
CH_3CHCH_3, $\begin{array}{c}CH_3\\[-2pt]\diagdown\\ CH_3\end{array}CH$—, or $(CH_3)_2CH$—	*i*-propyl	(methylethyl)
$CH_3CH_2CH_2CH_2$—	*n*-butyl	butyl
$CH_3CH_2CHCH_3$, CH_3CH_2CH—, $\quad\quad\quad CH_3$ or C_2H_5CH— $\quad\quad CH_3$	*s*-butyl	(1-methylpropyl)
CH_3CHCH_2— or CH_3 $(CH_3)_2CHCH_2$—	*i*-butyl	(2-methylpropyl)
CH_3 CH_3C— or $(CH_3)_3C$— CH_3	*t*-butyl	(dimethylethyl)

* All isoalkyl names and also *s*-butyl, *t*-butyl, and neopentyl may be used as alternates for the systematic names of alkyl groups.

a smaller group. Thus compound (a) would be called trimethyl-*i*-propyl-methane rather than dimethyl-*t*-butylmethane. On the other hand com-

$$
\begin{array}{cc}
\underset{|}{\overset{\displaystyle CH_3}{}} & \underset{|}{\overset{\displaystyle CH_3}{}} \\
CH_3-CH-C-CH_3 & CH_3-CH-C-CH_3 \\
\underset{\displaystyle CH_3\ \ CH_3}{|\ \ \ |} & \underset{\displaystyle CH_3-CH\ \ \ CH_3}{|} \\
 & \underset{\displaystyle CH_3}{|}
\end{array}
$$

(a)   (b)

pound (b) could be named methyl-*i*-propyl-*t*-butylmethane if the less highly branched carbon atom were considered to be the methane carbon atom but would require a name for a five-carbon group if the more highly branched carbon atom were chosen to represent methane.

The system which names compounds as derivatives of methane has the disadvantage that the eight groups given in Table 2 still are not suffi-cient for naming the more complicated compounds. This disadvantage is overcome to a considerable extent in the system adopted by the Interna-tional Congress held at Geneva, Switzerland, in 1892, which has come to be known as the *Geneva system*. This system, as extended by the meeting of the International Union of Chemistry at Liège in 1930 and of the Inter-national Union of Pure and Applied Chemistry at Amsterdam in 1949 and subsequently, attempts to cover all the more important phases of the nomenclature of organic chemistry. A summary of the rules for alkanes follows.

Geneva system (I.U.C. or I.U.P.A.C. system)

(*1*) The ending for alkanes is *ane*.

(*2*) The common names for the normal (straight-chain) hydrocarbons are used.

(*3*) Branched-chain hydrocarbons are regarded as derivatives of nor-mal hydrocarbons, the longest normal chain in the molecule being consid-ered as the parent hydrocarbon. If there are two or more chains of equal length, that chain is selected which has the most branches, that is, the one which is the most highly substituted.

Uses longest chain as starting point

(*4*) The carbon atoms of the parent hydrocarbon are numbered from the end that gives the branched atoms the smaller numbers.

(*5*) The names of the branches or side chains are attached as prefixes directly to the parent name. Their position is indicated by the number of the atom to which they are attached. If two branches are on the same car-bon atom, the number is repeated. The numbers precede the groups and are separated from the groups by hyphens. Consecutive numbers are sepa-rated from each other by commas.

(*6*) Alkyl groups containing more than four carbon atoms are named in the same way as the alkanes except that the ending is *yl*, and the point of attachment is numbered 1. The full name of the group is enclosed in parentheses (cf. Table 2).

These rules and the other methods of nomenclature are illustrated in Table 3 by the names for the five isomeric hexanes and for a still more com-plicated compound. The advantages of naming compounds as derivatives of parent hydrocarbons are that it is easy to assign a name to every com-

Formulas can be written from names

TABLE 3.   NOMENCLATURE OF ALKANES

STRUCTURE	COMMON NAME	AS A DERIVATIVE OF METHANE	BY GENEVA SYSTEM
$CH_3(CH_2)_4CH_3$	normal hexane	not used	hexane

$CH_3CH(CH_2)_2CH_3$
     $\vert$
    CH_3
	isohexane	dimethyl-n-propylmethane	2-methylpentane

$CH_3CH_2CHCH_2CH_3$
         $\vert$
        CH_3
	none	methyldiethylmethane	3-methylpentane

$CH_3CH—CHCH_3$
     $\vert$ $\vert$
    CH_3 CH_3
	(diisopropyl*)	dimethyl-i-propylmethane	2,3-dimethylbutane

CH_3
        $\vert$
 $CH_3—C—CH_2CH_3$
        $\vert$
       CH_3
	neohexane	trimethylethylmethane	2,2-dimethylbutane

$\overset{9}{C}H_3(CH_2)_3\overset{5}{C}H(CH_2)_3CH_3$
   $CH_3—\overset{4}{C}H$
        $\vert$
     $\overset{3}{C}H_2—\overset{2}{C}H\overset{1}{C}H_3$
          $\vert$
        CH_3
	none	not possible using the first eight groups	2,4-dimethyl-5-butylnonane

    * Occasionally a hydrocarbon is given a common name which indicates that it may be divided into two like groups.

pound and to write the formula from the name. Thus the structure for 2,2,5-trimethyl-3-ethylhexane is written by joining six carbon atoms in a row, numbering them from 1 to 6, attaching three methyl groups and an ethyl group at the proper positions, and satisfying the remaining valences of the carbon atoms with hydrogen atoms.

Formula may be checked against name

    A useful check on the correctness of a one-word name is that the sum of the carbon atoms in the various groups and in the parent hydrocarbon must equal the total number of carbon atoms in the molecule. In the last example of Table 3 each methyl group has one carbon atom, the butyl group has four, and the parent name nine, making a total of fifteen carbon atoms. This number checks with the number of carbon atoms in the formula. It should be noted also in this example that there are two different nine-carbon chains, but that by choosing the most highly substituted chain the necessity for naming a complicated six-carbon group is avoided. If it had been necessary to name this group, it would have been called the (1,3-dimethylbutyl) group. The parentheses are necessary to prevent confusion concerning the portion of the molecule to which the numbers refer. The compound

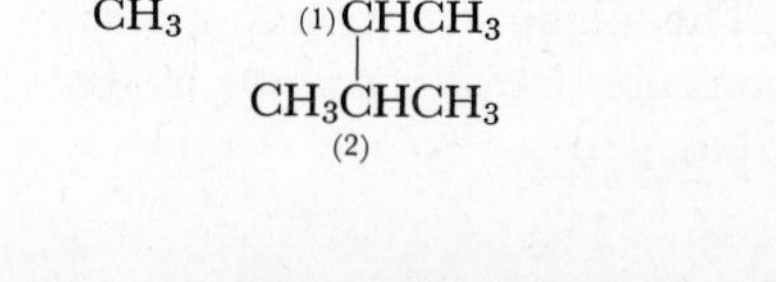

$$\overset{1}{C}H_3\overset{2}{C}H\overset{3}{C}H_2\overset{4}{C}H_2\overset{5}{C}H\overset{6}{C}H_2\overset{7}{C}H_2\overset{8}{C}H_2\overset{9}{C}H_3$$
$$\vert\qquad\qquad\qquad\vert$$
$$CH_3\qquad\quad {(1)}CHCH_3$$
$$\vert$$
$$CH_3CHCH_3$$
$$(2)$$

for example, would be called 2-methyl-5-(1,2-dimethylpropyl)nonane. The first five compounds in Table 3 are all hexanes because they have six carbon atoms, regardless of the fact that they are named as derivatives of methane, butane, and pentane. The last compound of the list is a pentadecane, even though it is named as a derivative of nonane.

In the naming of compounds as derivatives of another compound, it is conventional to consider the name as one word rather than to write the names of groups and parent compound as separate words or to use an unnecessary number of hyphens. It is preferable to limit the use of hyphens to the attachment of position numbers and symbols.

Physical properties

The physical properties of organic compounds depend in general on the number and kind of atoms in the molecule and on the way in which the atoms are linked together. At 25° and 760 mm., the normal hydrocarbons are gases from C_1 to C_4, liquids from C_5 to C_{17}, and solids for C_{18} and above.

The **boiling points** of the normal hydrocarbons increase with increasing molecular weight. When plotted against the number of carbon atoms, they fall on a smooth curve, as shown in Figure 10. The rise in boiling point

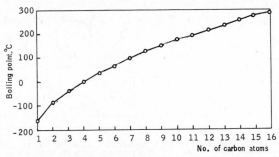

Figure 10.   Boiling points of normal alkanes.

Branching lowers boiling point

is due to the increased attraction between molecules as the number of atoms increases. Branching of the chain always results in a lower boiling point. Thus *n*-pentane boils at 36°, *i*-pentane at 28°, and neopentane at 9.5°.

Attractive forces between molecules are known as **van der Waals forces** because they are responsible for the a term in the van der Waals equation, $\left(P + \dfrac{a}{V^2}\right)(V - b) = RT$ for one mole of gas. The law for a perfect gas, $PV = RT$, holds only if the molecules of a gas have no attraction for each other and occupy no volume. By introducing a constant a to take care of the attraction between molecules and a constant b to offset the volume occupied by the molecules, the equation fits more closely the experimental data. Constants a and b are characteristic for each compound.

Nature of van der Waals forces

Van der Waals forces may be divided into three groups according to the magnitude of the effect: (1) those due to a transient polarization, which usually are called *London forces* after F. London; (2) those due to a permanent polarization, known as *permanent dipole association;* and (3) those due to so-called *hydrogen bonding* or *proton bonding*. Each of these types will be considered as examples arise.

Attractive forces between molecules

All attractive forces are electrical; that is, they are due to attraction between positive and negative charges. If there is a difference in charge between two parts of a molecule, the molecules behave much like an aggregation of bar magnets, with the positive and negative ends of one molecule attracting the negative and positive ends of the other. Even the inert gas helium can be liquefied when cooled under pressure, indicating that attractive forces exist between molecules when they are close enough together.

Although the negative electrons in a neutral molecule are balanced by the positive charges on the nucleus, the electrons are in motion, and the center of density of the electrons does not coincide continuously with the center of density of the positively-charged nuclei. Hence the molecules *Transient dipole* sometimes have a positive end and a negative end; that is, they acquire *attraction* what is called an *electrical dipole*. In this condition they are said to be *polarized* and can exert an attraction for other molecules having a dipole. In helium, for example, the atoms (i.e., molecules) are nonpolar only when the electrons are on opposite sides of the nucleus and in line with it. In all other positions the atoms are dipolar, resulting in slight attraction, as indicated in Figure 11. Because the molecules continuously revert to the nonpolar state, the dipole may be said to be transient.

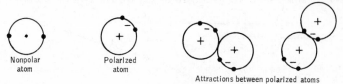

Figure 11.   Representation of source of attractive forces (London forces) between helium atoms.

It is this type of polarization that causes the attraction between hydrocarbon molecules. The ease of polarizability and hence the strength of the *Polarizability increases* attractive force increase as the number of electrons increases and hence *with number of electrons* as the number and complexity of the atoms in the molecule increase. For normal alkanes the force amounts to about 1.0 kcal. per carbon atom per mole and accounts for the regular increase in boiling point with increasing molecular weight within a homologous series. It is not possible to distill without decomposition hydrocarbons having more than around 80 carbon atoms, no matter how perfect the vacuum, because the energy of about 80 kcal. per mole required to separate the molecules is approximately the same as that necessary to break a carbon-carbon bond (p. 11). These forces vary inversely as the seventh power of the distance between the molecules and hence are operative only when molecules approach each other very closely. Branching of a molecule tends to decrease the magnitude of the transient dipole and prevents the optimum proximity of the molecules to each other, thus accounting for the lower boiling points of branched compounds.

The **melting points** of normal alkanes do not fall on a smooth curve *Melting points* but show alternation (Fig. 12). With the exception of methane they fall on *show alternation* two curves, an upper one for the hydrocarbons having an even number of carbon atoms and a lower one for those with an odd number of carbon atoms. X-ray investigations of solid hydrocarbons have shown that the chains of the saturated hydrocarbons are extended, the carbon atoms taking

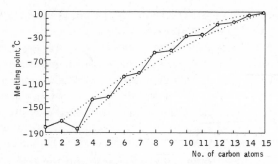

Figure 12.   Melting points of normal alkanes.

a zigzag arrangement. With compounds having an even number of carbon atoms, the end carbon atoms are on opposite sides of the chain; whereas for those having an odd number they are on the same side (Fig. 13). Apparently the molecules having an odd number of carbon atoms do not fit together so well as those having an even number, and the van der Waals force is not so effective.

Figure 13.   Extended chains having an even and an odd number of carbon atoms.

Unlike the variation in boiling points, there is no regularity in the change in melting point with branching, because the effectiveness of the attractive forces depends on how well the molecule fits into the crystal lattice. Thus n-pentane melts at $-129.7°$, isopentane at $-160°$, and neopentane at $-20°$. In general, however, the more symmetrical and compact the molecule, the higher its melting point. Hexamethylethane, $(CH_3)_3CC(CH_3)_3$, is interesting in that it melts at $100.7°$ and boils at $106.3°$.

The **density** of the normal alkanes gradually increases from 0.626 g. per cc. at 20° for pentane to 0.769 for pentadecane. Branching may cause a decrease or an increase in the density. All hydrocarbons float on water. They are the lightest of all organic compounds. The **viscosity** of the normal alkanes increases with increasing chain length, because the greater attraction between the molecules and the increased possibility for entanglement decreases the ease with which the molecules can slip past one another. The alkanes are almost completely *insoluble in water*, because they have little attraction for water molecules, whereas water molecules have considerable attraction for each other (pp. 61–63). They are miscible with many other organic compounds when the attractions between like molecules and unlike molecules are of the same order of magnitude.

The commercial sources of the saturated hydrocarbons are *natural gas* and *petroleum*. Paraffin hydrocarbons are present also in the *products of the destructive distillation of coal*. Natural gas usually is composed chiefly of **methane** and smaller amounts of **ethane, propane** and the **butanes** (p. 49). Petroleum contains a large number of hydrocarbons of the alkane, cyclane, and aromatic series. The composition varies depending on the location of the oil field from which the oil is obtained. Oil from Pennsylvania or Michi-

Density and viscosity increase with increasing chain length

Insoluble in water

Petroleum and natural gas chief sources of alkanes

gan consists chiefly of alkanes, whereas that from certain California fields contains chiefly cyclanes and aromatic hydrocarbons.

Methane is a product also of the action of anaerobic organisms on cellulose and other organic matter. For example it is formed during the decomposition of vegetable matter under water in marshes, whence the common name *marsh gas*. Large amounts are formed during the treatment of sewage by the activated sludge process. It also is present in coal mines where, because it is one of the causes of explosions, it is known as *fire damp*. **n-Heptane** is *Alkanes in plants* present in the volatile oil of the fruit of *Pittosporum resiniferum*, and in the turpentine of the digger pine (*Pinus sabiniana*) and the Jeffrey pine (*Pinus jeffreyi*) of California. It readily can be obtained pure and in quantity from the last source. The normal hydrocarbons having an odd number of carbon atoms from C_{25} to C_{37} occur in many plant and insect waxes. For example the waxes from leaves of members of the cabbage family (*Brassica*) contain the C_{29} and C_{31} normal hydrocarbons, and spinach wax contains the C_{33}, C_{35}, and C_{37} hydrocarbons. Individual alkanes of known structure usually are obtained by synthesis, that is, by making them from certain other compounds.

Chemical properties; very inert

The alkanes are not affected by aqueous solutions of acids, alkalies, strong oxidizing or reducing agents, or most other reagents at room temperature, and frequently resist reaction under more drastic conditions. This inertness gave rise to the name *paraffin* (L. *parum*, little; *affinis*, akin) for a saturated hydrocarbon.

Burn in air

Hydrocarbons in the presence of oxygen or strong oxidizing agents at high temperatures burn to carbon dioxide and water.

$$CH_4 + 2\,O_2 \longrightarrow CO_2 + 2\,H_2O$$
$$C_2H_6 + 3\tfrac{1}{2}\,O_2 \longrightarrow 2\,CO_2 + 3\,H_2O$$
$$C_3H_8 + 5\,O_2 \longrightarrow 3\,CO_2 + 4\,H_2O$$
$$C_nH_{2n+2} + \frac{3n+1}{2}\,O_2 \longrightarrow n\,CO_2 + (n+1)\,H_2O$$

When hydrocarbons are burned to carbon dioxide and water, heat is evolved. The amount of heat varies somewhat with the molecular weight and the structure of the compound but is approximately 11.5 kcal. per gram.

Use as fuel

The fact that the combustion of hydrocarbons is exothermic is the basis for their use as fuels. Their flammability depends on the volatility of the particular hydrocarbon. Mixtures of air and hydrocarbon vapors in the proper proportions explode on ignition, which gives rise to their use in the internal combustion engine. In a deficient oxygen supply, carbon monoxide or elementary carbon in the form of carbon black may be produced.

Decompose at high temperatures

At sufficiently high temperatures hydrocarbons decompose in the absence of oxygen, a phenomenon known as **cracking** or **pyrolysis** (Gr. *pyr*, fire, and *lysis*, loosing). Methane yields carbon and hydrogen as final products.

$$CH_4 \longrightarrow C + 2\,H_2$$

For the reaction to proceed rapidly with methane, temperatures above 1200° are required. Other hydrocarbons decompose rapidly at considerably lower temperatures. In the decomposition of ethane at 600° a new hydrocarbon is formed by the loss of one molecule of hydrogen from a molecule of ethane.

$$C_2H_6 \longrightarrow C_2H_4 + H_2$$
Ethylene

The new compound, ethylene, is an unsaturated hydrocarbon belonging to the alkene or olefin series (p. 29).

Alkenes among products

Propane at 600° decomposes to give four compounds which arise from the following reactions.

$$CH_3CH_2CH_3 \longrightarrow C_3H_6 + H_2$$
Propylene

$$CH_3CH_2CH_3 \longrightarrow C_2H_4 + CH_4$$
Ethylene   Methane

Actually ethylene and methane are the principal products. Higher alkanes on cracking give hydrogen and mixtures of alkanes and alkenes having varying numbers of carbon atoms. This cracking process is of great importance to the petroleum industry (p. 50), because it provides a means for making smaller, more volatile hydrocarbon molecules from the larger, less volatile molecules that predominate in most natural petroleum. When hydrocarbons are subjected to higher temperatures for very short periods, other products such as acetylene and benzene also are formed (p. 37).

CYCLANES

As mentioned previously, carbon atoms may be joined to each other to form a ring, giving rise to a series of cyclic saturated hydrocarbons known as **cyclanes.** The first member would of necessity have three carbon atoms and is called *cyclopropane.* Each carbon atom of the ring still has two unshared electrons and may combine with two hydrogen atoms. Hence the general formula for this series is $C_nH_{2n}.$ The four-carbon compound is *cyclobutane* and the five-carbon member is *cyclopentane.* One or more alkyl

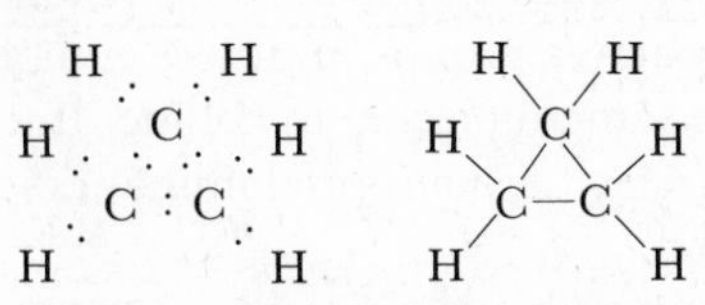

Nomenclature based on number of carbon atoms in ring

Cyclopropane 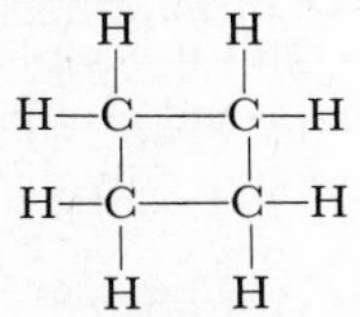   Cyclobutane 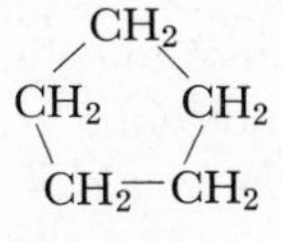   Cyclopentane

groups may be present in place of the hydrogens to give a mixed family. Members are named as derivatives of the parent cyclane. In the first formula the ring carbon atoms have been omitted, and in the second and third formulas the hydrogens attached directly to the ring have been omitted also.

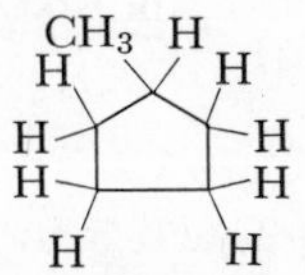

Skeletal formulas

Methylcyclo-   1,3-Dimethyl-   Methylcyclo-
pentane   cyclopentane   hexane

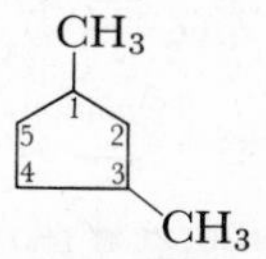

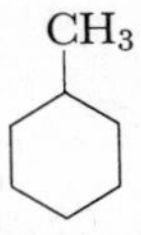

Where more than one group replaces hydrogen, the positions are indicated by numbers. The carbon atoms of the ring are numbered consecutively around the ring, starting at the point that gives the substituents the smallest numbers. Groups derived from the cyclanes having three-, four-, five-, and six-membered rings are called *cyclopropyl, cyclobutyl, cyclopentyl,* and *cyclohexyl* groups.

Ring size

Most of the known cyclic compounds contain five or six atoms in the ring. Ring formation must take place by joining two ends of a chain. Because the natural carbon-carbon single-bond distance of 1.54 Å and the tetrahedral angle of 109°28′ between valences tend to be maintained, there would be no possibility of joining terminal atoms, if the atoms were forced to remain in an extended chain. However, rotation about the single bonds permits the assumption of a spiral structure as indicated in Figure 14. If

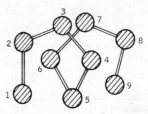

Figure 14.   Spiral conformation of a carbon chain.

in this figure the C—C—C angles are the tetrahedral angles of 109°28′ and the distance between C-1 and C-2 = 1.54 Å, then the distance C-1 to C-3 = 2.51 Å, C-1 to C-4 = 2.52 Å, and C-1 to C-5 = 1.67 Å. Hence the double bond and the five-membered ring can be formed readily, but it is more difficult to form three- and four-membered rings. Because of the flexibility of the molecule, C-1 and C-6 can approach each other to any desired distance. The same situation exists for longer chains, but above six carbon atoms other atoms in the chain begin to get in the way of the terminal reacting groups, and a greater amount of maneuvering of the chain is necessary to bring the reacting groups into the proper space relationship for reaction to take place. As a result it is easier for reactive groups of different molecules to collide than for end groups of the same molecule to collide. Intermolecular reaction to give polymeric products becomes predominant, and the yields of cyclic compounds are very low.

Small rings can be made

Since 1879, three-membered and four-membered rings have been prepared. Hence bond angles can contract sufficiently during the natural vibrations of the molecule to permit groups in the 1,3 and 1,4 positions to react in such a way that three- and four-membered rings are formed.

Cyclopropane, obtained in good yield by the reaction of zinc dust

$$CH_2\begin{array}{l}CH_2Cl\\\\CH_2Br\end{array} + Zn \longrightarrow \begin{array}{c}CH_2\\CH_2-CH_2\end{array} + ZnClBr$$

Trimethylene chlorobromide   Cyclopropane

Chemical properties; small rings open easily, others inert

with trimethylene chlorobromide, is a gas, b.p. −34°. It is used frequently instead of ether as a general anesthetic. Because the internal bond angles of three- and four-membered rings must be 60° and 90°, the rings are less stable than higher-membered rings and are said to be *strained*. Because of the strain, the rings open more easily. Thus cyclopropane and most of its derivatives react with the same reagents as do olefins (p. 32) to give open-chain compounds.

$$(CH_2)_3 + H_2SO_4 \longrightarrow CH_3CH_2CH_2OSO_3H$$

$$(CH_2)_3 + Br_2 \longrightarrow BrCH_2CH_2CH_2Br$$

$$(CH_2)_3 + H_2 \xrightarrow[80°]{Pt} CH_3CH_2CH_3$$

Cyclanes having five or more atoms in the ring are unreactive and in other respects resemble the alkanes. Cyclohexane is made by the catalytic hydrogenation of benzene (p. 41). It is present in petroleum from certain fields (p. 49). The chief use for pure cyclohexane is as a raw material for the production of adipic acid (p. 113), which is used to make nylon 66 (p. 238).

SUMMARY

1. Hydrocarbon molecules contain only carbon and hydrogen atoms. They are divided into acyclic and cyclic compounds, which are further subdivided into saturated, unsaturated, and aromatic compounds.

2. The alkanes have the general formula C_nH_{2n+2} and constitute a family in which each member differs from an adjacent member by one carbon atom and two hydrogen atoms. Any such series of compounds is known as an homologous series, and the members of the family are called homologs.

3. Compounds that have the same molecular formula but differ in chemical and physical properties are called isomers; the phenomenon is known as isomerism.

4. Alkanes may have common names, be named as derivatives of methane, or be named by the Geneva (I.U.C. or I.U.P.A.C.) system. The names of all alkanes end in *ane;* when more than four carbon atoms are present, a prefix indicates the number of carbon atoms in the compound.

5. For normal alkanes, the boiling point rises as the number of carbon atoms in the chain increases. For isomeric alkanes, branching of the chain lowers the boiling point. Hydrocarbons are insoluble in water but soluble in many organic liquids. They have the lowest density of any organic compounds.

6. The principal source of the alkanes is petroleum, but they are obtained also from other sources. Although the chief use of petroleum is as fuel, it is being used increasingly as raw material for the synthesis of other organic compounds.

7. Alkanes are characterized by their chemical inertness. They are remarkably resistant to the action of concentrated alkali, acid, and of oxidizing and reducing agents. At high temperatures they decompose into smaller hydrocarbon molecules, and in the presence of oxygen they are burned to carbon dioxide and water, evolving about 11.5 kcal. of heat per gram.

8. Cyclanes have the general formula C_nH_{2n} At least three of the carbon atoms are joined in a ring. The rings are named by placing the prefix *cyclo-* before the name of the alkane that has the same number of carbon atoms as are present in the ring.

9. Rings having five and six atoms are most abundant in natural products and are formed most readily, because the normal bond angles and interatomic distances

permit ring closure most readily between the 1 position and the 5 position, or the 1 position and the 6 position of a chain.

(10) Saturated carbon rings that have five, six, or a larger number of ring atoms are chemically inert like the alkanes. Rings having three and four atoms in the ring undergo reactions leading to opening of the ring.

EXERCISES

1. Give the molecular formulas of the members of the homologous series of alkanes having from one to ten carbon atoms.
2. Give condensed structural formulas for (a) each of the possible heptanes; (b) each of the octanes having a chain of five carbon atoms; (c) each of the alkylcyclohexanes having nine carbon atoms.
3. Write a condensed structural formula for each of the following compounds: (a) isoheptane; (b) tridecane; (c) dimethylethyl-*i*-butylmethane; (d) 2,3,4-trimethylpentane; (e) 4-*i*-propyl-5-*t*-butyloctane; (f) 5-*n*-propyl-5-*s*-butylnonane; (g) 1,1-dimethylcyclopropane; (h) 1-ethyl-3-*i*-propylcyclopentane; (i) 1-cyclopentyl-3-methylpentane.
4. Name the isomeric group to which each of the above compounds (a) to (f) belongs; i.e., tell whether it is a pentane, a hexane, a heptane, etc.
5. From the structure of the following alkanes, predict the order of increasing boiling points: *n*-hexane, neopentane, 3-methylpentane, *i*-hexane, 2,2-dimethylbutane, *n*-heptane.
6. Write balanced equations for the complete combustion of (a) *n*-hexane; (b) cyclohexane.
7. Which of the above compounds would have the higher heat of combustion per mole?

CHAPTER 4

UNSATURATED HYDROCARBONS

The saturated hydrocarbons were defined as having the maximum number of hydrogen atoms for a particular carbon skeleton. Compounds are known that have fewer than this number, and these are called *unsaturated hydrocarbons*. Two types of acyclic unsaturated hydrocarbons are known. Those having two fewer hydrogens than the alkanes, and hence the general formula C_nH_{2n}, are called *alkenes,* or by the older name *olefins*. The second type has four fewer hydrogen atoms than the corresponding alkane, and hence the general formula C_nH_{2n-2}, these are the *alkynes,* or *acetylenes*.

Two types of acyclic unsaturated hydrocarbons

The cyclic compounds corresponding to the alkenes are known as *cyclenes*. They have the same molecular formula, C_nH_{2n-2}, as the alkynes, but their properties resemble those of the alkenes. Cyclynes are possible only if the number of carbon atoms forming the ring is larger than ten.

ALKENES

The simplest member of this homologous series, ethylene, has the molecular formula C_2H_4. No stable compound having a single carbon atom is known for this series. Three electronic formulas suggest themselves. Either one carbon atom has two unshared electrons (*I*), each has one unshared electron (*II*), or the carbon atoms are joined by two pairs of electrons (*III*).

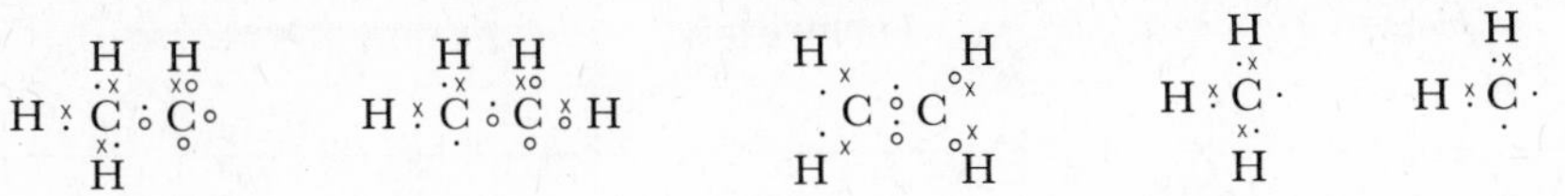

Structure of alkenes

If *I* or *II* were capable of existence, *IV* or *V* should be stable also, but these groups have been detected only as highly reactive, short-lived *free radicals* (p. 33). Formula *I* is ruled out also on chemical grounds because its reactions would involve only one carbon atom, whereas all known reactions of the olefins involve both carbon atoms. Formula *III* satisfies all requirements. Atoms sharing two pairs of electrons are said to be joined by a **double bond.** The double bond causes the ethylene molecule to be flat, all of its atoms lying in the same plane.

Contain double bond

Formulas for the homologs of ethylene can be constructed in the same way as formulas for the homologs of methane, that is, by inserting CH_2 groups (*methylene groups*) between hydrogen and carbon atoms or by replacing hydrogen atoms by alkyl groups. For example, the next member of the series, propylene, C_3H_6, has the formula $CH_3CH=CH_2$. Because the propylene molecule has three kinds of hydrogen atoms (see footnote, p. 17), there should be three structurally isomeric butylene, all of which are known.

$$CH_3CH_2CH=CH_2 \qquad CH_3CH=CHCH_3 \qquad CH_3\underset{\underset{\displaystyle CH_3}{|}}{C}=CH_2$$

The same formulas would have been obtained if the double bond had been put in all possible positions in normal butane and in isobutane.

Nomenclature; common and systematic names

The **common names** of the alkenes are derived by replacing the *ane* of the common name for the saturated hydrocarbon by *ylene*, but *n*-(normal) is omitted for straight-chain compounds. Greek letters sometimes are used to distinguish between isomers (see Table 4).

The **Geneva rules** for naming alkenes resemble the rules for naming alkanes (p. 19): (*1*) the ending *ane* of the corresponding saturated hydrocarbon is replaced by the ending *ene;* (*2*) the parent compound is considered to be the longest chain *containing the double bond;* (*3*) the chains are numbered from the end nearest the double bond, and the position of the double bond is indicated by the number of the lower-numbered carbon atom to which it is attached; (*4*) side chains are named and their position indicated by a number.

TABLE 4.   NOMENCLATURE OF ALKENES

FORMULA	COMMON NAME	BY GENEVA SYSTEM
$CH_2=CH_2$	ethylene	ethene
$CH_3CH=CH_2$	propylene	propene
$CH_3CH_2CH=CH_2$	α-butylene	1-butene
$CH_3CH=CHCH_3$	β-butylene	2-butene
$CH_3\underset{\underset{\displaystyle CH_3}{|}}{C}=CH_2$	isobutylene*	methylpropene
$C_2H_5CH=CHCH_3$	β-amylene†	2-pentene
$\overset{6}{C}H_3\overset{5}{C}H_2\overset{4}{C}HCH_3$ $\underset{\qquad}{\;}$ $CH_3\overset{3}{C}=\overset{2}{C}H\overset{1}{C}H_3$	none	3,4-dimethyl-2-hexene

* The name isobutene, which frequently is used, is undesirable because it mixes two systems.
† Olefins having five carbon atoms are known as *amylenes* instead of *pentylenes* (see *fusel oil,* p. 65).

Cyclenes have double bond in ring

The cyclenes contain a double bond between two carbon atoms of the ring.

$$\underset{\text{Cyclopropene}}{\overset{\displaystyle\text{CH}}{\underset{\displaystyle\text{H}_2\text{C}\!-\!\text{CH}}{\diagup\diagdown}}} \qquad \underset{\text{Cyclobutene}}{\overset{\displaystyle\text{H}_2\text{C}\!-\!\text{CH}}{\underset{\displaystyle\text{H}_2\text{C}\!-\!\text{CH}}{|\quad\;\|}}} \qquad \underset{\text{Cyclopentene}}{\square} \qquad \underset{\text{Cyclohexene}}{\hexagon}$$

In the last two formulas it is understood that a carbon atom is at each corner of the polygon and that each carbon atom has a sufficient number of hydrogens attached to it to satisfy the rules of valence. The cyclenes are named by adding the prefix *cyclo-* to the name of the alkene having the same number of carbon atoms. For the alkyl-substituted cyclenes, one of the carbon atoms bearing a double bond is number 1, namely that which will permit the use of the smaller numbers. If the double bond is in the side chain, the compound is named as a derivative of the alkene.

1,3-Dimethyl-
cyclohexene

$-\text{CH}_2\text{CH}\!=\!\text{CHCH}_3$

1-Cyclopentyl-2-butene

Sources and uses

Alkenes are produced commercially by the cracking of natural gas and petroleum hydrocarbons (p. 24). **Ethylene** is by far the most important olefin used as a raw material for the synthesis of other chemicals. Production in 1960 was 5.5 billion pounds, and the contract price less than 5 cents per pound. About 50 per cent was produced by cracking propane, 40 per cent from ethane, and 10 per cent from petroleum refinery gas (p. 50). About 25 per cent each was used for the synthesis of ethyl alcohol (p. 66) and ethylene oxide (p. 71), and 10 per cent each for styrene (p. 235), ethyl chloride (p. 91), and polyethylene (p. 234). **Propylene** and the **butylenes** find some use for the production of chemicals, but are used chiefly for the production of gasoline (p. 51), plastics, and synthetic rubber (p. 237).

Physical properties

The general physical properties of the alkenes are much the same as those of the corresponding saturated hydrocarbons. The solubility of the lower alkenes in water, though slight, is considerably greater than that of the alkanes, because the higher concentration of electrons in the double bond leads to a greater attraction for the positive end of the water dipole (p. 94).

Chemical properties; very reactive

In contrast to the saturated hydrocarbons, the unsaturated hydrocarbons are very reactive. Many reagents add to the two carbon atoms joined by the double bond. In this process the reagent itself is decomposed, one part combining with one carbon atom and the other part with the other carbon atom. Such reactions are known as **addition reactions.** The bonding properties of one pair of electrons in the double bond are not fully satisfied. These electrons frequently are referred to as *unsaturation electrons.* In the presence of a suitable reagent this pair reacts with the reagent to give a new bond system that is more stable. The reagent is said to have *added* to the double bond. The reactions may be divided into two groups, depending on whether the addenda are identical or nonidentical. Examples of the addition of like addenda are the reaction with halogen and the catalytic addition of hydrogen. The reaction with sulfuric acid illustrates the addition of nonidentical addenda.

Addition of halogen

The most characteristic reaction of the double bond is the rapid addition, in the liquid phase or in solution, of chlorine or bromine to those alkenes in which each of the doubly-bound carbon atoms is united to at least one hydrogen atom.

$$CH_2{=}CH_2 + Cl_2 \longrightarrow ClCH_2CH_2Cl$$
Ethylene chloride
(1,2-dichloroethane)

$$CH_3CH{=}CH_2 + Br_2 \longrightarrow CH_3CHBrCH_2Br$$
Propylene bromide
(1,2-dibromopropane)

The reaction in general may be expressed by the equation

$$RCH{=}CHR + X_2 \longrightarrow RCHXCHXR$$

where R is any alkyl group or a hydrogen atom, and X is any halogen atom. In practice the reaction is limited to chlorine and bromine, because fluorine reacts too violently to be controllable, and iodine does not give stable 1,2-diiodo derivatives except with a few simple olefins.

Decolorization of bromine as test for double bond

These halogen derivatives are colorless liquids. Hence decolorization of a solution of bromine in water, or better in a mutual solvent such as carbon tetrachloride or acetic acid, may be used as a *test for unsaturation,* provided no other group is present that reacts with bromine. To determine the amount of a known olefin in a mixture with other substances, the mixture can be titrated with a standardized solution of bromine. A similar titration of a pure unknown olefin would give the equivalent weight of the compound, that is, the weight associated with one double bond. The number of double bonds would be equal to the molecular weight divided by the equivalent weight. Because ethylene chloride is a liquid, ethylene originally was called *olifiant gas,* i.e., oil-making gas. Contraction led to *olefin* as a general term for unsaturated hydrocarbons.

Addition of hydrogen

In the presence of a suitable catalyst such as finely divided platinum, palladium, or nickel, hydrogen adds to a double bond with the evolution of about 30 kcal. of energy per mole. The process is called *catalytic hydrogenation.*

$$CH_2{=}CH_2 + H_2 \xrightarrow{\text{Pt, Pd, or Ni}} CH_3CH_3$$

$$R_2C{=}CR_2 + H_2 \xrightarrow{\text{Pt, Pd, or Ni}} R_2CHCHR_2$$

If the olefin is a gas, a mixture with hydrogen may be passed over the catalyst. Liquid olefins, or solid olefins dissolved in an inert solvent, may be shaken with hydrogen in the presence of a suspension of the finely divided catalyst. The reaction can be used for analytical as well as for preparative purposes. From the volume of hydrogen absorbed, the amount of an unsaturated compound of known structure in a mixture with saturated compounds, or the number of double bonds in a pure unknown compound whose molecular weight has been determined, can be calculated.

Action of catalysts

Many reactions, although energetically possible, do not take place at room temperature because the molecules do not possess sufficient kinetic energy to break the bonds when the molecules collide, a process that is necessary before the formation of new bonds can take place. The energy required to bring molecules into the reactive state is called the **activation energy** for the reaction. If the activation energy is low, collisions of molecules at room temperature may be sufficient to bring about reaction, or the application of heat may be sufficient to increase the kinetic energy enough to enable the reaction to proceed at a satisfactory rate.

Another way to bring about reaction is by the use of catalysts. Catalysts are reagents that make compounds more reactive by partly dissociating the bonds in the reacting molecules, or that produce intermediates that enable the reaction to proceed by one or more additional steps, each of which has a lower activation energy than that required by a single step. The catalyst usually is regenerated in the reaction, and hence merely speeds up the attainment of equilibrium but does not shift the position of equilibrium.

Metals such as platinum, palladium, nickel, and copper strongly adsorb hydrogen and unsaturated molecules. The atoms in the metal surface have unpaired electrons which can interact with the electrons of the hydrogen molecule and of the double bond. The resulting formation of weak bonds with the metal atoms causes adsorption. As indicated in the schematic representation, the hydrogen molecule can be dissociated to give adsorbed hydrogen atoms and the olefin to give an adsorbed free biradical. Reaction of the atom and free biradical leaves an adsorbed hydrogen atom and an adsorbed free radical. Further reaction gives the saturated hydrocarbon which is desorbed.

Mechanism of addition of hydrogen is by way of atoms and free radicals

$$
\begin{array}{llll}
\text{Pt}|\cdot & \text{Pt}|:\text{H} & \text{Pt}|\cdot & \text{Pt}|\cdot \\
\text{Pt}|\cdot + \text{H}:\text{H} & \text{Pt}|:\text{H} & \text{Pt}|:\text{H} & \text{Pt}|\cdot \\
\text{Pt}|\cdot \quad\quad \text{CH}_2 & \text{Pt}|:\text{CH}_2 & \text{Pt}|:\text{CH}_2\text{CH}_2 & \text{Pt}|\cdot \\
\text{Pt}|\cdot \quad\quad \text{CH}_2 & \text{Pt}|:\text{CH}_2 & \text{Pt}|\cdot & \text{Pt}|\cdot
\end{array}
$$

Because the various steps in the reaction involve unpaired electrons and weak bonds, none has a high activation energy.

Free radicals are neutral entities having unpaired electrons, and reactions involving free radical intermediates, such as catalytic hydrogenation and catalysis by light, are said to take place by **free radical mechanisms.** Entities that bear positive or negative charges are called **ions.** Reactions involving charged entities as intermediates are said to take place by **ionic mechanisms.** Catalysis by acids or bases belongs to the latter category and will be discussed as examples arise.

Numerous reagents add unlike groups to a double bond. For example, sulfuric acid adds H and OSO_3H. If the molecule is symmetrical, that is, if identical groups are on both of the doubly-bound carbon atoms, only one compound can be obtained on addition, even if the addenda are not alike. However *if the olefin molecule is unsymmetrical, two structural isomers could result.* Actually, *one isomer is formed in predominant amount, namely that in which the hydrogen of sulfuric acid adds to the carbon atom having the larger number of hydrogen atoms.* This generalization is known as the **Markovnikov rule,** named for the Russian chemist, Vladimir Vasil'evich Markovnikov (1838–1904).

Addition of sulfuric acid

The products of the reaction of olefins with sulfuric acid are _alkyl hydrogen sulfates._

Hydrogen adds to carbon with most hydrogen

$$CH_3CH_2CH=CH_2 + HOSO_3H \longrightarrow CH_3CH_2CHCH_3$$
$$\underset{\text{OSO}_3\text{H}}{|}$$

1-Butene   s-Butyl hydrogen sulfate

$$RCH=CR_2 + HOSO_3H \longrightarrow RCH_2CR_2$$
$$\underset{\text{OSO}_3\text{H}}{|}$$

2-Butene can give only one product, which is the same as that from 1-butene.

$$CH_3CH=CHCH_3 + HOSO_3H \longrightarrow CH_3CH_2CHCH_3$$
$$\underset{\text{OSO}_3\text{H}}{|}$$

2-Butene

Hydrolysis yields alcohols

The chief importance of this reaction lies in the fact that alcohols can be formed from the alkyl hydrogen sulfates by hydrolysis.

$$CH_3CH_2CHCH_3 + H_2O \longrightarrow CH_3CH_2CHCH_3 + H_2SO_4$$
$$\underset{\text{OSO}_3\text{H}}{|} \qquad\qquad\qquad \underset{\text{OH}}{|}$$

Mechanism of addition of sulfuric acid is ionic

The addition of acids to a double bond takes place by an ionic mechanism, the initial step being the transfer of a proton from the acid to one pair of electrons of the double bond. If the alkene is symmetrical, the molecule is nonpolar; that is, on a time average the electrons are symmetrically distributed about the center of the molecule. An alkyl group with its larger number of electrons is more polarizable than a hydrogen atom and releases electrons to a carbon atom more readily than hydrogen. Hence

Unsymmetrical olefins are polarized

in an unsymmetrical alkene the unsaturation electrons move away from the alkyl group and toward the hydrogen to give a polarized molecule.

$$R \rightarrow \overset{|}{\underset{\overset{|}{H}}{C}} - \overset{|}{\underset{\overset{|}{H}}{C}} - H \qquad \text{or} \qquad RCH-CH_2$$
$$\qquad\qquad\qquad\qquad\qquad\qquad \underset{\delta+}{} \quad \underset{\delta-}{}$$

The $\delta+$ and $\delta-$ indicate a difference in charge less than that which would result from the transfer of one electron.

Attack of the polarized molecule by a proton of an acid molecule occurs at the negative end of the double bond, thus explaining the Markovnikov rule. The reaction is completed by extraction of a negative ion from another molecule of acid.

$$RCH-CH_2 + HOSO_3H \longrightarrow [RCH-\overset{H}{\overset{..}{CH_2}}] + [^-OSO_3H]$$
$$\underset{\delta+}{} \quad \underset{\delta-}{} \qquad\qquad\qquad\qquad \underset{+}{}$$

$$[RCH-CH_3] + HOSO_3H \longrightarrow RCH-CH_3 + [H^+]$$
$$\underset{+}{} \qquad\qquad\qquad\qquad\qquad \underset{\text{OSO}_3\text{H}}{|}$$

The cyclenes behave similarly to the alkenes. Thus cyclohexene reacts with bromine to give cyclohexene bromide or 1,2-dibromocyclohexane. It can be reduced by catalytic hydrogenation to cyclohexane, and it adds sulfuric acid to give cyclohexyl hydrogen sulfate. 1-Methylcyclohexene adds sulfuric acid according to the Markovnikov rule to give 1-methylcyclohexyl hydrogen sulfate.

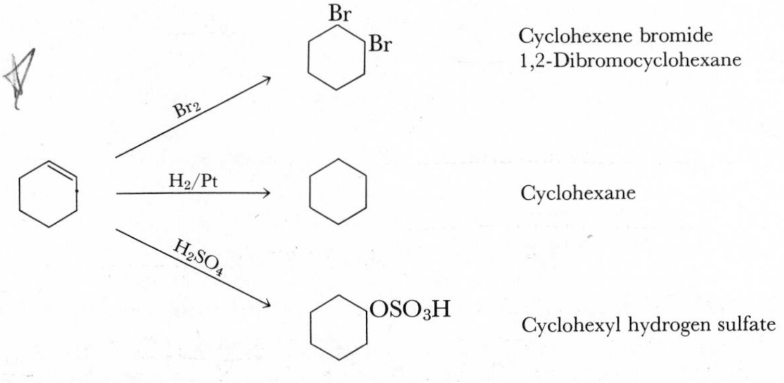

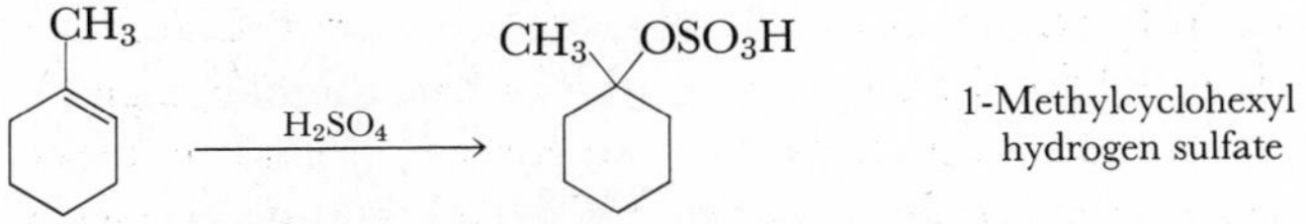

Reactions of cyclenes like those of alkenes

Cyclohexene bromide
1,2-Dibromocyclohexane

Cyclohexane

Cyclohexyl hydrogen sulfate

1-Methylcyclohexyl
hydrogen sulfate

Hydrocarbons having two double bonds are called **dienes.** If a molecule has two or more double bonds separated by at least two singly-bonded carbon atoms, each double bond reacts independently of the other; these are called **isolated double bonds.** If, however, double bonds alternate with single bonds in a molecule, they no longer react independently and are said to be **conjugated.** Usually a conjugated system is somewhat more stable than an isolated system. A characteristic chemical behavior of conjugated double bonds is addition of reagents to the ends of the system, with migration of the electrons to form a double bond at the center. Thus, although the addition of one mole of bromine to 1,4-pentadiene gives chiefly 4,5-dibromo-1-pentene,

Dienes

Reagents add to ends of conjugated system

$$CH_2{=}CH{-}CH_2{-}CH{=}CH_2 + Br_2 \longrightarrow Br\ CH_2CHBrCH_2CH{=}CH_2$$

1,4-Pentadiene   4,5-Dibromo-1-pentene

1,3-pentadiene yields chiefly 1,4-dibromo-2-pentene.

$$CH_2{=}CH{-}CH{=}CH{-}CH_3 + Br_2 \longrightarrow BrCH_2CH{=}CHCHBrCH_3$$

1,3-Pentadiene   1,4-Dibromo-2-pentene

Conjugated dienes can be detected easily because they absorb ultraviolet light strongly in the region of 220 to 250 mμ. If two double bonds are conjugated in a single ring, as in 1,3-cyclohexadiene, the absorption band lies between 250 and 290 mμ. Unconjugated double bonds absorb in the far ultraviolet range near 170 mμ.

Absorption in ultraviolet region

1,3-Butadiene and **2-methyl-1,3-butadiene** (*isoprene*) are important intermediates in the production of synthetic rubbers (p. 237).

Important dienes

Cyclopentadiene, b.p. 41°, is a component of coal gas (p. 51) and is a coproduct in the manufacture of isoprene by the cracking of petroleum fractions. It dimerizes spontaneously to dicyclopentadiene by the 1,4 addition of one molecule to the 1,2 position of the other (*Diels-Alder addition*). The reaction is reversible, and the dimer depolymerizes at its boiling point (170°) to the monomer.

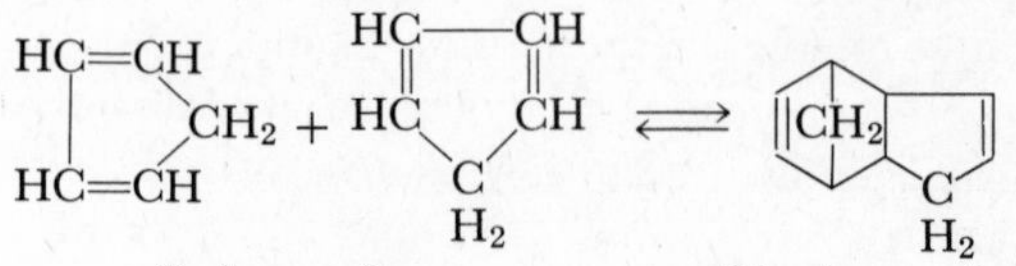

Cyclopentadiene   Dicyclopentadiene

ALKYNES (ACETYLENES)

Alkynes have triple bond

In addition to the olefins and cyclenes, a third homologous series of unsaturated hydrocarbons exists, called either **acetylenes,** from the first member of the series, or **alkynes.** Acetylene has the molecular formula C_2H_2. The acetylenes add two moles of halogen whereby two halogen atoms are united to each of two adjacent carbon atoms. Using the same arguments advanced for the structure of the olefins, the only logical structure for the acetylenes is one in which two carbon atoms are joined by a triple bond. Acetylene has the structure $HC\equiv CH$, and acetylenes in general have the structure $RC\equiv CR$.

Acetylene is a linear molecule; that is, the atomic centers of the two carbon atoms and of the two hydrogen atoms all lie in a straight line. Similarly, the bond angle between any group and the $C\equiv C$ group is 180°.

Physical properties and nomenclature

The physical properties of the alkynes closely resemble those of the alkanes and the alkenes, although the boiling points are somewhat higher and the solubility in water is greater. Alkynes may be named (*1*) as derivatives of acetylene, and (*2*) by the Geneva system. In the latter the ending is *yne*. These methods are illustrated by the following examples.

$$(CH_3)_2CHC\equiv CH \qquad\qquad CH_3CH_2CHC\equiv CC_2H_5$$
$$\overset{|}{CH_3}$$

i-Propylacetylene   Ethyl-*s*-butylacetylene
(methylbutyne)   (5-methyl-3-heptyne)

Chemical properties similar to alkenes

Acetylenes undergo addition reactions similar to those of the alkenes. Thus two moles of hydrogen or two moles of halogen can be added.

$$RC\equiv CR + 2\,H_2 \xrightarrow{Pt} RCH_2CH_2R$$
$$RC\equiv CR + 2\,Cl_2 \longrightarrow RCCl_2CCl_2R$$

Acetylene adds water in the presence of sulfuric acid and mercurous sulfate (mercury-mercuric sulfate mixture). However, instead of forming hydroxy compounds, as occurs in the reactions of olefins with sulfuric acid and water (p. 66), acetylene yields acetaldehyde.

$$HC\equiv CH + H_2O \xrightarrow[\text{Hg—HgSO}_4]{\text{H}_2\text{SO}_4} [H_2C=CHOH] \longrightarrow CH_3\overset{\text{H}}{\underset{}{C}}=O$$
$$\text{Acetaldehyde}$$

The initial mercury salt complex probably yields a hydroxyolefin having a hydroxyl group on a carbon atom united to another carbon atom by a double bond. Such structures are known as *enols*. The simple enols are unstable and rearrange to give the more stable isomer having the double bond between the carbon atom and the oxygen atom rather than between the two carbon atoms. To indicate that a structure is unstable and that a compound having this structure cannot be isolated, the formula is enclosed in brackets.

Unlike hydrogen on a saturated carbon atom or on a doubly-bound carbon atom, hydrogen on a triply-bound carbon atom is replaceable by metals. Acetylene reacts readily with aqueous ammoniacal silver nitrate or aqueous ammoniacal cuprous chloride solutions to give water-insoluble carbides. *Some acetylenes have acidic hydrogen*

$$HC\equiv CH + 2\,Ag(NH_3)_2NO_3 \longrightarrow Ag^{+-}C\equiv C^{-+}Ag + 2\,NH_4NO_3 + 2\,NH_3$$
$$\text{Silver carbide}$$

$$HC\equiv CH + 2\,Cu(NH_3)_2Cl \longrightarrow Cu^{+-}C\equiv C^{-+}Cu + 2\,NH_4Cl + 2\,NH_3$$
$$\text{Cuprous carbide}$$

The heavy metal carbides are thermodynamically unstable and when dry may be exploded by heat or shock, with the formation of the metal and carbon. Silver carbide, for example, explodes at 140°–150°. Sodium carbide, on the other hand, is stable up to 400°, and calcium carbide, which is made in the electric furnace, melts without decomposition at 2300°.

The acetylides and carbides are salts of the very weak acid, acetylene, and the alkali and alkaline earth metal salts are hydrolyzed by water. *Hydrolysis of salts regenerates alkyne*

$$[HC\equiv C]\,Na^+ + H_2O \longrightarrow NaOH + C_2H_2$$
$$\text{Sodium acetylide}$$

$$Ca^{++}[\overset{-}{C}\equiv\overset{-}{C}] + 2\,H_2O \longrightarrow Ca(OH)_2 + C_2H_2$$
$$\text{Calcium carbide}$$

A mineral acid is required to decompose the heavy metal salts.

$$Ag_2C_2 + 2\,HNO_3 \longrightarrow 2\,AgNO_3 + C_2H_2$$

Acetylene is the only commercially important compound of the series. It is made from coke by way of calcium carbide, or from natural gas. *Commercial importance of acetylene*

$$3\,C + CaO \xrightarrow[(2000°)]{\text{Electric furnace}} CaC_2 + CO$$
$$\text{Coke}\quad\text{Lime}\qquad\qquad\text{Calcium}$$
$$\text{carbide}$$

$$CaC_2 + 2\,H_2O \xrightarrow[\text{temp.}]{\text{Room}} HC\equiv CH + Ca(OH)_2$$

When methane is heated to a very high temperature, acetylene is one of the products.

$$2\,CH_4 \rightleftarrows C_2H_2 + 3\,H_2 - 95.5 \text{ kcal.}$$

Thermodynamically unstable

If the time of exposure to the high temperature (1400°–1600°) is short enough (0.1 to 0.01 second) and the products are cooled quickly enough, a reasonably high yield of acetylene can be obtained.

Acetylene is a colorless gas that boils at −84°. It cannot be liquefied safely, because it is thermodynamically unstable and explodes from shock with the formation of the elements.

$$C_2H_2 \longrightarrow 2\,C + H_2 + 56\,kcal.$$

At twelve atmospheres, 300 volumes of acetylene dissolve in one volume of acetone. This solution is stable, and acetylene is transported under pressure in tanks filled with a porous material saturated with acetone.

Important uses

About 45 per cent of the acetylene consumed in the United States is used for the welding, cutting, and cleaning of iron and steel by means of the oxyacetylene flame, which has a temperature in the neighborhood of 2800°. The remainder is used for the manufacture of other organic chemicals. It is the starting point for the synthesis of plastics, rubbers, dry-cleaning solvents, and numerous other useful materials. Large quantities are converted into chlorinated solvents. Addition of chlorine yields **tetrachloroethane** (*acetylene tetrachloride*).

Chlorinated solvents from acetylene

$$HC{\equiv}CH + 2\,Cl_2 \longrightarrow Cl_2CHCHCl_2$$
$$\text{Tetrachloroethane}$$
$$\text{(acetylene tetrachloride)}$$

Tetrachloroethane is an excellent solvent, but it is rather high-boiling (146°), is highly toxic, and corrodes metals in the presence of moisture. Most of it is used for the production of **trichloroethylene** by the action of an aqueous slurry of lime, which removes one mole of hydrogen chloride, or by pyrolysis.

$$Cl_2CHCHCl_2 \quad \xrightarrow{Ca(OH)_2} \quad Cl_2C{=}CHCl + \tfrac{1}{2}CaCl_2 + H_2O$$
$$\text{Trichloroethylene}$$
$$\xrightarrow{475°} \quad Cl_2C{=}CHCl + HCl$$

Degreasing and dry-cleaning agents

This product boils at 87° and is one of the most important of the chlorinated solvents. It is stable and noncorrosive and is less toxic than carbon tetrachloride. It is used chiefly for degreasing metal parts. The cold metal part is passed through the hot vapors, which condense on the metal and wash away the oil and dirt.

Addition of chlorine to trichloroethylene gives **pentachloroethane,** b.p. 162°, which can be converted to **tetrachloroethylene** (perchloroethylene), b.p. 118°, by the action of lime.

$$CHCl{=}CCl_2 \xrightarrow{Cl_2} CHCl_2CCl_3 \xrightarrow{Ca(OH)_2} CCl_2{=}CCl_2 \xrightarrow{Cl_2} CCl_3CCl_3$$
$$\text{Penta-} \qquad\qquad \text{Tetra-} \qquad\qquad \text{Hexa-}$$
$$\text{chloroethane} \qquad \text{chloroethylene} \qquad \text{chloroethane}$$

Pyrolysis of pentachloroethane over activated carbon is more economical because the anhydrous hydrogen chloride formed can be used for the manufacture of other chemicals.

$$CHCl_2CCl_3 \xrightarrow[250°]{Act.C, BaCl_2} CCl_2{=}CCl_2 + HCl$$

Tetrachloroethylene is the most important solvent used by the dry-cleaning industry. An advantage of chlorinated solvents is that they are nonflammable. A disadvantage is that all are more or less toxic; prolonged exposure to them results in fatty degeneration of the liver. Hence they should be used only in a closed system or with adequate ventilation. *Chlorinated hydrocarbons nonflammable but highly toxic*

SUMMARY

1. Unsaturated hydrocarbons have fewer than the maximum number of hydrogen atoms that can be attached to a particular carbon skeleton. Those having two fewer hydrogens than alkanes are called alkenes or olefins and have the general formula C_nH_{2n}. Compounds that have two fewer hydrogen atoms than the cyclanes are called cyclenes and have the general formula C_nH_{2n-2}.

2. To satisfy the rules of electronic structure, two adjacent carbon atoms of alkenes must each share two electrons with the other carbon atom, giving rise to what is known as a double bond.

3. The double bond has little effect on the physical properties of the molecule, as compared with those of the corresponding alkane, but is much more reactive than a single bond. All the reactions result in the addition of some other molecule to the double bond. In this process, the reagent dissociates into two parts, one of the bonds of the double bond is broken, and one part of the reagent adds to each carbon atom.

4. If the reagent is symmetrical, half adds to one carbon atom and the other half to the other carbon atom. If the reagent is not symmetrical, the more positive portion adds to the carbon atom having the greater number of hydrogens (Markovnikov rule).

5. For a reaction to take place, it must not only be thermodynamically favorable; the reacting molecules also must have sufficient kinetic energy to break bonds on collision before new bonds can be formed. The amount of energy required, which may be very little or quite large, is known as the activation energy. Catalysts are agents that introduce intermediate steps, each of which requires a lower activation energy than a one-step reaction, thus enabling a thermodynamically possible reaction to proceed at a lower temperature.

6. Compounds having two double bonds are called dienes. The double bonds may be isolated or conjugated.

7. Conjugated double bonds are characterized by 1,4-addition. They also absorb light in the ultraviolet range in the region of 220–290 mμ, whereas isolated double bonds absorb around 170 mμ.

8. Hydrocarbons in which two adjacent carbon atoms each share three electrons with the other are called alkynes or acetylenes. The carbon atoms are said to be joined by a triple bond.

9. The physical properties of alkynes are similar to those of the corresponding alkenes. The chemical properties of alkenes and alkynes also are similar, but the triple bond adds two moles of hydrogen or halogen instead of one mole. Moreover, if a triply-bonded carbon is bonded to a hydrogen atom, this hydrogen is sufficiently acidic to form salts with metals.

10. Acetylene itself is the most important alkyne and is used as the raw material for the commercial synthesis of other organic compounds.

EXERCISES

1. Write electronic formulas for each of the following compounds, using different symbols for the electrons to indicate their source: (a) *i*-butylene; (b) ethylene bromide; (c) 1,3-butadiene; (d) dimethylacetylene.
2. Write condensed structural formulas for the following compounds: (a) 3-methyl-4-ethyl-3-hexene; (b) tetramethylethylene; (c) 1-*s*-butylcyclohexene; (d) 2-methyl-1,3-butadiene; (e) *i*-butylacetylene; (f) 4-methyl-2-pentyne.
3. Write equations for the following reactions: (a) 2-pentene with bromine; (b) 1-hexene with sulfuric acid; (c) cyclopentene with chlorine; (d) catalytic reduction of 3-methyl-2-pentene; (e) 1,3-butadiene with one mole of bromine; (f) 2-butyne with two moles of chlorine; (g) methylacetylene with ammoniacal silver nitrate solution.
4. How may one distinguish readily by a chemical reaction between (a) *n*-pentane and 2-pentene; (b) ethylene and acetylene; (c) ethylacetylene and dimethylacetylene?

CHAPTER 5

AROMATIC
HYDROCARBONS

It was recognized at an early date that many organic compounds have a hydrocarbon portion with a higher ratio of carbon to hydrogen than the alkanes and have distinctly different chemical properties. These substances frequently are pleasantly odorous or derivable from aromatic substances. For example, the essential components of the volatile oils of cloves, cinnamon, sassafras, anise, bitter almonds, wintergreen, and vanilla exhibit these properties. The hydrocarbon *benzene* received its name because it was obtained from benzoic acid isolated from the aromatic substance *gum benzoin;* the name *toluene* was assigned to another hydrocarbon because it had been obtained by heating the fragrant *tolu balsam.* Loschmidt, an Austrian physicist (1821–1895), first stated in 1861 that most of the aromatic compounds could be considered as derivatives of the hydrocarbon, benzene, C_6H_6, just as the aliphatic compounds were considered as derivatives of methane, CH_4. Since then the term *aromatic compounds* has been applied to those compounds having the characteristic chemical properties of benzene. Compounds having alkane skeletons are termed *aliphatic* because the fats are related to the alkanes (Gr. *aliphatos,* fat). Compounds containing cyclane rings usually are designated as *alicyclic* because they are cyclic compounds with aliphatic properties.

Meaning of terms aromatic, aliphatic, and alicyclic

BENZENE AND ITS HOMOLOGS

Benzene has the molecular formula C_6H_6. All of the hydrogen atoms are alike, because replacement of one hydrogen by another group yields only one new compound, regardless of which hydrogen is replaced. Hence each hydrogen atom bears the same relationship to the molecule as a whole as every other hydrogen atom; that is, the molecule is symmetrically constituted.

Structure of benzene

Kekulé, who originated or consolidated most of the views concerning the structure of organic compounds (p. 12), assigned the first definite structural formula to benzene in 1865. He proposed that the six carbon atoms were at the corners of a regular hexagon and that one hydrogen atom was joined to each.

41

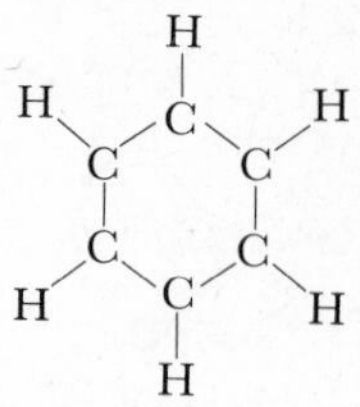

Kekulé formula explains number of substitution products

Kekulé's formula accounts also for the fact that if two hydrogen atoms are replaced by other groups, *Y,* three and only three isomers are known. If two adjacent hydrogen atoms are replaced, the resulting compound is known as the *ortho* isomer; if two alternate hydrogen atoms are replaced, the compound is known as the *meta* isomer; and if two opposite hydrogen atoms are replaced, it is known as the *para* isomer.

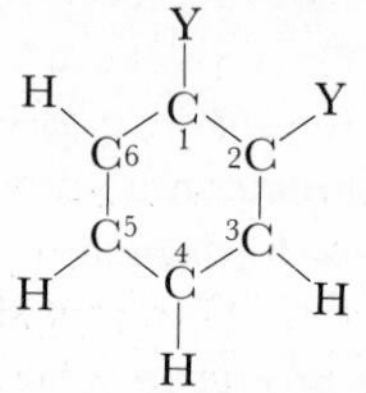

ortho Isomer 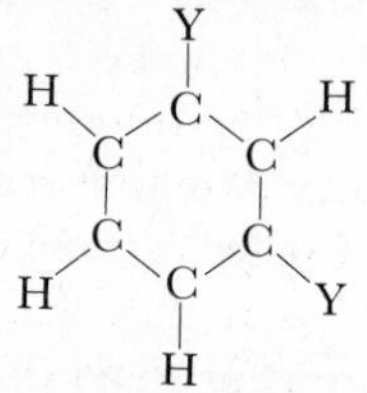   *meta* Isomer 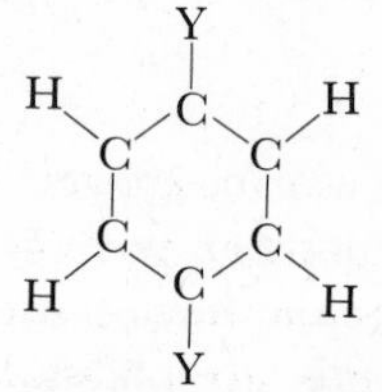   *para* Isomer

Regardless of which two adjacent hydrogen atoms are replaced, the same compound results. For example, if hydrogen atoms at positions 3 and 4 are replaced instead of those at 1 and 2, rotation through 120 degrees in the plane of the paper brings the two molecules into coincidence. Similar considerations hold for the *meta* and *para* isomer. Moreover the two groups, *Y,* may be alike or different without changing the number of isomers.

Objections to the simple hexagon formula for benzene are that it violates Kekulé's own advocacy of the tetravalence of carbon, and that it does not explain the fact that benzene can be made to add six atoms of halogen or six atoms of hydrogen. Both difficulties are overcome by the introduction of three double bonds in continuous conjugation. Now, however, the objection arises that two *ortho* substitution products would be expected, one in which the two carbon atoms carrying the *Y* groups are linked by a double bond (*a*), and another in which they are linked by a single bond (*b*).

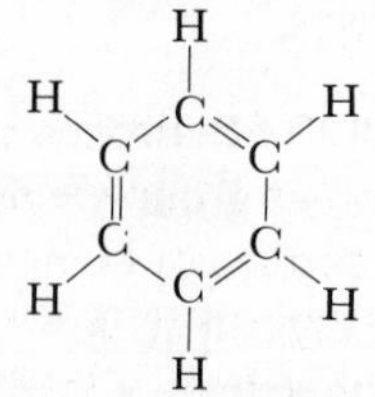

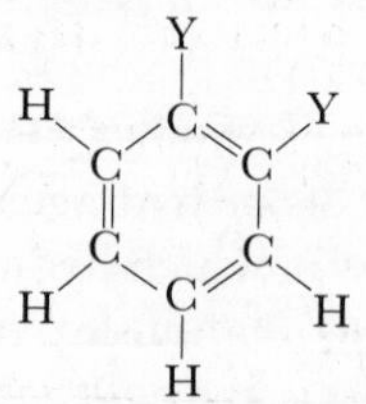

Double bonds cause trouble

(*a*) 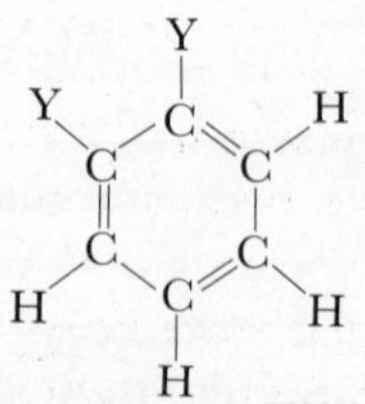   (*b*)

To overcome this difficulty, Kekulé proposed in 1872 that the positions of the double bonds are not fixed, but that an equilibrium exists between two structures which is so mobile that individual isomers such as (*a*) and (*b*) cannot be isolated.

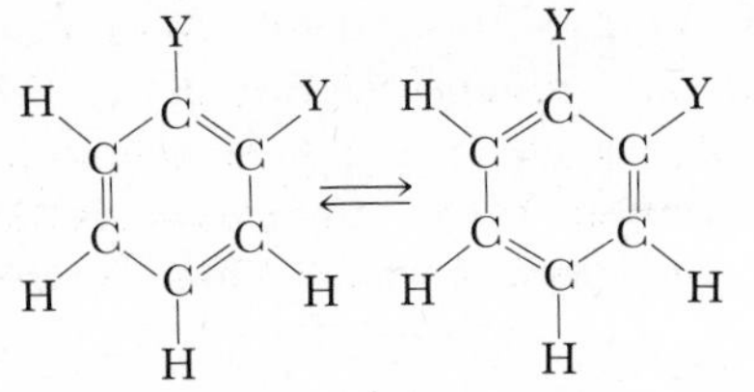

(a)   (b)

The current view is that in neither benzene nor its derivatives do molecules of two structures exist in mobile equilibrium with each other, but that only one kind of molecule is present, one that is a hybrid of the two structures. The most direct evidence for this view comes from the measurement of the distances between carbon atoms by means of electron diffraction. In ethane and other saturated compounds the distance between adjacent carbon atoms is 1.55 Å; in ethylene the carbon-carbon distance is 1.34 Å; and in acetylene it is 1.20 Å. In other words the distance is shorter for a double bond than for a single bond and shorter for a triple bond than for a double bond. This result is to be expected, because the attraction between atoms increases with the formation of each bond. In compounds containing both single bonds and double bonds, both distances are observed, but for benzene only a single carbon-carbon distance can be detected, namely 1.39 Å, which lies between the single bond and double bond distances. Therefore all of the carbon-carbon bonds in benzene are alike and benzene is a perfectly symmetrical molecule. To avoid the implication that an equilibrium is involved, a symbolism is adopted in which double arrows are replaced by a double-headed arrow, and the whole is enclosed in braces.

Hybrid structure preferred

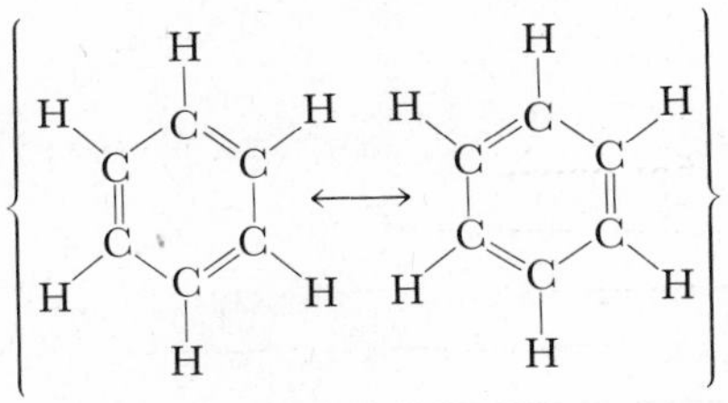

Because this hybrid structure is more stable than that having three double bonds by about 36 kcal. per mole, this amount of energy, which is known as the **resonance energy** of benzene, must be supplied before the unsaturation electrons become as reactive as they are in an alkene. Hence addition reactions of benzene take place only with difficulty, and usually the double bonds may be ignored.

Aromatic compounds may be named as derivatives of benzene or of some other aromatic compound. Thus the compound in which a chlorine atom has replaced a hydrogen atom in benzene is known as chlorobenzene. When more than one substituent is present the positions occupied are indicated by numbers. Usually the benzene ring is represented as a hexagon, the presence of hydrogen at each unsubstituted corner being understood. When substituents are present, one group usually is placed at the top carbon of the hexagon, which then becomes the number one carbon atom. To

Compounds named as derivatives of benzene

indicate the position of other substituents, the remaining carbon atoms are numbered consecutively around the ring in the direction that gives the substituents the smaller numbers. It is preferable to name the substituent groups in alphabetical order. When only two substituents are present, the designations *ortho* (*o-*), *meta* (*m-*), or *para* (*p-*) may be used.

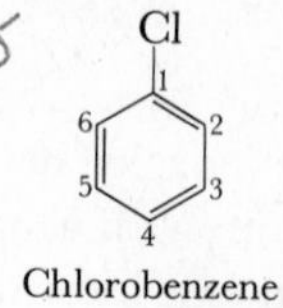

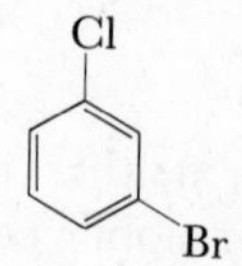

3-Bromo-1-chlorobenzene
3-Bromochlorobenzene
m-Bromochlorobenzene

Chlorobenzene

In these and subsequent formulas the carbon and hydrogen atoms of the benzene ring are represented by the simple hexagon and only those groups that replace hydrogen are given. The double bonds are included to indicate that the ring is aromatic and not alicyclic (p. 41), but it is understood that they are not the same as fixed aliphatic double bonds (p. 43).

Common names used extensively

Common names are used even more extensively for aromatic compounds than for aliphatic compounds. Thus many of the hydrocarbons have common names. Methylbenzene is called *toluene*, and 1,2-, 1,3-, and 1,4-dimethylbenzene are known as *ortho-*, *meta-*, and *para-xylene*.

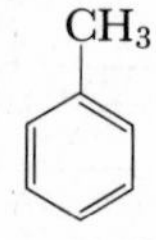

Toluene 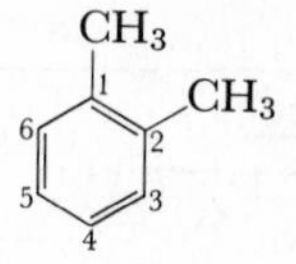　　　　*o*-Xylene 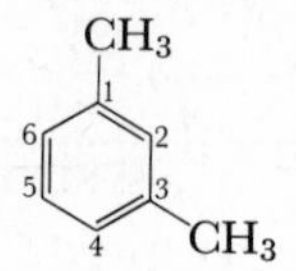　　　　*m*-Xylene 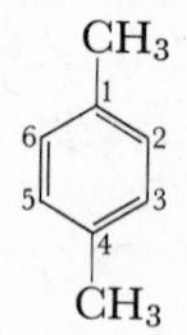　　　　*p*-Xylene

1,3,5-Trimethylbenzene is called *mesitylene*, isopropylbenzene is *cumene*, and 4-isopropyltoluene is *p-cymene*.

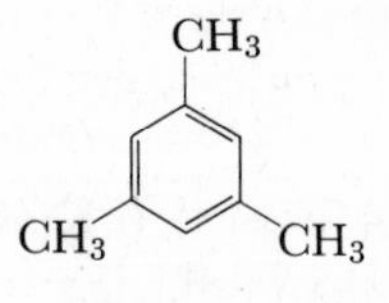

Mesitylene 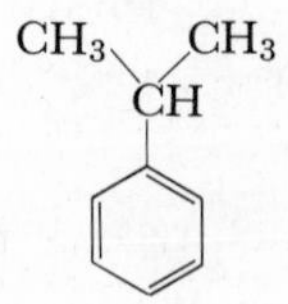　　　　Cumene 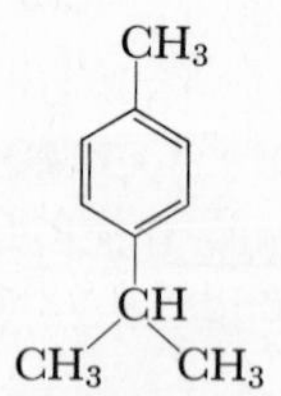　　　　*p*-Cymene

Meaning of terms nucleus and side chain

Kekulé introduced the terms *ring* and *nucleus* to designate the characteristic portion of aromatic compounds. The aliphatic portions he called *side chains*. Groups obtained by dropping a hydrogen atom from the nucleus are called *aryl* groups. Frequently they are indicated by the symbol Ar, just as R is used to designate an alkyl group. The group C_6H_5 derived from benzene is known as *phenyl*. This name comes from *phene*, a name that was proposed for benzene by the French chemist Laurent (1807–1853), because it is present in illuminating gas (Gr. *phainein*, to bring to light). The phenyl group frequently is designated by the Greek letter φ (phi); for example, φBr is phenyl bromide or bromobenzene.

If two hydrogen atoms are dropped, the residue, C_6H_4, is known as a *Names of aryl groups*
phenylene group. Because the two hydrogen atoms may be removed in three
ways, there are *o-*, *m-*, and *p-*phenylene groups. If a hydrogen atom is
dropped from the methyl group of toluene, the residue is known as a *benzyl*
group, but if from the nucleus, three *tolyl* groups, *ortho*, *meta*, and *para*,
result.

Bromobenzene
(phenyl bromide)

o-Dibromobenzene
(1,2-dibromobenzene or
o-phenylene bromide)

know

Benzyl chloride
(phenylmethyl chloride)

p-Chlorotoluene
(*p*-tolyl chloride)

Hexane, C_6H_{14}, boils at 68.8°. Because benzene has a lower molecular
weight, its boiling point might be expected to be lower. Actually benzene
boils at 80.1°. The higher boiling point can be ascribed to the fact that the
benzene molecules have a rigid flat structure, whereas the hexane chains
can undergo considerable twisting and bending on thermal agitation. Hence
the van der Waals forces can operate more effectively between the benzene
molecules. The more symmetrical structure for benzene accounts also for
its relatively high melting point of +5.5° compared with −95° for hexane
or for toluene.

Physical properties; boil higher and are better solvents than alkanes

Being a hydrocarbon, benzene is practically insoluble in water, but
the solubility at 15° of 0.18 g. per 100 g. of water is over ten times that of
the 0.014 g. per 100 g. of water for *n*-hexane. The greater attraction of benzene for water molecules would be expected because of the greater polarizability of the unsaturation electrons. The solubility of water in benzene is
0.06 g. per 100 g. of benzene. Aromatic hydrocarbons are more useful as
solvents and diluents for paints, lacquers, and synthetic enamels than are
alkanes. They can be used only with proper precautions, however, because
of their high toxicity. They cause the destruction of red blood corpuscles,
and even very low concentrations are dangerous on prolonged exposure.
All workers using materials containing volatile aromatic hydrocarbons
should be subjected to frequent blood counts to detect signs of poisoning.

The usual reagents for double bonds do not add readily to the benzene
nucleus. In general the reactivity of the unsaturation electrons of benzene
is so low that the double bonds usually can be disregarded. Frequently they
are not even indicated in the formula for benzene. In contrast to the non-
reactivity of the double bonds, the hydrogen atoms of the aromatic nucleus
are substituted more readily than those of the alkanes.

Chemical properties

Saturated hydrocarbons react with chlorine or bromine at high tem-

Controllable halogenation

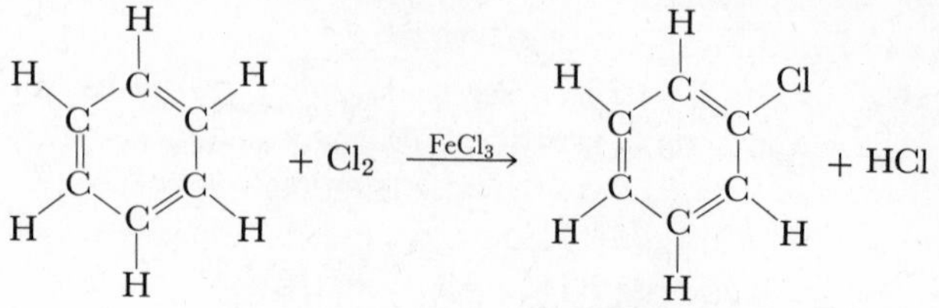

peratures or in the presence of light of short wave length, but the reaction is violent, the position of substitution is random, and considerable quantities of polysubstitution products are formed. At ordinary temperatures and in the absence of light, reaction is very slow. Benzene reacts with chlorine or bromine in the presence of light, but addition takes place rather than substitution. On the other hand, at moderately elevated temperatures, benzene reacts rapidly with chlorine or bromine to give halogen substitution products if a catalyst such as ferric chloride or bromide is present.

Chlorobenzene

Since a second halogen substitutes with more difficulty, the reaction can be controlled to give chiefly the monosubstitution product.

Controllable nitration

Propane or *n*-butane reacts with oxides of nitrogen at high temperatures. However, not only are all of the isomeric monosubstitution products obtained, but also all of the possible nitro compounds resulting from breaking the carbon-carbon bonds (p. 145). In contrast, benzene reacts with fuming nitric acid at moderate temperature, or better with concentrated nitric acid in the presence of concentrated sulfuric acid, to give good yields of the mononitro substitution products.

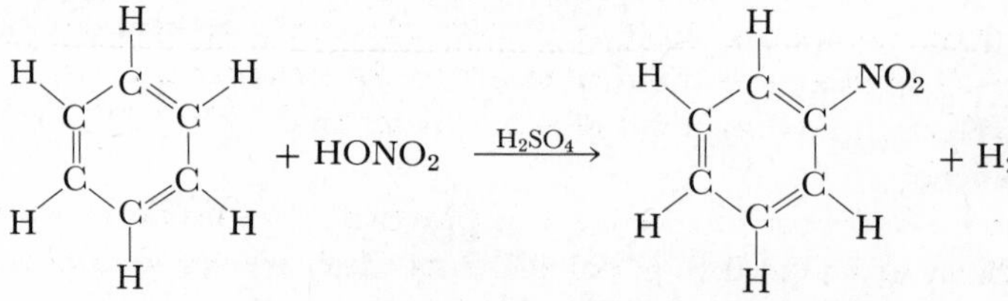

Nitrobenzene

Direct sulfonation

Straight-chain alkanes do not react with concentrated sulfuric acid, but sulfonation of benzene takes place readily to give the monosulfonic acid in good yield.

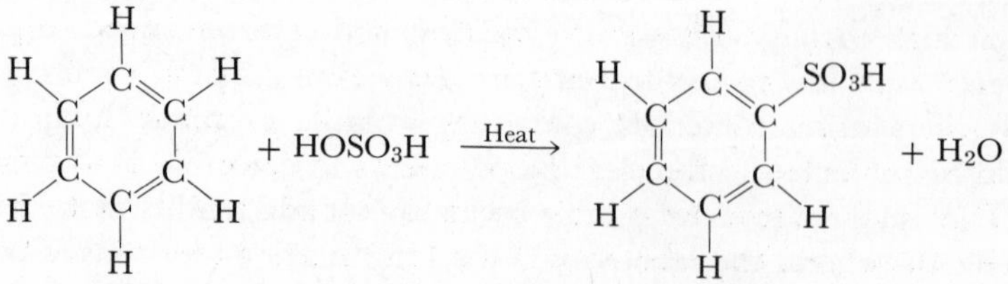

Benzenesulfonic acid

Aromatic hydrocarbons react with acyl chlorides (p. 109) in the presence of anhydrous aluminum chloride to give good yields of ketones.

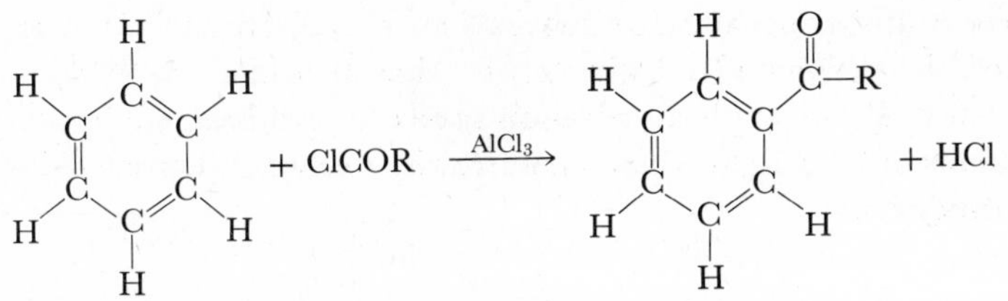

$$+ \text{ClCOR} \xrightarrow{\text{AlCl}_3} \quad + \text{HCl}$$

This behavior is known as the **Friedel-Crafts reaction** after its discoverers, a French professor, Charles Friedel (1832–1899), and his American co-worker, James Mason Crafts (1839–1917).

Friedel-Crafts reaction

It is the ability to undergo these substitution reactions that is characteristic of benzene and its derivatives. Compounds exhibiting these properties are classed as *aromatic compounds*.

Although the oxidation of side chains does not involve the aromatic nucleus, it usually is considered as one of the typical reactions of aromatic compounds. When the alkylbenzenes are subjected to vigorous oxidation with dichromic acid (sodium dichromate and sulfuric acid) or potassium permanganate, the alkyl group is converted to a carboxyl group.

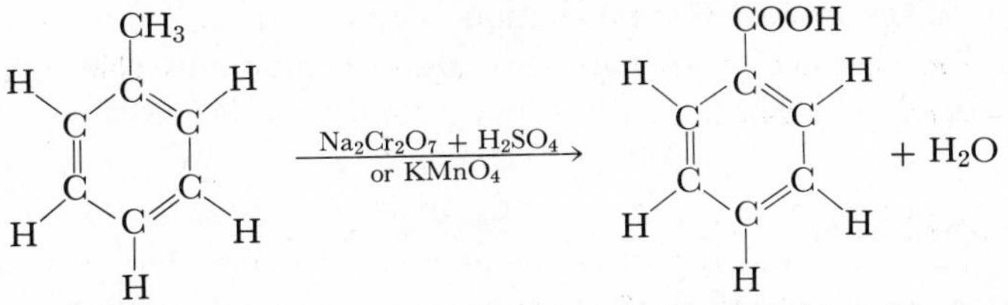

Oxidation of side chains

$$\xrightarrow[\text{or KMnO}_4]{\text{Na}_2\text{Cr}_2\text{O}_7 + \text{H}_2\text{SO}_4} \quad + \text{H}_2\text{O}$$

Toluene   Benzoic acid

Since the point of attack is the carbon atom attached to the benzene nucleus, a carboxyl group results regardless of the size of the alkyl group or the type of substituent present in the alkyl group.

OTHER AROMATIC NUCLEI

Besides benzene, other compounds have similar properties. Obviously compounds having more than one benzene ring should be possible. Toluene is phenylmethane, and **diphenylmethane, $(C_6H_5)_2CH_2$, triphenylmethane, $(C_6H_5)_3CH$, and tetraphenylmethane, $(C_6H_5)_4C$,** also are known. The compound in which a phenyl group replaces one hydrogen of benzene is called **biphenyl.**

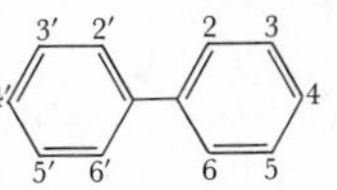

Multiple ring compounds

Biphenyl 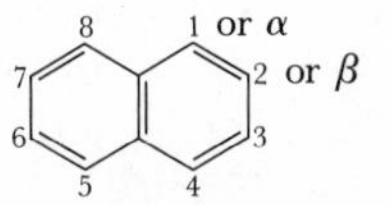   Naphthalene 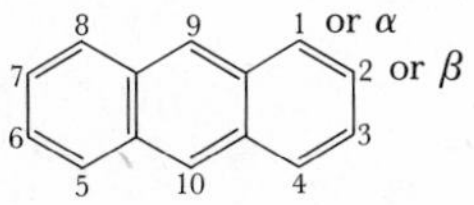   Anthracene 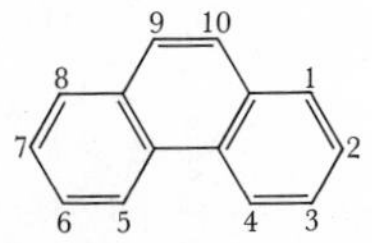   Phenanthrene

Compounds having benzene rings fused to each other are called *condensed nuclear hydrocarbons.* **Naphthalene, $C_{10}H_8$, anthracene, $C_{14}H_{10}$, and phenanthrene, $C_{14}H_{10}$,** which are present in coal tar, are common examples. The numbering and designations of the positions in the rings are indicated in the formulas. Naphthalene has two kinds of hydrogen and yields two different monosubstitution products. Anthracene has three different kinds of hydrogen, which can give rise to three different monosubstitution products.

SUMMARY

1. Benzene has the molecular formula C_6H_6. It yields only one monosubstitution product and only three disubstitution products. These facts, together with x-ray and electron-diffraction data, show that the six carbon atoms are at the corners of a regular hexagon, that all of the atoms lie in the same plane, and that all bond angles measure 120°.

2. Despite the deficiency of hydrogen, benzene has little tendency to add reagents. A system of six unsaturation electrons in a six-membered ring is more stable by 36 kcal. per mole than three isolated double bonds. This increased stability accounts for the difficulty with which reagents add to the benzene nucleus.

3. The characteristic reactions of benzene are controllable halogenation, controllable nitration, direct sulfonation, and the Friedel-Crafts reaction.

4. Aromatic compounds, from the chemical viewpoint, are those compounds that undergo the reactions characteristic of benzene.

EXERCISES

1. Write structural formulas for all of the possible compounds in each of the following groups: (a) the monobromomononitrotoluenes; (b) the dichloronaphthalenes; (c) the monobromo-anthracenes; (d) the mononitrophenanthrenes.

2. Write structural formulas for (a) the phenyl group; (b) the phenylene groups; (c) the tolyl groups; (d) the benzyl group.

3. Write structural formulas for (a) o-toluenesulfonic acid; (b) 2-chloro-4-i-propyltoluene; (c) nitromesitylene; (d) 3-bromocumene; (e) 2,2'-dinitrobiphenyl.

4. Three tribromobenzenes are known that melt at 44°, 87.4°, and 119°, respectively. When each is nitrated, they give, respectively, three, two, and one mononitrotribromobenzenes. Give the structures of the three tribromobenzenes and of their nitration products.

5. How could one distinguish readily by a chemical reaction (a) between benzene and cyclohexane; (b) between benzene and cyclohexene?

CHAPTER 6

NATURAL GAS, PETROLEUM, AND COAL

The chief use for natural gas, petroleum, and coal is as fuel to supply heat for various purposes. However, either directly or indirectly, these substances also are the principal raw materials for the production of organic chemicals.

NATURAL GAS AND PETROLEUM

Natural gas and petroleum are the chief sources of hydrocarbons. **Natural gas** varies greatly in composition. Unprocessed gases contain 60 to 80 per cent methane, 5 to 9 per cent ethane, 3 to 18 per cent propane, and 2 to 14 per cent higher hydrocarbons. Most of the natural gas is used for fuel, although an increasing amount is being used as raw material for the synthesis of organic compounds (pp. 31, 37). *Composition*

Petroleum is a complex liquid mixture of organic compounds. The chief components are hydrocarbons, which may be aliphatic, alicyclic, or aromatic in varying proportions. In addition to carbon and hydrogen, petroleum contains 1 to 6 per cent of sulfur, nitrogen, and oxygen.

The separation of the individual components is very difficult, but between 1927 and 1960, at the U.S. Bureau of Standards and at the Carnegie Institute of Technology, 145 pure hydrocarbons were isolated from the gas, gasoline, and kerosene fractions of a midcontinent petroleum. Of the 145 hydrocarbons, 49 were paraffinic, 48 were alicyclic, and 48 were aromatic. It is estimated that the portion of petroleum boiling up to 200° contains at least 500 compounds.

Petroleum is *refined,* that is, separated into useful products, by distilling into fractions of different boiling ranges, converting the less desirable components into more valuable products, and treating fractions in various ways to remove undesirable components. **Gasoline** is the fraction boiling between 0° and 200°. However, qualities other than volatility also are important, especially the *octane number.* Everyone is familiar with *knocking* in an automobile gasoline engine, the *ping* that develops when pulling up a long grade *Refining of petroleum* or attempting to accelerate a car too rapidly. Knocking varies with the fuel and depends on the structures of the hydrocarbon molecules.

Octane number of gasoline

As a means of measuring the knocking properties of a fuel, two pure hydrocarbons were selected as standards. One is *n*-heptane, which was worse in its tendency to cause knocking than any ordinary gasoline, and the other is 2,2,4-trimethylpentane, which was better than any gasoline known at the time. Blends of these two pure hydrocarbons could be made to match the knocking characteristics of any known fuel. The knocking property of the fuel then could be described by its **octane number,** the per cent of 2,2,4-trimethylpentane in the synthetic blend that matched the gasoline in knocking properties. Investigation of a large number of pure hydrocarbons has shown that in general the octane number increases with an increase in branching, and that olefins and aromatic hydrocarbons are better than saturated hydrocarbons.

Increased yield of gasoline by cracking

Besides the fraction obtained from the first distillation of petroleum, referred to as *straight-run* gasoline, large amounts of gasoline are obtained by *cracking* (p. 24) the higher-boiling fractions. Purely thermal cracking is being replaced rapidly by catalytic cracking in which the oil vapors are heated in the presence of aluminum silicate. Not only is the yield of gasoline increased by cracking; the octane number of straight-run gasoline may be 50–55, that of thermally cracked gasoline 70–72, and of catalytically cracked gasoline 77–81. Cracking in the presence of hydrogen and special catalysts yields a saturated product, free of oxygen, sulfur, and nitrogen.

$$R - R + H_2 \longrightarrow 2\,RH$$
$$ROH + H_2 \longrightarrow RH + H_2O$$
$$R_2S + 2\,H_2 \longrightarrow 2\,RH + H_2S$$
$$R_2NH + 2\,H_2 \longrightarrow 2\,RH + NH_3$$

Moreover, because no coke is produced and because the density of hydrocarbons decreases with decreasing molecular weight, up to 115 barrels of products result from 100 barrels of feed stock. Although the octane number of gasoline produced in this way is low, it can be raised to as high as 100 by *reforming*. In this process gasolines are heated in the presence of platinum catalysts. The acyclic and alicyclic hydrocarbons are converted by cyclization and dehydrogenation to aromatic hydrocarbons. Hydrogen from the reforming operation is used in the cracking process.

Increased octane number by reforming

n-Heptane   Methylcyclohexane   Toluene

By adding tetraethyl- or tetramethyllead

Octane number is improved also by the addition of *tetraethyllead,* Pb(C_2H_5)_4. One of the disadvantages of tetraethyllead when used alone is that the product of combustion is lead oxide, which is reduced to lead and causes pitting of the cylinder walls. If ethylene halides are added with the tetraethyllead, lead halides are formed, which are more resistant to reduction and are volatile at the temperature of combustion. Commercial *Ethyl Fluid*, which is added to gasoline, consists of approximately 59 per cent tetraethyllead, 13 per cent ethylene bromide, 24 per cent ethylene chloride, and 4 per cent kerosene and dye. *Tetramethyllead* is more effective than tetraethyllead in gasolines having a high aromatic content.

In the cracking operations considerable amounts of gaseous hydrocarbons are produced. The olefins may be converted by *polymerization* (p. 232) to higher-boiling olefins, or they may be used to synthesize other organic chemicals. The saturated compounds may be *dehydrogenated* to olefins or dienes. Straight-chain hydrocarbons can be *isomerized* to branched-chain compounds.

Other commercial fractions of petroleum are **kerosene, turbine fuel,** and **jet fuel** (b.p. 175°–275°), **gas oil, fuel oil,** and **diesel oil** (b.p. 250°–400°), and **lubricating oil.** Lubricating oil is purified by distillation at reduced pressure and by extraction with solvents to remove undesirable components. It then is mixed with various *additives* to improve the lubricating properties of the oil. **Paraffin** is the mixture of solid saturated hydrocarbons that crystallizes from various high-boiling fractions. **Greases** are made by dispersing metallic soaps (p. 124) in hot lubricating oils.

Products other than gasoline

CARBONIZATION OF COAL

Coal is a compact stratified mass derived from plants that have suffered partial decay and have been subjected to various degrees of heat and pressure. Most normal banded coals are believed to have originated in peat swamps. The substances peat, lignite, soft or bituminous coal, and anthracite or hard coal are progressive stages of metamorphosis in which the ratio of the amount of carbon to the amount of other elements increases. When bituminous coal is heated to a sufficiently high temperature (350°–1000°) in the absence of air, volatile products are formed, and a residue of impure carbon remains which is called *coke.* The process is known as the *destructive distillation* or *carbonization* of coal. When the volatile products cool to ordinary temperature, a portion condenses to a black viscous liquid known as *coal tar.* The noncondensable gases are known as *coal gas.* One ton of coal yields about 1500 pounds of coke, 8 gallons of tar, and 10,000 cubic feet of coal gas. About 20 pounds of ammonium sulfate is obtained by washing the gas with sulfuric acid to remove ammonia.

Coal carbonization produces coal gas, coal tar, and coke

The principal reason for the commercial carbonization of coal is the production of **coke,** which is used for the reduction of ores in blast furnaces. Coke is used also as a smokeless industrial and household fuel.

Coal gas varies in composition during the course of the distillation but consists chiefly of hydrogen and methane in about equal volumes, along with some carbon monoxide, ethane, ethylene, benzene, carbon dioxide, oxygen, and nitrogen, and smaller amounts of cyclopentadiene (p. 36), toluene, naphthalene (p. 47), water vapor, ammonia, hydrogen sulfide, hydrogen cyanide, cyanogen, and nitric oxide. After removal of the noxious components the gas is run into mains for use as illuminating gas and as a domestic fuel. When profitable, the benzene, toluene, and other less volatile hydrocarbons also are extracted from the gas by washing (*scrubbing*) with a high-boiling petroleum fraction (b.p. 285°–350°) known as *straw* *oil.* The hydrocarbons are recovered by heating (*stripping*) the oil and condensing the vapors. The condensate contains chiefly benzene and toluene and is known as *light oil* because of its low specific gravity. Although the benzene and toluene are liquids at room temperature, the coal gas is saturated with them, and a larger amount can be obtained by washing the coal gas than by distilling the coal tar. About three gallons of light oil can be recovered per ton of coal carbonized.

The composition of **coal tar** varies with the process used for carbonization. Tar obtained from high temperature distillation is the most useful for chemical purposes. The first step in the separation of the black foulsmelling liquid into its components is distillation. The fractions obtained in a typical procedure are (*1*) *light oil* (so-called because it floats on water) distilling up to 200°, 5 per cent; (*2*) *middle oil* (carbolic oil), 200°–250°, 17 per cent; (*3*) *heavy oil* (dead oil, creosote oil), 250°–300°, 7 per cent; (*4*) *anthracene oil* (green oil), 300°–350°, 9 per cent; and (*5*) *pitch,* the residue, 62 per cent.

The further separation of the fractions depends on a combination of chemical and physical methods. Three main groups of substances are present: (*1*) *neutral compounds,* chiefly hydrocarbons; (*2*) *tar acids,* very weakly acidic substances soluble in sodium hydroxide solution; (*3*) *tar bases,* weakly basic substances soluble in dilute sulfuric acid.

The **light oil** fraction from coal tar is rather small, but about eight times as much can be recovered by scrubbing coal gas. It usually is separated directly into its components by fractional distillation. The distilled fractions are treated with concentrated sulfuric acid to polymerize the olefins and to remove any basic or oxygenated compounds. The insoluble portions then are washed with 10 per cent aqueous sodium hydroxide and distilled to give benzene, toluene, and xylenes.

The **middle** or **carbolic oil** is combined with the high-boiling fraction from the light oil and cooled in large shallow pans. The solid hydrocarbon *naphthalene* (p. 47) crystallizes and is removed by centrifuging. The crude naphthalene is distilled, washed while molten with sulfuric acid, water, and aqueous alkali, and distilled again to give refined naphthalene. The oil that is separated from the crude naphthalene during the initial crystallization is washed with aqueous sodium hydroxide to remove the tar acids. Steam is passed into the aqueous extract to remove volatile materials, and then the solution is cooled and saturated with carbon dioxide, which liberates the weakly acidic tar acids from their salts. The tar acid layer is separated and fractionally distilled to give phenol (p. 73), which is purified further by crystallization. The oil remaining after the extraction of acidic substances with alkali is washed with aqueous sulfuric acid, which forms salts with the tar bases and takes them into solution. The tar bases are liberated by the addition of sodium hydroxide and are distilled to give chiefly *pyridine* (p. 131). The oil remaining from the acid treatment is distilled to give solvent naphtha and a solid residue of polymerized olefins known as *cumar resin.*

The **heavy oil** may be treated in much the same way to yield naphthalene, the higher tar acids (cresols, p. 73), and the higher tar bases. The tendency in recent years has been not to separate the higher fractions into their components but to use them as wood preservatives under the name *creosote oil.*

The extent, expressed as a percentage, to which the more important components are present in coal tar is as follows: benzene, 0.1; toluene, 0.2; xylenes, anthracene, and carbazole, 1.0 each; crude tar bases, 2.0 (pyridine 0.1); crude tar acids, 2.5 (phenol 0.7); phenanthrene, 4.0; naphthalene, 11.0. The percentages of benzene, toluene, and xylenes do not include the amounts present in the light-oil fraction extracted from coal gas by scrubbing.

Relative amounts of products

SUMMARY

1. Although used chiefly as fuel, petroleum and coal also are the principal raw materials for the commercial synthesis of organic compounds and derived products such as plastics, protective coatings, dyes, rubbers, and fibers.

2. Petroleum is refined, that is, separated into useful products such as gasoline, gas oil, and lubricants, chiefly by distillation and by removal of deleterious substances.

3. In order to increase the quantity of lower-boiling products, the higher-boiling fractions are subjected, usually in the presence of catalysts, to thermal decomposition, a process known as cracking.

4. Next to proper volatility, the most important characteristic of gasoline is its octane number, which is a measure of its tendency to cause knocking in gasoline engines. The higher the octane number, the higher the compression ratio that may be used without knocking, and hence the greater thermal efficiency that may be obtained.

5. Tetraethyllead or tetramethyllead added to gasoline increases the octane number, and other additives may be used to decrease the tendency of the fuel to foul spark plugs or to deposit gum in the piston rings.

6. The middle fractions may be cracked or may be used to produce kerosene, jet engine fuel, diesel fuel, or gas turbine fuel.

7. The higher-boiling portion of petroleum is distilled at reduced pressure to yield fractions from which paraffin and lubricating oils are produced. Various additives are used in the latter to increase the lubricating properties, to decrease the tendency of the oil to thin out with rising temperature, and to keep the cylinder walls and pistons of the engine clean.

8. Coal must be converted by destructive distillation into coke to yield a fuel suitable for use in blast furnaces. During the coking, volatile products are formed. The mixture of products noncondensable at room temperature is known as coal gas, and the mixture of condensable products is called coal tar.

9. Coal tar is a complex mixture from which over 200 compounds have been isolated. It is an important source, along with coal gas, of aromatic compounds such as benzene, toluene, xylene, and naphthalene. However, increasing quantities of these hydrocarbons are being synthesized by the dehydrogenation of cyclanes isolated from petroleum.

EXERCISES

1. What is meant by the statement that a gasoline has an octane number of 85?
2. (a) What volume of carbon dioxide (S.T.P.) is produced when one gallon (3.78 liters) of gasoline is burned? Assume that the gasoline contains only octanes and that its density is 0.7 g. per cc. (b) What weight of water is formed?
3. What types of hydrocarbons are present in (a) most gasolines; (b) paraffin wax?
4. Benzene is produced both from coal and from petroleum. How do the processes differ?

CHAPTER 7

COMMON
FUNCTIONAL
GROUPS

The saturated hydrocarbons are relatively unreactive compounds. The presence of one or more double or triple bonds greatly increases the reactivity of the molecule. Reactions of these unsaturated molecules are associated with the multiple bonds, and the reactions of organic molecules in general are associated with a specific structure, usually called the **function** or the **functional group** of the molecule.

Reactive portions of molecule called functional groups

In addition to multiple bonds, many other functions are known which contain elements other than or in addition to carbon and hydrogen. Thus several functional groups such as the hydroxyl group, the ether linkage, the aldehyde or ketone groups, or the carboxyl group contain oxygen. Nitrogen and sulfur are present in other functional groups, and various combinations of oxygen, nitrogen, sulfur, carbon, and hydrogen account for other functions. All of these groups confer their own special properties on the molecule and give rise to the various classes of organic compounds. Some of these classes will be considered in detail and others mentioned only in passing.

The names and the electronic and bond structures of some of the groups that will be discussed are summarized in Table 5. If at any time an unfamiliar group is encountered, or if its structure has been forgotten, it will be convenient to refer to this table, which also gives the page at which the group or class is discussed in more detail.

TABLE 5. IMPORTANT FUNCTIONAL GROUPS

NAME OF GROUP	CLASS OF COMPOUNDS IN WHICH GROUP OCCURS	ELECTRONIC FORMULA	BONDED FORMULA (SEE FOOTNOTE A)	REFERENCE PAGE NO.
Double bond	Alkenes, olefins, or unsaturated compounds	·C⫶C×	$-\overset{\mid}{C}=\overset{\mid}{C}-$	29
Triple bond	Alkynes, acetylenes, or acetylenic compounds	·C⫶C×	$-C\equiv C-$	36
Hydroxyl	Alcohols	R⫶O⬝⬝H	R—O—H or ROH	58
Hydroxyl	Phenols	Ar⫶O⬝⬝H	Ar—O—H or ArOH	73
Halogen (X = F, Cl, Br, or I)	Halides	R⫶X⫶ (Ar)	R—X (Ar)	88
Oxide or ether	Ethers	R⫶O⫶R (Ar)	R—O—R or ROR (Ar)	80
Carbonyl	Aldehydes, ketones, carboxylic acids and their derivatives	·C⫶O×	$-\overset{\mid}{C}=O$ or $-CO-$	93, 102
Aldehyde	Aldehydes	$\overset{H}{R\,C\,O}$ (Ar)	$R-\overset{H}{\underset{\mid}{C}}=O$ or RCHO (Ar)	93
Keto or oxo	Ketones	$\overset{}{R\,C\,O}$ (Ar) R	$R-\overset{}{\underset{\mid}{C}}=O$ or RCOR (Ar) R	93
Carboxyl	Carboxylic acids	·C⫶O⬝⬝H	$-\overset{O}{\overset{\|}{C}}-O-H$ or $-COOH$	102
Acid chloride or chlorocarbonyl	Acid chlorides or acyl chlorides	·C⬝Cl⬝	$-\overset{O}{\overset{\|}{C}}-Cl$ or $-COCl$	109
Ester or alkoxycarbonyl	Esters	·C⫶O⬝⬝R (Ar)	$-\overset{O}{\overset{\|}{C}}-O-R$ or $-COOR$ (Ar)	109
Anhydride	Anhydrides, acid anhydrides, or carboxylic anhydrides	R C⫶O⫶C R (Ar)	$R-\overset{O}{\overset{\|}{C}}-O-\overset{O}{\overset{\|}{C}}-R$ or $(RCO)_2O$ (Ar)	108
Amino	Primary amines	R⫶N⫶H (Ar) H	R—N—H or RNH_2 (Ar) H	126

TABLE 5. IMPORTANT FUNCTIONAL GROUPS (*Continued*)

NAME OF GROUP	CLASS OF COMPOUNDS IN WHICH GROUP OCCURS	ELECTRONIC FORMULA	BONDED FORMULA (SEE FOOTNOTE A)	REFERENCE PAGE NO.
Imino	Secondary amines	$R\!:\!\overset{xx}{\underset{ox}{N}}\!:\!H$ R	R—N—H or R_2NH (Ar) R	126
	Tertiary amines	$R\!:\!\overset{xx}{\underset{ox}{N}}\!:\!R$ (Ar) R	R—N—R or R_3N (Ar) R	126
Amide or amido	Amides	$\cdot\overset{x\,O\,x}{\underset{\cdot o}{C}}\!:\!\overset{}{N}\!:\!H$ H	$-\overset{O}{\overset{\|}{C}}-\underset{H}{N}-H$ or $-CONH_2$	136
Imide or imido	Imides	$R\!:\!\overset{xOx}{C}\!:\!\overset{}{N}\!:\!\overset{xOx}{C}\!:\!R$ H (Ar)	$R-\overset{O}{\overset{\|}{C}}-\underset{H}{N}-\overset{O}{\overset{\|}{C}}-R$ or $(RCO)_2NH$ (Ar)	137
Cyano or nitrile	Cyanides or nitriles	$R\!:\!\overset{o}{\underset{x}{C}}\!:\!\overset{o}{\underset{x}{N}}\!:$ (Ar)	R—C≡N or RCN (Ar)	90
Isocyano or isonitrile	Isocyanides or carbylamines	$R\!:\!\overset{x}{\underset{o}{N}}\!:\!\overset{x}{\underset{x}{C}}\!:$ (Ar)	R—N≡C or RNC (Ar) (see footnote b)	—
Isocyanate	Isocyanates	$R\!:\!\overset{xx}{\underset{o}{N}}\!:\!\overset{x}{\underset{x}{C}}\!:\!\overset{o}{\underset{x}{O}}\!:$	R—N=C=O or RNCO (Ar)	142
Nitroso	Nitroso compounds	$Ar\!:\!\overset{o}{\underset{xx}{N}}\!:\!\overset{o}{\underset{x}{O}}\!:$	Ar—N=O or ArNO	144
Nitro	Nitro compounds	$\overset{oo}{\underset{o}{O}}$ $R\!:\!\overset{xx}{\underset{o}{N}}\!:\!\overset{o}{\underset{o}{O}}$ (Ar)	$R-\overset{O}{\overset{\uparrow}{N}}=O$ or RNO_2 (Ar) (see footnote b)	144
Azo	Azo compounds	$R\!:\!\overset{xx}{\underset{x}{N}}\!:\!\overset{o\,oo}{N}\!:\!R$ (Ar)	R—N=N—R (Ar)	208
Diazonium	Diazonium salts	$\left[Ar\!:\!\overset{+\,x}{\underset{x}{N}}\!:\!\overset{}{\underset{o}{N}}\!:\right]$	$\left[Ar-\overset{+}{N}\!\equiv\!N\right]$ or $\left[ArN^+{}_2\right]$	208
Thiol or sulfhydryl	Thiols or mercaptans	$R\!:\!\overset{xx}{\underset{xx}{S}}\!:\!H$	R—S—H or RSH (Ar)	84
Sulfide or thioether	Sulfides or thioethers	$R\!:\!\overset{xx}{\underset{xx}{S}}\!:\!R$	R—S—R or R_2S (Ar)	84
Disulfide	Disulfides	$R\!:\!\overset{xx}{\underset{xx}{S}}\!:\!\overset{oo}{\underset{oo}{S}}\!:\!R$	R—S—S—R or R_2S_2 (Ar)	84
Sulfoxide	Sulfoxides	$\overset{oo}{\underset{o}{O}}$ $R\!:\!\overset{xx}{\underset{xx}{S}}\!:\!R$	$R-\overset{O}{\overset{\uparrow}{S}}-R$ or R_2SO (Ar) (see footnote b)	—

TABLE 5. IMPORTANT FUNCTIONAL GROUPS (*Continued*)

NAME OF GROUP	CLASS OF COMPOUNDS IN WHICH GROUP OCCURS	ELECTRONIC FORMULA	BONDED FORMULA (SEE FOOTNOTE A)	REFERENCE PAGE NO.
Sulfone	Sulfones	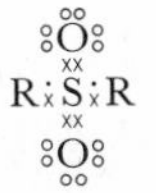 $\overset{O}{R:S:R}\underset{O}{}$	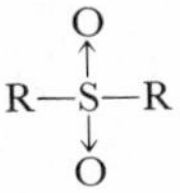 $R—\overset{O}{\underset{O}{\overset{\uparrow}{\underset{\downarrow}{S}}}}—R$ or R_2SO_2 (Ar)	—
Sulfonic acid	Sulfonic acids	 $\overset{O}{R:S:O:H}\underset{O}{}$	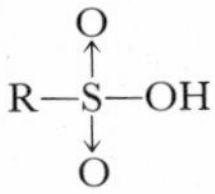 $R—\overset{O}{\underset{O}{\overset{\uparrow}{\underset{\downarrow}{S}}}}—OH$ or RSO_3H	115
Sulfonyl chloride or chlorosulfonyl	Sulfonyl chlorides or sulfone chlorides	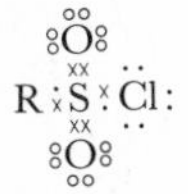 $\overset{O}{R:S:Cl:}\underset{O}{}$	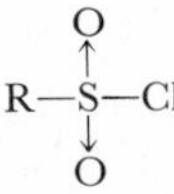 $R—\overset{O}{\underset{O}{\overset{\uparrow}{\underset{\downarrow}{S}}}}—Cl$ or RSO_2Cl	115
Sulfonic ester or alkoxysulfonyl	Sulfonic esters	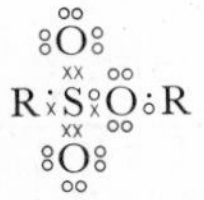 $\overset{O}{R:S:O:R}\underset{O}{}$	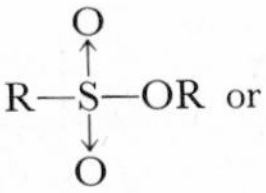 $R—\overset{O}{\underset{O}{\overset{\uparrow}{\underset{\downarrow}{S}}}}—OR$ or RSO_3R	—
Sulfonamide	Sulfonamides	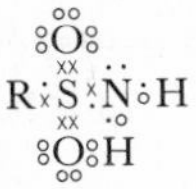 $\overset{O}{R:S:N:H}\underset{O:H}{}$	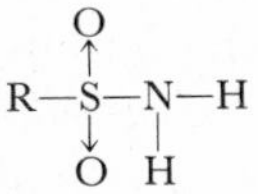 $R—\overset{O}{\underset{O}{\overset{\uparrow}{\underset{\downarrow}{S}}}}—\overset{}{\underset{H}{N}}—H$ or RSO_2NH_2	143

ᵃ Where no group is attached to the free valence, the quadrivalence of carbon may be satisfied by bonding to either hydrogen, H, an alkyl group, R, or an aryl group, Ar. If R or Ar is attached to carbon it indicates either an alkyl group or an aryl group, but not hydrogen. (Ar) indicates that an aryl group may replace one or both R groups.

ᵇ The arrowhead on a bond indicates that the bond is semipolar. For an explanation of this symbol, see p. 144. Such bonds may be represented also by showing the difference in charge on the atoms involved, for example, $R\overset{+}{N}\equiv\overset{-}{C}$ or $R_2\overset{+}{S}—\overset{-}{O}$.

EXERCISE

Using different symbols for the electrons to indicate their source, write electronic formulas for (a) nitric acid; (b) nitrous acid; (c) sulfuric acid; (d) sulfurous acid; (e) sulfur dioxide; (f) sulfur trioxide; (g) carbon dioxide; (h) phosphoric acid; (i) hydrogen peroxide.

CHAPTER 8

ALCOHOLS, PHENOLS, AND ETHERS. SOME SULFUR ANALOGS

As noted previously, the saturated hydrocarbons are very inert. The presence of a double bond permits the molecule to react with a variety of reagents, but the increased reactivity is associated only with the double bond portion of the molecule. The double bond was referred to as a function or functional group. In this chapter several functions containing oxygen or sulfur are considered, each of which imparts a distinctive chemical character to the molecule.

Structural relations to water molecule

The water molecule, H_2O, is the simplest compound of oxygen with another element and has the electronic structure $H:\overset{..}{O}:$, with a hydrogen-
oxygen-hydrogen bond angle of 105° and two unshared pairs of electrons in the valence shell. Molecules having an alkyl group instead of one of the hydrogens of water are called *alcohols*. If the aryl group is present rather than an alkyl group, the chemical properties are sufficiently different from those of alcohols for the molecules to be classified separately under the term *phenols*, named after the first member of the series. In both classes the functional group, O—H, is called a *hydroxyl group.* If it is necessary to distinguish between the two types of hydroxyl groups, that in alcohols is called an *alcoholic hydroxyl* group and that in phenols, *phenolic hydroxyl.* If the oxygen atom is joined to two alkyl groups, two aryl groups, or an alkyl and an alkyl group, the compounds are classed as *ethers.*

ALCOHOLS

Structure of alcohols and number of isomers for each homolog

The simplest alcohol, called **methyl alcohol,** has the molecular formula CH_4O, and only one structural formula is possible, namely $H-\overset{\overset{\displaystyle H}{|}}{\underset{\underset{\displaystyle H}{|}}{C}}-OH$, or CH_3OH.

The number of possible structures for the other members of this homologous series can be predicted in much the same way as was done for the olefins, namely, from a consideration of the possible positions which the functional group, in this case the *hydroxyl group* (OH), can occupy in the carbon skeletons of the alkanes. This procedure leads to one C_2 alcohol, two C_3 alcohols, four C_4 alcohols, and eight C_5 alcohols.

Three systems of nomenclature are in general use. In the first the alkyl group attached to the hydroxyl group is named and the separate word *alcohol* is added. In the second system the higher alcohols are considered as derivatives of the first member of the series, which is called *carbinol.* The third method is the modified Geneva system in which (*1*) the longest carbon chain containing the hydroxyl group determines the surname; (*2*) the ending *e* of the corresponding saturated hydrocarbon is replaced by *ol*, (*3*) the carbon chain is numbered from the end that gives the hydroxyl group the smaller number, and (*4*) the side chains are named and their positions indicated by the proper number. The following examples illustrate these various systems.

Nomenclature by three systems

CH_3OH

methyl alcohol
carbinol[1]
methanol[1]

C_2H_5OH

ethyl alcohol[2]
methylcarbinol[2]
ethanol

$CH_3CH_2CH_2OH$

normal propyl alcohol (*n*-propyl alcohol)
ethylcarbinol
1-propanol

$CH_3\overset{|}{\underset{OH}{C}}HCH_3$

isopropyl alcohol (*i*-propyl alcohol)
dimethylcarbinol
2-propanol

$CH_3CH_2CH_2CH_2OH$

normal butyl alcohol (*n*-butyl alcohol)
n-propylcarbinol
1-butanol

$CH_3CH_2\underset{OH}{C}HCH_3$

secondary butyl alcohol (*s*-butyl alcohol)
methylethylcarbinol
2-butanol

$CH_3\underset{CH_3}{C}HCH_2OH$

isobutyl alcohol (*i*-butyl alcohol)
i-propylcarbinol
2-methyl-1-propanol

$CH_3-\overset{CH_3}{\underset{CH_3}{C}}-OH$

tertiary butyl alcohol (*t*-butyl alcohol)
trimethylcarbinol
2-methyl-2-propanol

$CH_3-CH_2-\overset{1}{\overset{CH_3}{\underset{2}{\underset{CH}}}}\overset{CH_3}{\underset{3}{C}}-OH$
$\overset{4}{CH}$
$\overset{6}{CH_3}-\overset{5}{CH_2}\quad CH_3$

ethyl-*i*-propyl-*s*-butylcarbinol
2,4-dimethyl-3-ethyl-3-hexanol

---

[1] With the exception of the word *alcohol*, the ending *ol* is pronounced with a long *o*. Thus *carbinol* and *methanol* are pronounced as if they were spelled *carbinole* and *methanole*.

[2] Whether a chemical name for an organic compound is written as one word or more than one depends on whether the compound is being named as a derivative of a chemical entity. Thus *carbinol* is a definite compound, CH_3OH, and names for compounds considered to be derivatives of it are written as one word, for example *methylcarbinol*. On the other hand *alcohol* is not the name of any compound but is the name of a class of compounds. Hence *ethyl alcohol* is written as two words.

Alcohols in general are divided into three classes. In *primary* alcohols the hydroxyl group is united to a primary carbon atom, that is, a carbon atom united directly to only *one* other carbon atom. *Secondary* alcohols have the hydroxyl group united to a secondary carbon atom, that is, one united to *two* other carbon atoms. *Tertiary* alcohols have the hydroxyl group united to a tertiary carbon atom, that is, one joined directly to three other carbon atoms. The three classes can be represented by the general formulas RCH_2OH, R_2CHOH, and R_3COH. In the above list ethyl, n-propyl, n-butyl, and i-butyl alcohols are primary alcohols, i-propyl and s-butyl alcohols are secondary alcohols, and t-butyl alcohol and ethyl-i-propyl-s-butylcarbinol are tertiary alcohols. Ordinarily methyl alcohol is grouped with the primary alcohols, although really it is unique in that it is the only alcohol having only hydrogen atoms attached to the carbon atom that bears the hydroxyl group.

Physical properties; boiling points higher than alkanes

Methyl alcohol, the first member of the series, is a liquid boiling at 65°, in contrast to methane which boils at −161°. Even ethane, which has almost the same molecular weight as methyl alcohol, boils at −88°. The alcohols in general boil at a considerably higher temperature than the saturated hydrocarbons of the same molecular weight. The rise in boiling point of the straight-chain primary alcohols with increasing molecular weight is about 18° for each additional CH_2 group, as shown by Figure 15. For a given molecular weight, branching of the carbon chain lowers

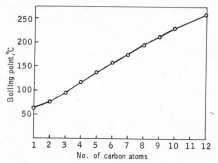

Figure 15.   Boiling points of normal alcohols.

the boiling point just as it does in hydrocarbons. The boiling points of n-, i-, and t-butyl alcohols are respectively 117°, 107°, and 83°. The boiling point of s-butyl alcohol is 100° indicating that the hydroxyl group acts like a branch, as might be expected.

Proton or hydrogen bonding

The much higher boiling point of water and of alcohols as compared with alkanes of the same molecular weight means that an attractive force, in addition to the transient dipole caused by polarizability (p. 21), must be operating. This second type of van der Waals force appears between molecules having hydrogen bound to oxygen or nitrogen and molecules containing an unshared pair of electrons on oxygen or nitrogen, and in a few other isolated instances.

The hydrogen atom is unique in that it has a single electron surrounding the nucleus. When it is bonded to other elements, the hydrogen nucleus, that is, the proton, is less protected by a cover of electrons than the nuclei of other elements, and it can approach the electron shells of other molecules more closely. The result is that an attractive force can appear between the proton and any concentration of negative charge in another molecule.

If the other molecule contains an atom having an unshared pair of electrons, and if this atom can share this pair of electrons more nearly equally with the proton than can the atom to which the proton is attached, that is, form a more nearly covalent bond, transfer of the proton from one atom to the other takes place. The usual acid-base reactions are of this type.

$$H_3N: + H:Cl \longrightarrow [H_3\overset{+}{N}:H]\,[Cl^-]$$

If the new bond were less covalent than the original bond, no transfer would take place. Thus there is no tendency for an alkane to transfer a proton to other elements, because hydrogen forms a more nearly covalent bond with carbon than with any other element except another hydrogen.

Conceivably an intermediate condition should be possible in which the relative electrical forces are such that the tendency of hydrogen to form covalent bonds with two atoms is equal or nearly so. Then, if the molecules approach each other closely enough and in the right orientation for transfer of a proton to take place, there will be a stage where the proton is attracted equally or almost equally by the atoms of two molecules. Under such conditions the proton may or may not transfer from one molecule to the other; and if transfer does take place, it is reversible. Nevertheless during the time when the molecules are close enough for the transfer to take place, there is a strong attraction of the proton for both molecules and hence an increased attraction between the molecules. This type of attraction is called *proton bonding* or *hydrogen bonding*. The former term is more descriptive of the process and avoids confusion with the normal covalent hydrogen bond. The phenomenon also is known as *association,* and compounds exhibiting proton bonding are said to be *associated.*

On this basis, the high boiling point of water as compared with methane is due to the association of water molecules by proton bonding. The high boiling point of the alcohols as compared with the boiling point of alkanes of similar molecular weight may be explained in the same way.

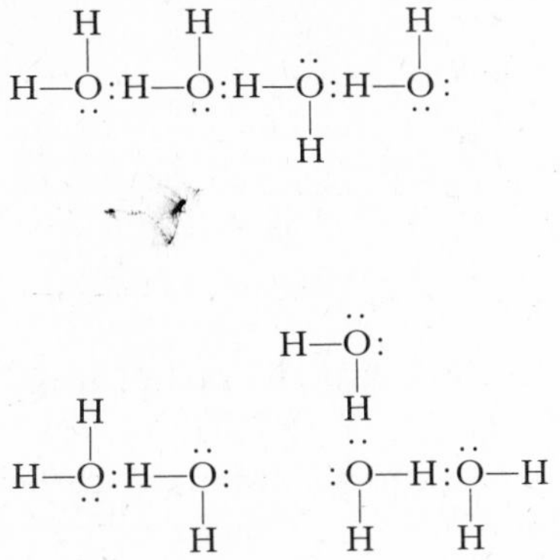

Water and alcohols highly associated

H—O:H—O:H—O:H—O :
(with H below)

CH₃—O:H—O:
(liquid structures)

Liquid water 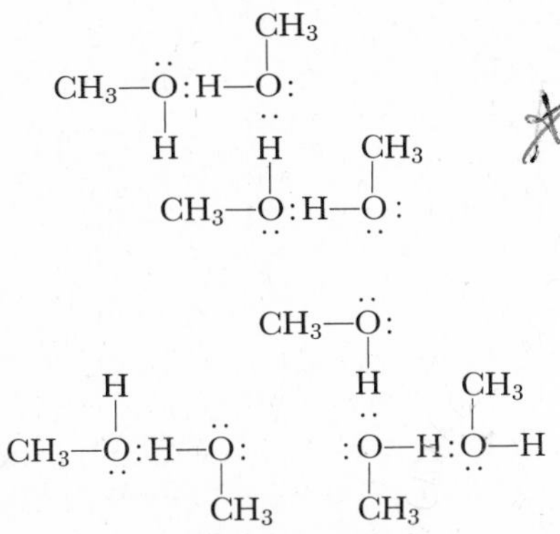   Liquid methyl alcohol

However, the attractive forces between alcohol molecules are not so great as those between water molecules, because the hydrogen atoms of the alkyl groups do not form proton bonds, and the bulk of the alkyl groups decreases the chance that collision of two alcohol molecules will form a proton bond between two hydroxyl groups.

Proton can attract no more than two other nuclei

In proton bonding, a single proton cannot attract more than two other atoms. Because of the small size of the proton, two water molecules or two alcohol molecules approach each other so closely that a third molecule cannot approach the proton closely enough to be attracted appreciably. However, a proton of a third molecule can bond to one of the oxygen atoms, and this process can be repeated until the attractive forces balance the disruptive forces caused by thermal agitation.

Oxygen and nitrogen chiefly involved

The reason that proton bonding occurs most frequently between molecules having hydrogen on oxygen or on nitrogen and those having an unshared pair of electrons on oxygen or nitrogen is simply that then the balance of electrical forces is such that proton bonding is possible. The proton is held neither too strongly nor too loosely by oxygen or nitrogen, and the negative charge resulting from the unshared pair on oxygen or nitrogen is sufficiently concentrated to be effective. Fundamentally the attraction is not concerned with an unshared pair of electrons. However, only when an atom has an unshared pair is the negative charge sufficiently exposed for a proton attached to another oxygen or nitrogen atom in another molecule to get close enough to the electrons for an attractive force to operate.

The attractive force resulting from hydrogen bonding is eight to ten times that caused by the polarizability of a single methylene group but does not increase with increasing molecular weight. The rise in boiling point of alcohols beyond the first carbon atom is of the same order of magnitude as that for alkanes and results from the London forces (p. 21).

Melting points and solubility

Dodecyl alcohol is the first straight-chain alcohol that is solid at room temperature, although the more nearly spherical branched alcohols with fewer carbon atoms, for example *t*-butyl alcohol, also may be solids at room temperature. There is no evidence for alternation in melting point (Fig. 16) as is exhibited by saturated hydrocarbons (Fig. 12, p. 23).

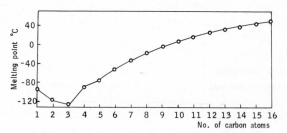

Figure 16.   Melting points of normal alcohols.

The alcohols containing three carbon atoms or less and *t*-butyl alcohol are miscible with water at 20°, but *n*-butyl alcohol is soluble to the extent of only about 8 per cent, and primary alcohols with more than five carbon atoms are less than 1 per cent soluble in water.

Solubility has been mentioned previously on page 5 and page 23. Solution is nothing more than the intermingling of molecules. Two liquids do not mix if the attractive forces of like molecules for each other are much greater than the attractive forces between unlike molecules. Moreover the more closely molecules are related in composition and structure, the more similar will be the attractive and repulsive forces between them. These statements explain the very approximate rule that _like dissolves like._

It is desirable to have a somewhat clearer picture of the factors producing solubility and insolubility. From the differences in boiling points, it was concluded that the attraction between water molecules is considerably greater than between alcohol molecules, and it might be predicted that water and methyl alcohol should not mix. However, alcohol molecules can form proton bonds with water molecules and _vice versa,_ with the result that the differences in attractive forces are decreased and intermingling takes place.

Hydration of alcohol molecules leads to solubility in water

$$
\begin{array}{cccc}
\overset{\text{H}}{\underset{|}{}} \quad \overset{\text{H}}{\underset{|}{}} &
\overset{\text{H}}{\underset{|}{}} \quad \overset{\text{H}}{\underset{|}{}} &
\overset{\text{H}}{\underset{|}{}} \quad \overset{\text{H}}{\underset{|}{}} &
\overset{\text{H}}{\underset{|}{}} \quad \overset{\text{R}}{\underset{|}{}} \\
\text{R—O:H—O:} & \text{H—O:H—O:} & \text{R—O:H—O:} & \text{H—O:H—O:} \\
 & & \overset{|}{\text{H}} & \overset{|}{\text{H}} \\
 & & \overset{|}{\text{H—O:}} & \overset{|}{\text{:O—R}}
\end{array}
$$

As the length of the hydrocarbon chain increases, the attractive forces resulting from the polarizability of the molecule (p. 22) increase until a point is reached at which the association with water molecules no longer is sufficient to prevent alcohol molecules from being attracted more strongly to each other than to water complexes, and two phases result. The separation is not complete, however. Some alcohol-water complexes remain in the water layer, and some remain in the alcohol layer. Thus 100 g. of _n_-butyl alcohol dissolves 37 g. of water, and 100 g. of water dissolves 7.3 g. of _n_-butyl alcohol at 15°. The fact that _t_-butyl alcohol is miscible with water agrees with the fact that it boils lower than _n_-butyl alcohol; both the higher solubility and lower boiling point are dependent on the lower attractive forces between _t_-butyl alcohol molecules.

Methyl alcohol is produced in larger amount than any other synthetic organic chemical. The word _methyl_, first used by Dumas and Peligot in 1834, was derived from the Greek word _methy_ meaning wine and _yle_ meaning wood or material, and refers to the fact that it is the chief alcohol formed by the destructive distillation of wood. Previous to 1919 it commonly was called _wood alcohol_ or _Columbian spirits_ in the United States. During the operation of the Volstead Act, which outlawed alcoholic beverages in the United States, anything called alcohol was used by many for intoxicating drinks. Because methyl alcohol is highly toxic, the result was an alarming number of deaths and cases of blindness. As one combative measure the use of the Geneva name _methanol_ was urged, and it now largely has displaced the older term.

Important alcohols

Some methyl alcohol still is obtained by wood distillation, but most of it is made by a synthetic process. In **wood distillation** dried hardwood such as beech, birch, hickory, maple, or oak is decomposed in an oven or retort at a temperature increasing from about 160° to 450°. The products are gases, which are burned as fuel, a liquid condensate, and a residue of charcoal. The liquid condensate separates into an aqueous layer called _pyroligneous acid_ and a tarry layer. The pyroligneous acid, of which 200 to 250 gallons per cord of wood is obtained, is mostly water but contains 1 to

Destructive distillation of wood

6 per cent of methyl alcohol, 4 to 10 per cent acetic acid, 0.1 to 0.5 per cent of acetone, and smaller amounts of methyl acetate and numerous other organic compounds. Removal of the acetic acid and distillation gives a liquid containing 8 to 10 per cent of methyl alcohol, which is purified further by fractional distillation.

During the year 1924 the total importation of methyl alcohol by the United States was 48 gallons. This material was of high purity, the import duty of 12 cents per gallon being sufficient to prevent importation of the commercial grade of foreign wood alcohol. During the first five months of 1925, the Badische Company of Germany shipped into the United States almost a quarter of a million gallons of methyl alcohol. Wood alcohol was selling for 88 cents per gallon, but the imported material was being made by a synthetic process perfected in 1923 which could produce methanol at a cost of around 20 cents per gallon. This new process soon was put into operation in the United States.

Synthesis of methanol

The **synthetic process** starts with carbon monoxide and hydrogen, which combine over a zinc oxide catalyst containing other promoter oxides, for example 10 per cent chromium oxide, at a temperature of 300°–400° and at pressures of 200 to 300 atmospheres.

$$CO + 2 H_2 \xrightarrow{\quad ZnO-Cr_2O_3 \quad} CH_3OH$$

The total production of synthetic methanol in the United States in 1960 was 2 billion pounds, or 311 million gallons. About 45 per cent was used for the manufacture of formaldehyde (p. 96), 25 per cent for the synthesis of other chemicals, 15 per cent as radiator antifreeze, and 15 per cent as solvent[3] and as a denaturant for ethyl alcohol. Production of wood alcohol was around 2.5 million gallons. Practically all of it was used to denature ethyl alcohol (p. 67).

Ethyl alcohol is the equal of methanol in technical importance. Although the suffix *yl* was used in 1834 by Dumas and Peligot in the word *methyl* to indicate its derivation from wood, Liebig and Woehler had used the same suffix in 1832 in the term *benzoyl* in the sense of stuff or material. It is in the latter sense that it ordinarily is used. *Ethyl* means the material which gives rise to *ether* (p. 80).

Ethanol by fermentation of sugars

One important source of ethyl alcohol is the *fermentation of sugars*. **Fermentation** is the decomposition of organic compounds into simpler compounds through the agency of enzyme catalysts. **Enzymes** are complex organic compounds secreted by living cells. The name *enzyme* means *in yeast* and was given because the earliest known enzymes were those produced by yeast cells. Pasteur (1822–1895), the French chemist and microbiologist who discovered the nature of fermentation, thought that the living cell was necessary, but this view was disproved by Buchner in 1897. He showed that

---

[3] The term *solvent* refers to the use of organic liquids for the purpose of dissolving other organic substances. Solvents may be used as reaction media, or for extraction of organic compounds from solids or from aqueous solutions. Following the operation the solvent is removed by distillation or evaporation. Hence they usually are low-boiling liquids. Solvents may be used also to dissolve solid organic materials in order to form the latter into sheets or fibers or to coat other materials with them.

juice expressed from yeast cells that had been completely destroyed still was capable of bringing about fermentation.

The chief sources of sugars for fermentation are the various starches and the molasses residue from sugar refining. Corn (maize) is the chief source of starch in the United States, and ethyl alcohol made from corn commonly is known as *grain alcohol*. Potatoes are the chief source of starch in Europe, and rice in Asia. In preparing alcohol from corn the grain, with or without the germ, is ground and cooked to give the mash. Malt (sprouted barley which has been killed by heat and ground), or a mold such as *Aspergillus oryzae,* both of which contain the enzyme *diastase,* is added, and the mixture is kept at 40° until all of the starch has been converted into the sugar maltose (p. 187). This solution is known as the *wort.*

Starch as source of sugars

$$2\,(C_6H_{10}O_5)_n + n\,H_2O \xrightarrow[\text{in malt}]{\text{Diastase}} n\,C_{12}H_{22}O_{11}$$
$$\text{Starch} \qquad\qquad\qquad\qquad \text{Maltose}$$

The wort is cooled to 20°, diluted to 10 per cent maltose, and a pure yeast culture added, usually a strain of *Saccharomyces cerevisiae* (or *ellipsoidus*). The yeast cells produce two enzymes, *maltase,* which converts the maltose into glucose, and *zymase,* which converts the glucose into carbon dioxide and alcohol.

$$C_{12}H_{22}O_{11} + H_2O \xrightarrow{\text{Maltase}} 2\,C_6H_{12}O_6$$
$$\text{Maltose} \qquad\qquad\qquad \text{Glucose}$$

$$C_6H_{12}O_6 \xrightarrow{\text{Zymase}} 2\,CO_2 + 2\,C_2H_5OH + 26\text{ kcal.}$$

Heat is liberated, and the temperature must be kept below 32° by cooling to prevent destruction of the enzymes. After 40 to 60 hours, fermentation is complete, and the product is distilled to remove the alcohol from solid matter. Redistillation yields a small amount of acetaldehyde (b.p. 21°, p. 97), followed by 95 per cent alcohol. **Fusel oil,** another product, consists of a mixture of higher alcohols, chiefly *n*-propyl, *i*-butyl, *i*-amyl (3-methyl-1-butanol), and active amyl[4] (2-methyl-1-butanol). The exact composition of fusel oil varies considerably, being dependent particularly on the type of raw material that is fermented. These higher alcohols are not formed by fermentation of glucose but arise from certain amino acids (p. 195) derived from the proteins present in the raw material and in the yeast.

Industrial alcohol is ethyl alcohol used for nonbeverage purposes and usually is not produced from starch. Previous to the development of efficient synthetic processes, the chief source of industrial alcohol was the fermentation of blackstrap molasses, the noncrystallizable residue from the refining of sugar. It contains about 50 per cent of sucrose. Malt is unnecessary in the fermentation, since yeast contains an enzyme, *sucrase (invertase),*

Molasses as source of sugars

---

[4] The five-carbon alcohols commonly are referred to as *amyl alcohols,* because they first were obtained from the products of fermentation (L. *amylum,* starch). The term *active* refers to the effect of the compound on plane-polarized light (p. 155). The higher alcohols are toxic even in small amounts. The term *fusel oil* comes from the German word *fusel* meaning *bad liquor.*

capable of converting sucrose into glucose and fructose, both of which are fermentable by zymase.

$$C_{12}H_{22}O_{11} + H_2O \xrightarrow{\text{Sucrase}} C_6H_{12}O_6 + C_6H_{12}O_6$$
$$\text{Sucrose} \qquad\qquad\qquad \text{Glucose} \qquad \text{Fructose}$$

$$C_6H_{12}O_6 \xrightarrow{\text{Zymase}} 2\ CO_2 + 2\ C_2H_5OH$$
$$\text{Glucose or}$$
$$\text{fructose}$$

Other sources

The waste liquors from the production of wood pulp by the sulfite process (p. 192) contain a low concentration of fermentable sugars and can yield about 20 gallons of alcohol per ton of wood pulp produced. Numerous plants utilizing waste sulfite liquors are operated in the Scandinavian countries and in Germany, and a few plants are operating in Canada and in the United States. Glucose formed by the hydrolysis of wood cellulose (pp. 177, 192) also is a possible source of carbohydrate for fermentation and has been used in Germany. Experimental plants have been built in the United States, but they have not been able to compete with other processes under normal economic conditions. The flowers of *Bassia latifolia* and other species have a high content of glucose and fructose and are used extensively for the production of alcohol in India.

Synthetic ethanol

Several processes for the **synthesis of ethyl alcohol** are possible. The first synthesis was reported by Hennel, an English apothecary, in 1828, the same year Woehler reported the synthesis of urea (p. 138). In 1826 Hennel had reported the isolation of potassium ethyl sulfate from a sample of sulfuric acid which had absorbed 80 volumes of ethylene, and which had been given to him by Faraday (1791–1867), the English chemist and physicist, for investigation. In 1828 Hennel reported the hydrolysis of potassium ethyl sulfate to ethyl alcohol. Hennel's discovery was overlooked, however, and the synthesis was rediscovered in 1855 by the French chemist Berthelot (1827–1907), who absorbed the ethylene from coal gas in concentrated sulfuric acid, and diluted and distilled the solution.

$$CH_2{=}CH_2 + HOSO_3H \longrightarrow CH_3CH_2OSO_3H$$
$$CH_3CH_2OSO_3H + HOH \longrightarrow CH_3CH_2OH + H_2SO_4$$

Although the possibility of industrial synthesis by this process was discussed in the following year and a claim made in France in 1862 that the cost of synthetic alcohol was about one-third that of fermentation alcohol, the first continuously successful process was started in the United States in 1930. The ethylene used as the raw material is produced by the cracking of hydrocarbons. It is absorbed in concentrated sulfuric acid at 100° to give a mixture of ethyl hydrogen sulfate and ethyl sulfate. Dilution with water and distillation brings about hydrolysis and removal of ethyl alcohol. The dilute sulfuric acid is concentrated for reuse. Since 1949 ethyl alcohol has been manufactured also by direct hydration of ethylene in the vapor phase. The conditions reported are a large excess of water, high temperature (300°) and pressure (1000–4000 p.s.i.), and a solid catalyst such as phosphoric acid on a carrier. By 1940, the synthetic process accounted for 25 per cent of the total U.S. production of industrial alcohol and in 1960 for 90 per cent.

Various grades of ethyl alcohol are produced. **Ordinary alcohol** is 92–95 per cent ethyl alcohol by weight, the remainder being chiefly water. Anhydrous alcohol cannot be obtained by simple distillation because a constant-boiling mixture (also called an *azeotrope*) containing 95.6 per cent alcohol by weight boils lower (78.15°) than pure alcohol (78.3°).

Various grades of ethanol

Absolute alcohol (anhydrous, 99.9 + per cent) usually is prepared in the laboratory by removing the water by chemical means, for example by heating with calcium oxide, which reacts with the water, and distilling the dried alcohol from the calcium hydroxide. The 5 per cent water in ordinary alcohol has a marked effect on its solvent properties, and there is a considerable demand for the anhydrous product. Commercial methods of dehydration depend on distillation with an "entrainer," such as benzene, which removes the water as a low-boiling azeotrope.

Because all countries have derived a sizeable portion of their revenue by taxing alcohol for beverage purposes, ethyl alcohol for industrial use first must be converted into **denatured alcohol** if the payment of tax is to be avoided. Denaturing is the addition of substances which render the alcohol unfit to drink. Many formulas are available to the manufacturer in order that he may choose one suitable for his purpose. Only denatured alcohols containing obnoxious mixtures that are difficult to remove may be sold to the general public without payment of tax. On January 1, 1940, the price of tax-free denatured alcohol was 31 cents per gallon, compared with $4.55 per gallon for taxed grain alcohol; on January 1, 1961, the prices were 53 cents and $20.63 respectively. The difference in each case is approximately the tax per gallon. The United States tax is based on "100 U.S. proof" alcohol, which contains half of its volume of absolute alcohol. Ordinary so-called 95 per cent alcohol is 190 proof, one volume containing 0.95 volume of alcohol. It is 92.4 per cent alcohol by weight.

Tax on ethanol for beverage purposes

Production of industrial alcohol in 1960 was 270 million gallons, over 90 per cent of which was synthesized from ethylene. About 45 per cent was used for the synthesis of acetaldehyde (p. 97) and 26 per cent for solvent purposes. The remainder was used for the synthesis of other chemicals and for miscellaneous purposes.

Previous to 1915 the chief source of higher alcohols was fusel oil, from which *n*-propyl, *i*-butyl, *i*-amyl, and active amyl alcohols were separated by distillation (p. 65). Since then many other alcohols have become available. **n-Butyl alcohol** is made by a special bacterial fermentation process. Corn mash or black-strap molasses is inoculated with a pure culture of one of several strains of *Clostridium acetobutylicum* in closed tanks under anaerobic conditions. The products of fermentation are *n*-butyl alcohol, acetone, and ethyl alcohol in proportions varying from 60:30:10 to 74:24:2. The evolved gas contains hydrogen and carbon dioxide in the ratio of 1 volume:2 volumes.

Higher alcohols

Secondary and tertiary alcohols are manufactured on a large scale from the lower olefins obtained by cracking saturated hydrocarbons.

$$CH_3CH{=}CH_2 \xrightarrow{H_2SO_4} CH_3\underset{\underset{OSO_3H}{|}}{CH}CH_3 \xrightarrow{H_2O} CH_3\underset{\underset{OH}{|}}{CH}CH_3 + H_2SO_4$$

Propylene   *i*-Propyl alcohol

$$CH_3CH{=}CHCH_3$$

2-Butene
and

$$CH_3CH_2CH{=}CH_2$$

1-Butene

$\xrightarrow{H_2SO_4}$

$$CH_3CH_2\underset{\underset{OSO_3H}{|}}{C}HCH_3$$

$\xrightarrow{H_2O}$

$$CH_3CH_2\underset{\underset{OH}{|}}{C}HCH_3 + H_2SO_4$$

s-Butyl alcohol

$$(CH_3)_2C{=}CH_2$$

Isobutylene

$\xrightarrow{H_2SO_4}$

$$(CH_3)_2\underset{\underset{OSO_3H}{|}}{C}CH_3$$

$\xrightarrow{H_2O}$

$$(CH_3)_3COH + H_2SO_4$$

t-Butyl alcohol

Cyclanols

Technically, the most important cyclic alcohol is **cyclohexanol.** It is made by the catalytic hydrogenation of phenol (hydroxybenzene, p. 73).

Phenol   Cyclohexanol

Chemical properties of alcohols similar to those of water; complexes with metallic salts

Because both water and alcohols contain a hydroxyl group, alcohols would be expected to undergo reactions analogous to those of water, and in many respects they do. Alcohols resemble water in that they associate readily, as evidenced by their abnormally high boiling points. Just as water forms hydrates of inorganic salts, alcohols form complexes which might be called *alcoholates*. Corresponding to $MgCl_2 \cdot 6\ H_2O$ there exist the molecular complexes, $MgCl_2 \cdot 6\ CH_3OH$ and $MgCl_2 \cdot 6\ C_2H_5OH$. Although calcium chloride forms a hexahydrate, the reported complexes with methyl and ethyl alcohols have the composition, $CaCl_2 \cdot 4\ CH_3OH$ and $CaCl_2 \cdot 3\ C_2H_5OH$. Some salts which form hydrates, for example anhydrous calcium sulfate, do not form complexes with alcohols.

In general, salts are not as soluble in alcohols as in water. If a salt, such as calcium chloride, forms a definite coordination complex with the alcohol, the complex may be highly soluble.

Oxonium salt formation

When a strong acid is dissolved in water, there is practically complete transfer of the proton from the acid to the water molecule as illustrated by the following equation.

$$H:\overset{..}{\underset{..}{O}}: + H:\overset{..}{\underset{..}{Cl}}: \longrightarrow \left[H:\overset{..}{\underset{..}{O}}:H\right]\left[:\overset{..}{\underset{..}{Cl}}:\right]_{+}$$

The product from hydrogen chloride is called *hydronium chloride,* and the $[H_3O^+]$ ion is the *hydronium ion.* The explanation of this reaction is that the negative charge on the larger chlorine atom is more diffuse than that on the oxygen atom. Hence the proton can form a more nearly covalent bond with the water molecule than with a chloride ion. The relative ability to combine with a proton or an electron-deficient molecule is called the *basicity* of a group. The proton is transferred to a water molecule because the water molecule is a stronger base than the chloride ion.

Alcohols also are stronger bases than the anions of strong acids. Hence alcohols dissolve in strong acids with the formation of alkonium salts.

$$\text{R:}\overset{\cdot\cdot}{\underset{\cdot\cdot}{\text{O}}}\text{:} + \text{H:}\overset{\cdot\cdot}{\underset{\cdot\cdot}{\text{Cl}}}\text{:} \longrightarrow \left[\text{R:}\overset{\cdot\cdot}{\underset{\cdot\cdot}{\underset{+}{\text{O}}}}\text{:H}\right]\left[\text{:}\overset{\cdot\cdot}{\underset{\cdot\cdot}{\text{Cl}}}\text{:}^-\right]$$

(with H above R:O:)

The general term for this type of compound is *oxonium salt.* Concentrated sulfuric acid dissolves practically all organic compounds containing oxygen, frequently without chemical change other than salt formation. This fact is used *to distinguish oxygen-containing compounds from saturated hydrocarbons.*

Test for oxygenated compounds

Alcohols and all other oxygen-containing compounds are more soluble in aqueous solutions of strong acids than in water because of the competition of alcohol and water molecules for the proton.

$$\text{R:}\overset{\text{H}}{\underset{\cdot\cdot}{\text{O}}}\text{:} + \left[\text{H:}\overset{\text{H}}{\underset{+}{\text{O}}}\text{:H}\right] \rightleftharpoons \left[\text{R:}\overset{\text{H}}{\underset{+}{\text{O}}}\text{:H}\right] + \text{H}_2\text{O}$$

For example, *n*-butyl alcohol is miscible with concentrated aqueous hydrochloric acid although it is soluble only to the extent of 8 per cent in water.

Just as water reacts with metallic sodium to give hydrogen and sodium hydroxide, the alcohols react with sodium to give hydrogen and sodium alkoxide.

Reaction with metals to give alkoxides

$$\text{HOH} + \text{Na} \longrightarrow \text{HO}^-{}^+\text{Na} + \tfrac{1}{2}\text{H}_2$$
Sodium hydroxide˙

$$\text{CH}_3\text{OH} + \text{Na} \longrightarrow \text{CH}_3\text{O}^-{}^+\text{Na} + \tfrac{1}{2}\text{H}_2$$
Sodium methoxide

$$\text{ROH} + \text{Na} \longrightarrow \text{RO}^-{}^+\text{Na} + \tfrac{1}{2}\text{H}_2$$
Sodium alkoxide

Metallic alkoxides are hydrolyzed extensively by water because the acidity of water and of alcohols is about the same.

$$\text{RONa} + \text{H}_2\text{O} \rightleftharpoons \text{ROH} + \text{NaOH}$$

Inorganic acids in general react with alcohols with the elimination of water. The products of reaction with halogen acids are alkyl halides.

Reaction with halogen acids replaces hydroxyl by halogen

$$\text{ROH} + \text{HX} \longrightarrow \text{RX} + \text{H}_2\text{O}$$

The rate of this reaction varies with the acid and with the type of alcohol. The order for halogen acids is hydrogen iodide > hydrogen bromide > hydrogen chloride > hydrogen fluoride. The order for the alcohols is tertiary > secondary > primary.

Primary and secondary alcohols may be dehydrogenated to aldehydes and ketones respectively by passing the vapors over an activated copper, copper-chromium, or copper-nickel catalyst at 300°–325°.

Dehydrogenation or oxidation to aldehydes or ketones

$$\text{RCH}_2\text{OH} \underset{325°}{\overset{\text{Cu}}{\rightleftarrows}} \text{RC} \overset{\text{H}}{=}\text{O} + \text{H}_2$$
An aldehyde

$$\text{R}_2\text{CHOH} \underset{325°}{\overset{\text{Cu}}{\rightleftarrows}} \text{R}_2\text{C}=\text{O} + \text{H}_2$$
A ketone

If air is used along with the alcohol, the hydrogen is converted into water and the reaction goes to completion.

$$RCH_2OH + \tfrac{1}{2} O_2 \xrightarrow[600°]{Cu \ or \ Ag} RCHO + H_2O$$

$$R_2CHOH + \tfrac{1}{2} O_2 \xrightarrow[600°]{Cu \ or \ Ag} R_2CO + H_2O$$

Tertiary alcohols, which do not have a hydrogen atom on the carbon atom united to the hydroxyl group, do not undergo these reactions.

The same type of dehydrogenation can be brought about by chemical oxidizing agents. The reagent most commonly employed is dichromic acid in aqueous sulfuric acid (sodium dichromate and sulfuric acid), or chromic anhydride (chromium trioxide) dissolved in glacial acetic acid.

$$3\ RCH_2OH + Na_2Cr_2O_7 + 4\ H_2SO_4 \longrightarrow 3\ RCHO + Na_2SO_4 + Cr_2(SO_4)_3 + 7\ H_2O$$

$$3\ R_2CHOH + 2\ CrO_3 + 6\ HC_2H_3O_2 \longrightarrow 3\ R_2CO + 2\ Cr(C_2H_3O_2)_3 + 6\ H_2O$$

The formation of aldehydes by this method is successful only if the aldehyde is removed rapidly from the oxidizing mixture by distillation; otherwise it is oxidized further to an organic acid (p. 96).

$$RCHO + [O] \longrightarrow RCOOH$$

Reaction with inorganic oxygen acids gives esters Some oxygen-containing inorganic acids react with alcohols to form alkyl esters.

$$ROH + HONO \rightleftharpoons \underset{\text{Alkyl nitrite}}{RONO} + H_2O$$

$$ROH + HONO_2 \rightleftharpoons \underset{\text{Alkyl nitrate}}{RONO_2} + H_2O$$

$$ROH + H_2SO_4 \rightleftharpoons \underset{\substack{\text{Alkyl hydrogen} \\ \text{sulfate}}}{ROSO_3H} + H_2O$$

$$ROH + HOSO_2OR \rightleftharpoons \underset{\text{Alkyl sulfate}}{ROSO_2OR} + H_2O$$

$$3\ ROH + H_3BO_3 \rightleftharpoons \underset{\text{Alkyl borate}}{(RO)_3B} + 3\ H_2O$$

In **esters of oxygen acids** the hydrocarbon group always is linked to the acid group through oxygen. Although the esters are named like salts, they are covalent compounds. The esters of lower molecular weight are volatile liquids, and the higher esters can be distilled under reduced pressure. They are insoluble in water and soluble in organic solvents.

Esters can be hydrolyzed to alcohol and acid The esters are hydrolyzed by water with varying degrees of ease. Ethyl borate, for example, is hydrolyzed readily by water at room temperature.

$$(C_2H_5O)_3B + 3\ H_2O \longrightarrow 3\ C_2H_5OH + B(OH)_3$$

Ethyl nitrate and ethyl perchlorate are hydrolyzed only very slowly by water, even at elevated temperatures. Care should be exercised in handling these compounds as they decompose explosively. It is stated that ethyl perchlorate in the anhydrous condition explodes on pouring from one vessel to another.

One alkyl group of sulfates and phosphates is hydrolyzed much more readily than a second group. For example, at 95° and low concentration the first methyl group of methyl sulfate is completely removed in 3 minutes, whereas only 25 per cent of the second methyl group is removed after 3 hours.

Methyl sulfate, which is used extensively to convert hydroxyl groups to methoxyl groups, is highly toxic, and care must be exercised to avoid exposure to its vapors. Nitrites relax the smooth muscles of the body and produce a rapid lowering of the blood pressure. *i*-**Amyl nitrite** is used for the relief of pain in acute angina pectoris.

POLYHYDRIC ALCOHOLS

Of the polyhydric alcohols, that is, compounds containing two or more hydroxyl groups, 1,2-dihydroxyethane, called *ethylene glycol* or simply *glycol;* 1,2-dihydroxypropane, called *propylene glycol;* and 1,2,3-trihydroxypropane, called *glycerol* (sometimes called glycerine), are of special interest. **Ethylene glycol** is made by the hydrolysis of the cyclic ether, ethylene oxide (p. 83), which is made by the direct oxidation of ethylene in the presence of a silver catalyst.

Ethylene glycol from ethylene

$$CH_2{=}CH_2 + \tfrac{1}{2}O_2 \underset{(air)}{\xrightarrow[250°]{Ag}} \underset{O}{CH_2{-}CH_2} \xrightarrow{H_2O} \underset{OH \quad OH}{CH_2{-}CH_2}$$

Ethylene oxide   Ethylene glycol (glycol)

Glycol is a toxic compound, is miscible with water in all proportions, and is not volatile at moderate temperatures.

The chief uses of ethylene glycol are as a permanent antifreeze for radiators of motor cars and as an intermediate for the preparation of other organic compounds. Reaction with a mixture of nitric and sulfuric acids gives the ester, **glycol nitrate.**

Use as permanent antifreeze for radiators

$$HOCH_2CH_2OH + 2\,HNO_3(H_2SO_4) \longrightarrow O_2N{-}O{-}CH_2CH_2{-}O{-}NO_2 + 2\,H_2O$$
Glycol nitrate

The nitrate is an explosive that is added to glyceryl nitrate (*nitroglycerine*) to prevent the latter from freezing. Dynamite containing only glyceryl nitrate is much more sensitive to shock, and hence more dangerous to handle, if the glyceryl nitrate has crystallized. Ethylene glycol is used in the production of numerous other products, including detergents (p. 83), plastics, fibers, and synthetic rubbers (p. 238).

Nitrate is an explosive

Propylene glycol is made by the alkaline hydrolysis of **propylene chlorohydrin** (*1-chloro-2-hydroxypropane*), which is obtained by the addition of the elements of hypochlorous acid (HOCl) to propylene.

Propylene glycol from propylene

$$CH_3CH = CH_2 + Cl_2 + H_2O + Na_2CO_3 \longrightarrow CH_3CHOHCH_2Cl + NaCl + NaHCO_3$$
Propylene chlorohydrin

$$CH_3CHOHCH_2Cl + Na_2CO_3 + H_2O \longrightarrow CH_3CHOHCH_2OH + NaHCO_3 + NaCl$$
Propylene glycol

Propylene glycol has properties similar to those of ethylene glycol. Unlike ethylene glycol, however, it is nontoxic and can be used to replace glycerol in tobacco and cosmetics. It is toxic to lower forms of life, and aerosols of it have been used in hospitals and schools to reduce the incidence of airborne infections. Mixed with ethylene glycol it is used as radiator antifreeze.

Glycerol from fats and by synthesis

Glycerol is one of the products obtained in the manufacture of soap from fats (p. 121). Demand for it has increased greatly in recent years, and large quantities now are synthesized from propylene. In one process propylene is chlorinated in the vapor phase at 600°, at which temperature substitution of hydrogen takes place instead of addition to the double bond. The product is called **allyl chloride.**

$$CH_2{=}CHCH_3 + Cl_2 \xrightarrow{600°} CH_2{=}CHCH_2Cl$$
$$\text{Allyl chloride}$$

Alkaline hydrolysis of allyl chloride gives **allyl alcohol.** When allyl alcohol is treated with an alkaline aqueous solution of chlorine, it adds the elements of hypochlorous acid to form 1,2-dihydroxy-3-chloropropane.

$$CH_2{=}CHCH_2Cl + Na_2CO_3 + H_2O \longrightarrow CH_2{=}CHCH_2OH + NaCl + NaHCO_3$$
$$\text{Allyl alcohol}$$
$$CH_2{=}CHCH_2OH + HOCl \longrightarrow ClCH_2CHOHCH_2OH$$

A final hydrolytic step yields glycerol.

$$ClCH_2CHOHCH_2OH + Na_2CO_3 + H_2O \longrightarrow HOCH_2CHOHCH_2OH + NaHCO_3 + NaCl$$
$$\text{Glycerol}$$

In a more recent process, the propylene is oxidized catalytically by air to the unsaturated aldehyde **acrolein.**

$$CH_2{=}CHCH_3 + O_2(\text{air}) \xrightarrow[370°]{Cu_2O} CH_2{=}CHCHO + H_2O$$
$$\text{Acrolein}$$

Controlled catalytic reduction to allyl alcohol, followed by addition of hydrogen peroxide to the carbon-carbon double bond, yields glycerol.

$$CH_2{=}CHCH{=}O + H_2 \xrightarrow{Ni} CH_2{=}CHCH_2OH \xrightarrow{H_2O_2} HOCH_2CHOHCH_2OH$$

Used chiefly as humectant and in manufacture of alkyd resins

Glycerol is hygroscopic (absorbs moisture from the air) and hence prevents materials from becoming too dry and brittle. About 60 per cent of the total production is used for this purpose in cellophane, tobacco, cosmetics, printing inks, etc. About 30 per cent is used for the manufacture of alkyd resins (p. 239) and 10 per cent to make **glyceryl nitrate** (*nitroglycerin*).

$$\begin{array}{c} CH_2OH \\ | \\ CHOH \\ | \\ CH_2OH \end{array} + 3\ HNO_3 \xrightarrow{(H_2SO_4)} \begin{array}{c} CH_2ONO_2 \\ | \\ CHONO_2 \\ | \\ CH_2ONO_2 \end{array} + 3\ H_2O$$
$$\text{Glyceryl nitrate}$$
$$\text{(nitroglycerin)}$$

The term *nitroglycerin* is a misnomer because the compound is an ester of nitric acid and not a nitro compound. In nitro compounds (p. 144), nitrogen is linked directly to carbon and not through oxygen.

Glyceryl nitrate is an oil which freezes at 13°. Formerly it was the chief explosive ingredient of **dynamite,** being mixed in amounts up to 40 per cent with a combustible mixture such as powdered wood pulp and sodium nitrate in the ratio of about 1 to 3. At present, dynamites contain up to 55 per cent ammonium nitrate mixed with about 15 per cent each of sodium nitrate, wood pulp, and *explosive oil.* Explosive oil is a mixture of glycol nitrate and glyceryl nitrate, and is added merely as a sensitizer for the ammonium nitrate. **Gelatin dynamite** is a mixture of wood pulp, sodium nitrate, and glyceryl nitrate gelatinized with 2 to 6 per cent of cellulose nitrate (p. 193). It is plastic and can be loaded solidly into bore holes. It has a high water resistance, a requirement for work in wet places. Dynamite has many useful applications, such as in mining, road building, and agriculture; over 600 million pounds per year is used in the United States. Double-base military smokeless powders such as *Ballistite* and *Cordite* consist of about 60 per cent cellulose nitrate gelatinized with 40 per cent of glyceryl nitrate. Similar compositions have been used as solid fuels for rockets.

Dynamite composition

PHENOLS

The phenols are compounds having a hydroxyl group attached directly to an aromatic nucleus. The name *phenol* for hydroxybenzene is derived from *phene,* an old name for benzene (p. 44). The hydroxy derivatives of toluene have the common name *cresols,* and those of xylene are called *xylenols.* Phenols in general are named as derivatives of phenol.

Nomenclature for phenols

o-Cresol   *p*-Aminophenol

Phenol, cresols, and xylenols occur in coal tar, wood tar, and petroleum distillates along with other phenolic compounds and are known as *tar acids.* The mixture of phenols from the cresol fraction is known technically as *cresylic acid.* Derivatives of phenols frequently occur as plant products (pp. 79, 99).

The pure phenols are colorless solids or liquids, although as usually encountered they are colored red by oxidation products. Like the aromatic hydrocarbons (p. 45), they boil higher than the normal aliphatic analogs of the same molecular weight. For example, phenol boils at 181°, whereas 1-hexanol boils at 157°. Phenol is soluble in water to the extent of 9 g. per 100 g. of water at 25° and becomes miscible at 65°. Water is soluble in phenol to the extent of 29 g. per 100 g. Since the melting point of phenol is only 42°, a small amount of water lowers the melting point below room temperature. This liquid form containing about 5 per cent water is called **carbolic acid.** In the monosubstituted phenols, the *para* isomer has the highest melting point.

Physical properties

Phenols differ from alcohols in two important respects. First, the

Chemical properties

chemical reactions involving the hydroxyl group differ considerably; second, the hydroxyl group in phenols has a marked effect on the reactivity of the hydrogens of the aryl group, but is without effect on those of the alkyl group. Aryl groups have a greater attraction for electrons than hydrogen, whereas alkyl groups have slightly less electron attraction than does hydrogen. The result is that phenols are considerably more acidic than either alcohols or water. Thus water-insoluble phenols usually dissolve in dilute aqueous solutions of strong bases such as sodium hydroxide.

$$ArOH + NaOH \longrightarrow ArO^{-+}Na + H_2O$$

Metallic salts of the alcohols, on the other hand, result only from the reaction with active metals under anhydrous conditions. The phenols, however, usually are not as acidic as carbonic acid and are liberated when carbon dioxide is passed into aqueous solutions of their sodium salts.

$$ArO^{-+}Na + H_2CO_3 \longrightarrow ArOH + NaHCO_3$$

Because the hydroxyl group in phenols cannot leave as readily with the bonding pair of electrons, it is not as readily replaceable by halogen as the hydroxyl group in alcohols. Thus halogen acids do not react with phenols. In contrast to alcohols, which are not affected by ferric ion, phenols give green to purple colors with ferric chloride. In the aliphatic series, the formation of colored complexes with ferric chloride takes place only with enols,

i.e., compounds having the grouping $-\overset{|}{C}=\overset{|}{C}-OH$.

Reactions of nucleus

Concerning the effect of the hydroxyl group on the reactivity of the hydrogens of the aromatic ring, the hydroxyl group, and especially the oxygen of the negative phenoxide ion, can supply electrons, thus increasing the ease of oxidation of the ring. Complex mixtures of oxidation products are formed by either air or other oxidizing agents. One of the oxidation products of phenol by air is *quinone* (p. 80), which forms a brilliant red addition product with phenol known as *phenoquinone*.

Oxidation

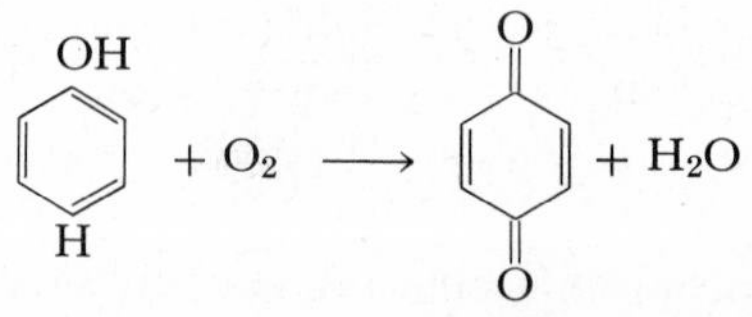

Quinone

$$C_6H_4O_2 + 2 C_6H_5OH \longrightarrow C_6H_4O_2 \cdot 2 C_6H_5OH$$

Phenoquinone

Simple phenols when pure are all colorless compounds, but samples that have stood for some time may be deeply colored because of exposure to air.

Sulfonation

Sulfonation, halogenation and nitration all take place more readily with phenol than with benzene. If a second group is present in a benzene ring, three isomers are possible, because the groups may be *ortho, meta,* or *para* to each other (p. 42). At room temperature concentrated sulfuric acid yields chiefly the *ortho* isomer, whereas at 100° the *para* isomer predominates.

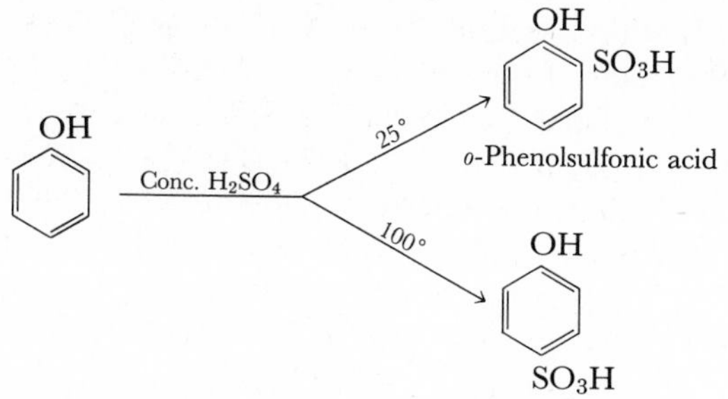

OH
SO₃H
o-Phenolsulfonic acid

OH

Conc. H₂SO₄

25°

100°

OH

SO₃H
p-Phenolsulfonic acid

Halogenation

By controlled halogenation in anhydrous solvents, it is possible to obtain the monohalogenated phenols in satisfactory yields. The *ortho* and *para* isomers are obtained almost exclusively.

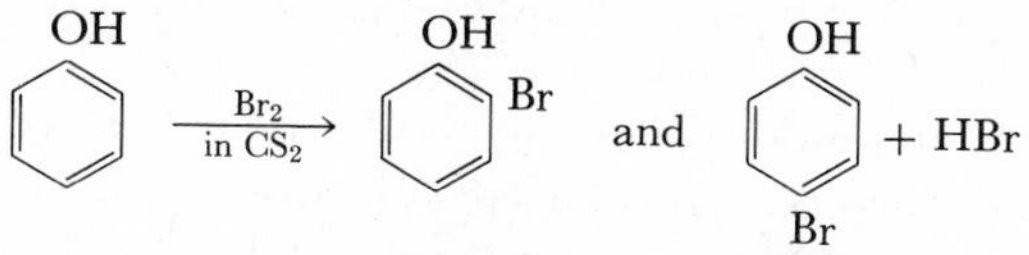

OH

Br₂
in CS₂

OH
Br

and

OH

+ HBr

Br

o-Bromo-
phenol

p-Bromo-
phenol

When bromine water is added to an aqueous solution of phenol, a quinonoid tetrabromo derivative precipitates. Reaction with sodium bisulfite produces 2,4,6-tribromophenol.

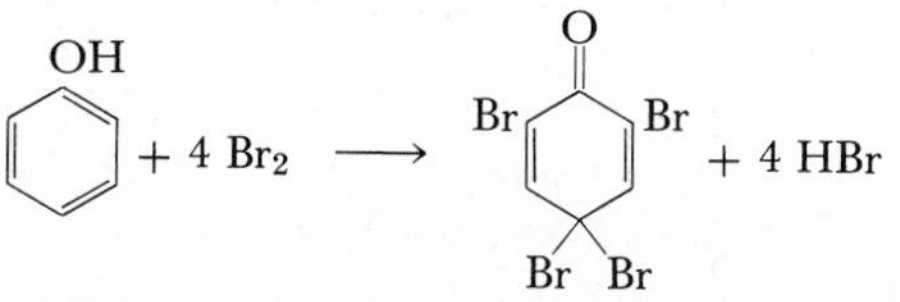

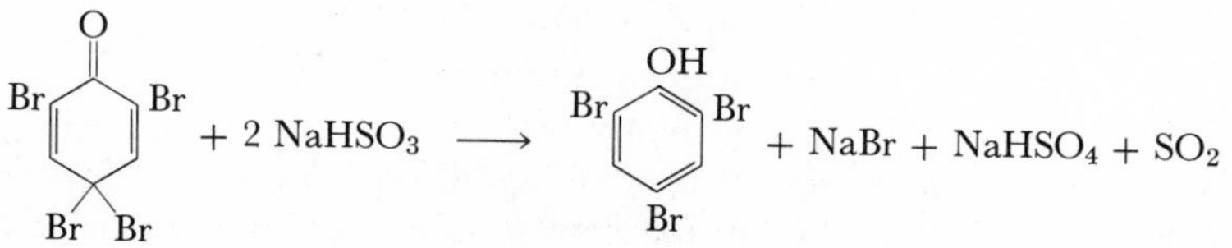

OH

+ 4 Br₂ ⟶

O
Br   Br

+ 4 HBr

Br Br

O
Br   Br

+ 2 NaHSO₃ ⟶

OH
Br   Br

+ NaBr + NaHSO₄ + SO₂

Br Br

Br

Nitration

Phenol nitrates so rapidly that if mononitration is desired, dilute nitric acid at room temperature is used. Again the *ortho* and *para* isomers predominate.

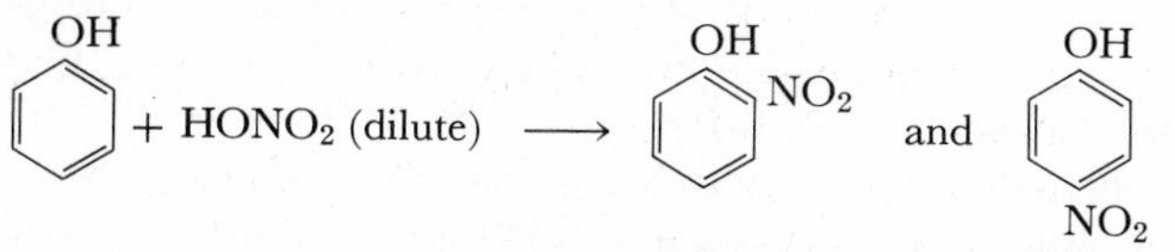

OH

+ HONO₂ (dilute) ⟶

OH
NO₂

and

OH

NO₂

o-Nitro-
phenol

p-Nitro-
phenol

Nitration of phenol with concentrated nitric acid gives 2,4,6-trinitrophenol (*picric acid*, p. 78), but the amount of oxidation is excessive, and indirect methods of preparation are used. The nitrophenols are colorless or pale yellow. Their salts are deep yellow.

Benzene is not affected by nitrous acid, but the activating effect of the hydroxyl group is so great that phenol reacts to give **p-nitrosophenol.** This compound is in equilibrium with the monoxime of quinone (cf. pp. 80, 95).

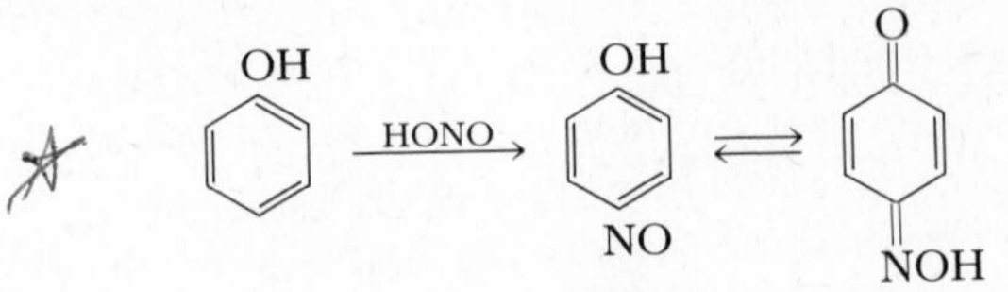

p-Nitrosophenol Quinone monoxime

If the reaction is carried out in the presence of concentrated sulfuric acid, further condensation with phenol takes place to give a dark blue solution of phenolindophenol acid sulfate. When the acid solution is diluted with water, the red **phenolindophenol** is liberated. When excess sodium hydroxide is added, the deep blue sodium salt is formed.

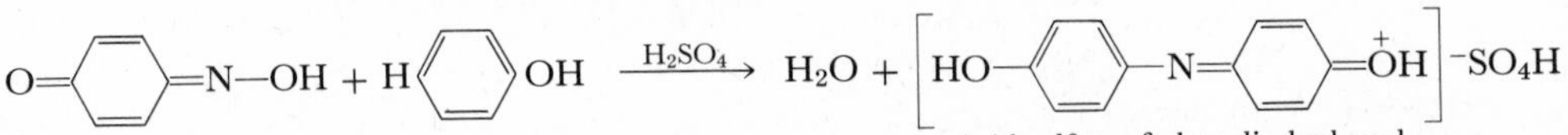

Acid sulfate of phenolindophenol (deep blue)

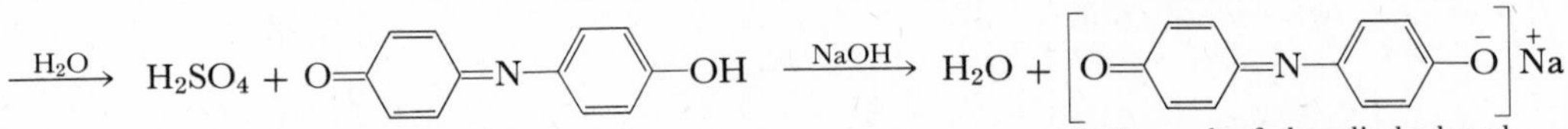

Phenolindophenol (red)

Sodium salt of phenolindophenol (deep blue)

Compounds of this type are called phenolindophenols, because they are hydroxy analogs of indophenol which contains an amino group instead of a hydroxyl group. The reaction is used as a test for phenols and for nitrites and is known as the **Liebermann nitroso reaction.**

All phenols having a sufficiently high vapor pressure have a characteristic odor. Phenol is highly toxic, killing all types of cells. It precipitates proteins, and, when applied to the skin, produces a white spot which soon turns red; later the dead skin sloughs. If allowed to remain in contact with the skin, it penetrates to the deeper tissues and severe burns result. It also is absorbed into the blood stream and acts as a systemic poison. Phenol is eliminated in the urine as sodium phenyl sulfate, $C_6H_5OSO_3Na$. Frequently other toxic aromatic compounds, for example naphthalene and bromobenzene, are detoxified in the body by oxidation to the phenol and elimination as the ester of sulfuric acid.

The phenols in general are toxic to microorganisms. Although many substances had been discovered empirically to have a preservative and healing action long before the nature of bacterial infection was known, phenol itself was the first compound to be used widely for the avowed purpose of antisepsis. It was introduced by Lister in 1867. Much more effective and less toxic compounds have been developed since then, but antiseptic activity still is reported in terms of the **phenol coefficient,** a number which compares the effectiveness of a preparation with that of a 5 per cent solution of phenol against *Staphylococcus aureus*.

Some **phenol** is obtained from coal tar and a still smaller amount from the refining of petroleum. By far the largest amount is produced by synthesis. Phenol in 1960 held third place among synthetic aromatic chemicals, the volume of production being exceeded only by that of styrene (p. 235) and its precursor, ethylbenzene.

Production of phenol

Three processes account for most of the production in the United States. The oldest process (1867) involves sulfonating benzene, neutralizing with sodium hydroxide, heating the sodium benzenesulfonate with molten sodium hydroxide, and liberating the free phenol with carbon dioxide.

from sodium benzenesulfonate

$$C_6H_6 + H_2SO_4 \longrightarrow C_6H_5SO_3H + H_2O$$
$$\text{Benzenesulfonic acid}$$

$$C_6H_5SO_3H + NaOH \longrightarrow C_6H_5SO_3Na + H_2O$$
$$\text{Sodium benzenesulfonate}$$

$$C_6H_5SO_3Na + NaOH \longrightarrow C_6H_5ONa + NaHSO_3$$
$$\text{Sodium phenoxide}$$

$$C_6H_5ONa + CO_2 + H_2O \longrightarrow C_6H_5OH + NaHCO_3$$
$$\text{Phenol}$$

In the Dow process, introduced in 1928, benzene is chlorinated to give chlorobenzene, which then is hydrolyzed with sodium hydroxide at 320°. Besides phenol, about 20 per cent of phenyl ether (p. 83) is formed.

from chlorobenzene

$$C_6H_5Cl + 2\,NaOH \longrightarrow C_6H_5ONa + NaCl + H_2O$$

$$C_6H_5Cl + NaOC_6H_5 \longrightarrow C_6H_5OC_6H_5 + NaCl$$
$$\text{Phenyl ether}$$

The phenyl ether is extracted with chlorobenzene, and the phenol is liberated with hydrochloric acid.

$$C_6H_5ONa + HCl \longrightarrow C_6H_5OH + NaCl$$

Since 1954 phenol has been synthesized from cumene, prepared from benzene and propylene.

from cumene

$$C_6H_6 + CH_3CH{=}CH_2 \xrightarrow{\text{HF}} C_6H_5CH(CH_3)_2$$
$$\text{Cumene}$$

Oxidation of the cumene by air gives cumene hydroperoxide. Strong acids catalyze the decomposition of the hydroperoxide into phenol and acetone.

$$C_6H_5CH(CH_3)_2 + O_2 \text{ (air)} \longrightarrow C_6H_5\underset{\underset{\text{O—OH}}{|}}{C}(CH_3)_2 \xrightarrow{H_2SO_4} C_6H_5OH + (CH_3)_2CO$$

Cumene   Cumene hydro-
               peroxide

About half of the phenol is used for the manufacture of phenol-formaldehyde resins and plastics (p. 240). Most of the remainder is used for the synthesis of other aromatic compounds.

Bisphenol-A is the condensation product from acetone and two moles of phenol.

Other important phenols

$$2\ C_6H_5OH + (CH_3)_2CO \xrightarrow{H_2SO_4} HO\text{—}\bigcirc\text{—}C(CH_3)_2\text{—}\bigcirc\text{—}OH + H_2O$$

Bisphenol-A

It is an important intermediate for the production of epoxy resins (p. 238). **Pentachlorophenol,** C_6Cl_5OH, dissolved in oil is used extensively for treating wood to prevent destruction by fungi and termites. The sodium salt is used to treat industrial water to prevent the growth of slime and algae.

Nitro groups increase acidity

Although phenol is a very weak acid, the introduction of electron-attracting groups into the benzene ring, especially in the *ortho* and *para* positions, causes an increase in acidity. Nitro groups are strongly electron-attracting, and 2,4,6-trinitrophenol is approximately as strong as sulfuric acid. Because of its high acidity and its bitter taste (Gr. *pikros,* bitter) it was given the name **picric acid.** In the past it has been used as a yellow dye for silk and as a military explosive. The aromatic ring of trinitrophenol is oxidized by alkaline hypochlorite to give **chloropicrin** (trichloronitromethane), which is used as a tear gas for dispelling mobs and as a warning agent for toxic gases.

$$O_2N\text{—}\underset{NO_2}{\bigcirc}\text{—}NO_2 + 11\ NaOCl \longrightarrow 3\ Cl_3CNO_2 + 3\ Na_2CO_3 + 3\ NaOH + 2\ NaCl$$

Chloropicrin

The *aryl phosphates* are made by the reaction of the phenol with phosphorus oxychloride.

$$3\ ArOH + POCl_3 \longrightarrow (ArO)_3PO + 3\ HCl$$

Phosphates are important

They are used extensively as plasticizers and flame retarders. Technical **cresyl phosphate** (*tricresyl phosphate*), prepared from the mixed cresols, is one of the most important of the plasticizers, particularly for vinyl polymers. It is used also as a nonflammable hydraulic fluid and as an additive for lubricating oils. It is added also to gasoline under the trade name **TCP** or **ICA** to prevent preignition and the fouling of spark plugs.

Creosote oil, a coal, wood, or petroleum tar fraction boiling at 225°–270°, contains considerable amounts of the cresols and is used on a large scale for wood preservation. *p***-Cresol** is synthesized from the hydroperoxide formed by the air-oxidation of *p*-cymene (cf. phenol from cumene, p. 77). Alkylation of *p*-cresol with isobutylene gives **2,6-di-*t*-butyl-4-methylphenol,**

Antioxidants

which is used widely as an antioxidant for gasoline, lubricating oils, rubber, and edible fats and oils (p. 122). *Antioxidants* are agents that prevent unwanted oxidation and polymerization of organic substances.

$$(CH_3)_3C\text{—}\underset{CH_3}{\overset{OH}{\bigcirc}}\text{—}C(CH_3)_3$$

2,6-Di-*t*-butyl-
4-methylphenol

$$\underset{(CH_3)_2CH}{\overset{CH_3}{\bigcirc}}\text{—}OH$$

Thymol

Thymol (*3-hydroxy-4-isopropyltoluene*) occurs in thyme oil. Being anti-septic in high dilutions and having a more pleasant aromatic odor than phenol or the cresols, it frequently is used in proprietary preparations. In the absence of a sufficient supply of the natural product, it is synthesized from *m*-cresol and propylene.

Naphthols

α- and β-Naphthol are made by the fusion of the corresponding sulfo-nates with sodium hydroxide. The sulfonic acids are obtained by the direct sulfonation of naphthalene.

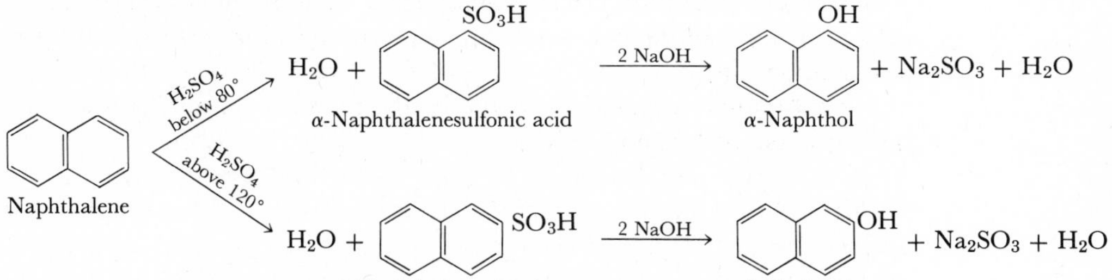

The naphthols and substituted naphthols are important intermediates for the manufacture of dyes (p. 209).

POLYHYDRIC PHENOLS

Dihydroxybenzenes

The *o*-, *m*-, and *p*-dihydroxybenzenes are known as *pyrocatechol, resorci-nol,* and *hydroquinone,* respectively. **Pyrocatechol** is so named because it is one of the distillation products of *gum catechu,* obtained from certain Asiatic tropical plants. It can be prepared by the general method of synthesis, namely the fusion of sodium *o*-phenolsulfonate with caustic soda.

Vesicants in poison ivy and poison oak

The toxic irritants of poison ivy (*Rhus toxicodendron*), poison oak (*Rhus diversiloba*), and certain related plants of the *Anacardiaceae* are mixtures of pyrocatechols having unbranched 15-carbon side chains in the 3-position. Four compounds in which the side chain is saturated or contains one, two, or three double bonds in the 8, the 8,11, or the 8,11,14 positions have been isolated from poison ivy. Three of the components of **urushiol,** the toxic principle of one of the lac trees (*Rhus vernicifera*), are identical with three of the compounds obtained from poison ivy, but the triply-unsaturated com-pound has two of the double bonds conjugated in the 12,14 positions.

Pyrocatechol   *Rhus* allergens   Resorcinol   4-*n*-Hexylresorcinol

Antiseptics

Resorcinol is a product of the distillation of certain natural resins but is manufactured by the fusion of sodium *m*-benzenedisulfonate with caustic soda. It undergoes substitution reactions readily in the 4 position. The con-densation products with formaldehyde (cf. p. 240) are used as cold-setting adhesives. Resorcinol also is an intermediate for the preparation of dyes and **4-*n*-hexylresorcinol.** The last compound is a popular antiseptic.

The antiseptic power of phenol is increased greatly by the substitution of alkyl groups into the nucleus. Thus the cresols are nearly as toxic as phenol, but their phenol coefficients (p. 76) are about 3. As the length of the alkyl group is increased the effectiveness increases up to six carbon atoms, and then decreases. *n*-Hexylphenol is 500 times more effective than phenol. Evidently a hydrocarbon chain of six carbon atoms corresponds to the optimum solubility in water and in fats, both of which are present in cells. The effect of the compound in lowering the surface tension of water also is important.

Hydroquinone is manufactured by the reduction of quinone, which is made by the oxidation of aniline.

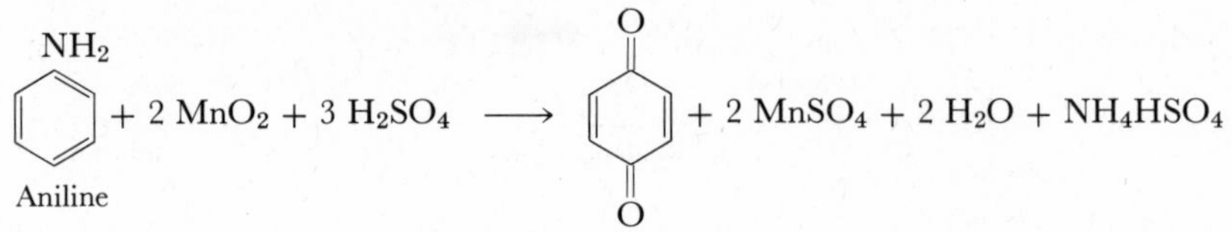

Aniline

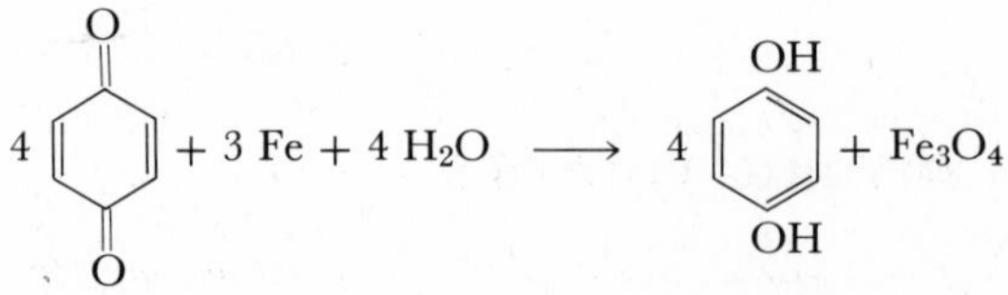

$$+ 2\,MnO_2 + 3\,H_2SO_4 \longrightarrow \quad + 2\,MnSO_4 + 2\,H_2O + NH_4HSO_4$$

Quinone　　　　　　Hydroquinone

$$4 \quad + 3\,Fe + 4\,H_2O \longrightarrow 4 \quad + Fe_3O_4$$

Trihydroxybenzenes

Pyrogallol (*pyrogallic acid; 1,2,3-trihydroxybenzene*) is prepared by decarboxylating gallic acid, obtained by hydrolysis of gallotannin (p. 172).

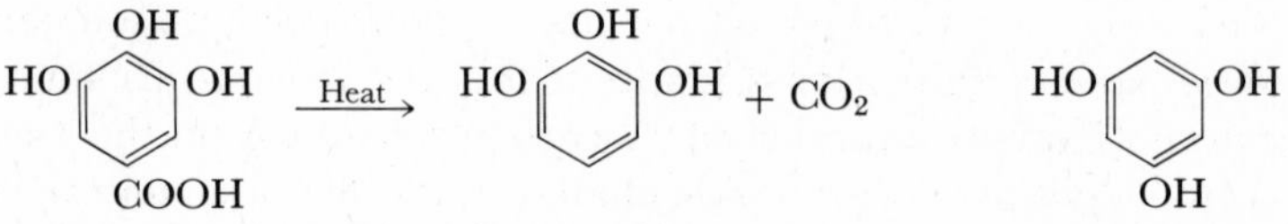

Gallic acid　　　　　Pyrogallol　　　　　Phloroglucinol

$$\xrightarrow{\text{Heat}} \quad + CO_2$$

Photographic developers

Hydroquinone and pyrogallol are important photographic developers. Alkaline pyrogallol solutions absorb oxygen very readily and are used to remove oxygen from mixtures with other gases. Hydroquinone is used extensively as an antioxidant. **Phloroglucinol** (*sym-trihydroxybenzene; 1,3,5-trihydroxybenzene*) is a useful reagent for the estimation of furfural and hence of pentoses (p. 184).

ETHERS

Nomenclature for ethers; two systems

The word *ether* (Gr. *aither,* applied to the material filling heavenly space) was given to ethyl ether because of its volatility. The ethers commonly are divided into two groups, the simple ethers, ROR, in which both R groups are alike, and the mixed ethers, ROR′, in which the R groups are different. They generally are designated by naming the alkyl groups and adding the word *ether.* For the simple ethers no indication need be given that two alkyl groups are present in the molecule; $(CH_3)_2O$ is methyl ether, $CH_3OC_2H_5$ is methyl ethyl ether, $(C_2H_5)_2O$ is ethyl ether, and $(C_6H_5)_2O$ is phenyl ether.[5]

The group RO is known as an *alkoxyl group,* although as a substituent it is called *alkoxy.* In the Geneva system the ethers are named as alkoxy derivatives of hydrocarbons. Methyl ether is methoxymethane, and methyl ethyl ether is methoxyethane. This system usually is used only when other functional groups are present. For example $CH_3OCH_2CH_2CH_2OH$ may be called 3-methoxy-1-propanol.

Ethers do not contain hydrogen united to the oxygen atom. Hence there is no tendency for molecules to associate with each other by proton bonding, and the boiling points are nearly normal. Methyl ether boils at $-24°$ and propane at $-42°$, methyl ethyl ether boils at $6°$ and n-butane at $-0.5°$, and ethyl ether boils at $35°$ and n-pentane at $36°$. *Resemblance to alkanes in boiling point and to alcohols in solubility*

Ethers have, however, unshared pairs of electrons on oxygen and can form proton bonds with water molecules. As would be expected, the solubilities in water are roughly the same as those of alcohols having the same number of carbon atoms. A saturated solution of ethyl ether in water at $25°$ contains 6 per cent by weight of the ether, and a saturated solution of n-butyl alcohol in water at $25°$ contains 7.5 per cent by weight of the alcohol. Water is soluble in both but only to the extent of 1.5 per cent in ether at $25°$ compared with 26 per cent in n-butyl alcohol.

A general method for the preparation of ethers involves the reaction of a metallic alkoxide with an alkyl halide. This procedure is known as the *Williamson synthesis.* *Preparation from alkoxides and alkyl halides or sulfates*

$$RONa + XR' \longrightarrow ROR' + NaX$$

The reaction may be used to prepare mixed ethers as well as simple ethers, because it is not reversible. Alkyl sulfates resemble alkyl halides in displacement reactions and may be used instead of alkyl halides to prepare ethers.

$$RONa + (R'O)_2SO_2 \longrightarrow ROR' + NaSO_3OR'$$

Phenols can be converted easily into aryl alkyl ethers, because sodium phenoxides are formed in aqueous solutions of sodium hydroxide, and the alkylation can be carried out in this medium. Most aryl halides cannot be used in the Williamson synthesis, because the halogen is too unreactive (p. 90).

Methyl and ethyl ether are prepared best by adding an alcohol to the alkyl hydrogen sulfate at a temperature of around $140°$. Under these conditions the ether distills from the mixture, and the process is continuous. *Preparation from alcohols and sulfuric acid*

$$ROH + H_2SO_4 \rightleftharpoons ROSO_3H + H_2O$$
$$ROSO_3H + HOR \rightleftharpoons ROR + H_2SO_4$$

---

[5] As there is no ambiguity in the term methyl ether, it is redundant to call it dimethyl ether. The situation is comparable to naming Na_2SO_4 sodium sulfate rather than disodium sulfate. Similarly the addition product of chlorine to ethylene was called ethylene chloride rather than ethylene dichloride (p. 32), just as $MgCl_2$ is called magnesium chloride rather than magnesium dichloride. This same principle will be followed later in naming derivatives of other polyvalent compounds such as the ketones (p. 94), sulfides (p. 84), esters of polycarboxylic acids (p. 114) and peroxides (p. 112).

Relatively unreactive

Ethers are relatively inert. Because the oxygen atom contains unshared electrons, ethers are capable of forming oxonium salts with any strong acid, HB, and addition complexes with any molecule having an atom that lacks a pair of electrons in its valence shell.

$$R:\overset{..}{\underset{..}{O}}: + HB \rightleftarrows \left[R:\overset{\overset{+}{..}}{\underset{..}{O}}:H \right] [B^-]$$
$$R$$

$$+ BF_3 \rightleftarrows R:\overset{..}{\underset{..}{O}}:BF_3$$
$$R$$

A reaction of ethers which has not found a use but which always should be kept in mind because of its potential danger is the absorption of atmospheric oxygen (*autoxidation*) to form peroxides.

$$R_2O + O_2 \longrightarrow R_2O_3$$

These peroxides are unstable and decompose violently on heating. An instance has been reported in which a can containing *i*-propyl ether that had been exposed to air for some time exploded on being moved. Hence ethers should not be exposed to air unnecessarily and always should be tested for peroxides before use.

Tests for peroxides

The ether may be tested by shaking a sample vigorously with a clean globule of mercury or with an acidified aqueous solution of potassium iodide. If the globule of mercury becomes badly tarnished or if the ether layer above the potassium iodide solution develops more than a pale yellow color, peroxides should be removed, especially before distillation.

Individual ethers

Methyl ether boils at $-24°$ and can be used as a solvent and extracting agent at low temperatures and as a propellant for aerosol sprays. The preparation of impure **ethyl ether** first was recorded in the sixteenth century. Since 1846, ethyl ether has been used as a general anesthetic and still is the most widely used substance for this purpose. It is used also as a solvent for fats. It frequently is used in the laboratory as a solvent for extracting organic compounds from aqueous solutions, although it is not always the best solvent for this purpose. The objections are that ether is highly flammable and that it is very soluble in strongly acid solutions. Moreover it emulsifies readily, making separation of the ether and water layers difficult. Finally it usually contains peroxides, which should be removed both for safety and because the peroxides may oxidize the product being extracted. One of the lower-boiling chlorinated hydrocarbons, such as methylene chloride (p. 91) or ethylene chloride (p. 92), may be preferable. One advantage of ether is that the equilibrium distribution of a compound between the water and the ether is attained rapidly, because ether and water are appreciably soluble in each other.

Ordinary ether contains some water and alcohol which are detrimental for some purposes. Both impurities can be removed by allowing the ether to stand over metallic sodium. The sodium hydroxide and sodium ethoxide formed are insoluble in ether and nonvolatile. The pure product is known as **absolute ether.**

Phenyl ether is a coproduct in the manufacture of phenol by the Dow process (p. 77). It is used to some extent in the perfume industry. The eutectic mixture consisting of 74 parts of phenyl ether and 26 parts of biphenyl (p. 47) is stable up to 400° at 135 p.s.i. and is used as a heat transfer medium in industrial operations.

Anethole, the chief component of anise oil, is the methyl ether of 4-propenylphenol. **Guaiacol,** the monomethyl ether of pyrocatechol, occurs in the distillation products of guaiac, the resin from American tropical trees of the genus *Guaiacum,* but is produced commercially from wood tar. The technical product, because of its antioxidant properties, is used as an antiskinning agent for paints. **Guaiacol carbonate** is used as an expectorant in cough remedies. **Eugenol** from oil of cloves is 2-methoxy-4-allylphenol.

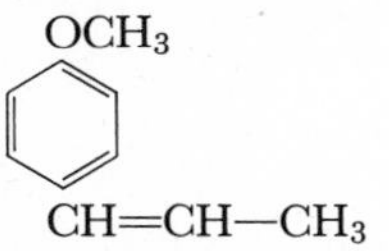

OCH3
CH=CH—CH3
Anethole

OCH3
OH
Guaiacol

OCH3
OCO
O
OCH3
Guaiacol carbonate

OH
OCH3
CH2CH=CH2
Eugenol

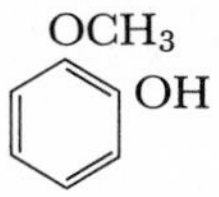

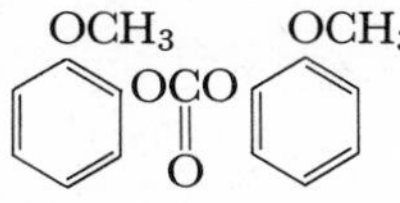

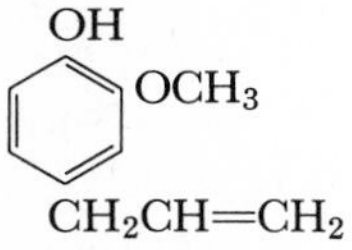

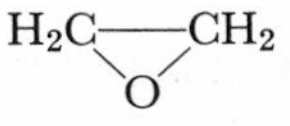

Heterocyclic ethers

Cyclic ethers belong to the **heterocyclic class of compounds,** that is, cyclic compounds having more than one kind of atom in the ring. Examples are ethylene oxide, tetrahydrofuran, tetrahydropyran, and 1,4-dioxane.

H2C—CH2
O
Ethylene oxide

H2C—CH2
H2C CH2
O
Tetrahydrofuran

HC—CH
HC CH
O
Furan

CH2
H2C CH2
H2C CH2
O
Tetrahydropyran

O
H2C CH2
H2C CH2
O
Dioxane

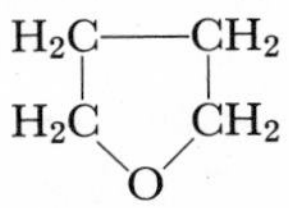

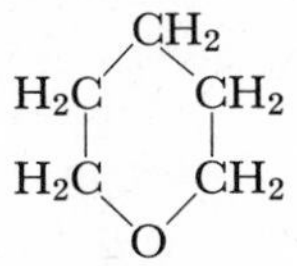

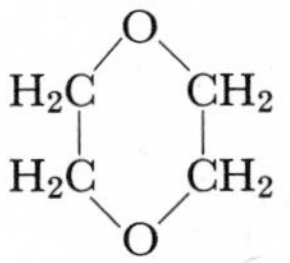

The reaction of ethylene oxide with ethylene glycol (p. 71) gives β-hydroxyethyl ether, commonly called **diethylene glycol,** and further reaction leads to the **polyethylene glycols** or *Carbowaxes* (p. 235).

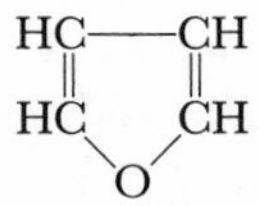

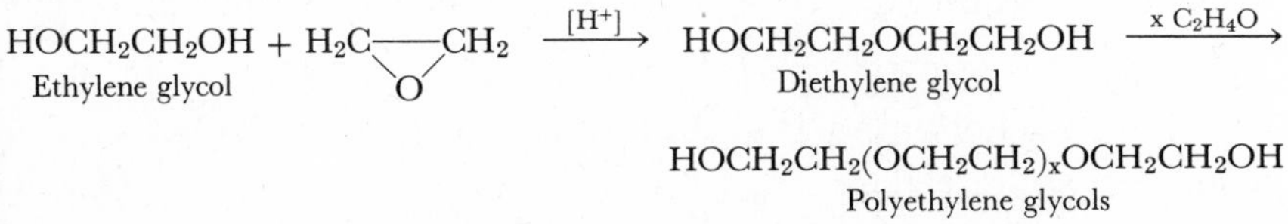

HOCH2CH2OH + H2C—CH2
O
[H+]
HOCH2CH2OCH2CH2OH
x C2H4O
Ethylene glycol
Diethylene glycol
HOCH2CH2(OCH2CH2)xOCH2CH2OH
Polyethylene glycols

Nonionic detergents (p. 123) are made by a similar reaction of ethylene oxide with an alkylated phenol or a fat acid.

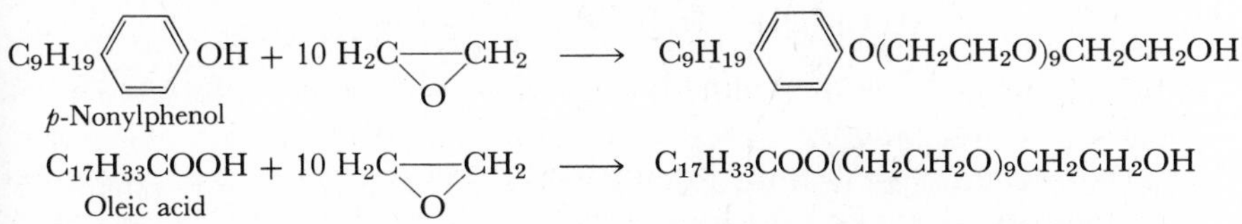

C9H19
OH + 10 H2C—CH2
O
C9H19
O(CH2CH2O)9CH2CH2OH
p-Nonylphenol
C17H33COOH + 10 H2C—CH2
O
C17H33COO(CH2CH2O)9CH2CH2OH
Oleic acid

Furan has aromatic properties

Furan has two conjugated double bonds. However, the presence of an unshared pair of electrons on oxygen provides a system of six electrons analogous to that provided by the six electrons of the three double bonds

in benzene. This situation reduces the ease of addition of reagents to the double bonds and gives the furan ring aromatic properties.

SOME SULFUR ANALOGS

Thiols are sulfur analogs of alcohols

Sulfur occurs below oxygen in the periodic table, and sulfur analogs of most oxygen compounds are known. Only a few are of general interest. The **thio alcohols** are known also as *thiols* or *mercaptans* and have the general formula RSH. They can be made by the reaction of an alkyl halide with sodium hydrosulfide.

$$RX + NaSH \longrightarrow RSH + NaX$$

The volatile members have a foul odor and are toxic. The thio alcohols do not form proton bonds. Hence they have normal boiling points and are insoluble in water.

More acidic than alcohols

Just as hydrogen sulfide is more acidic than water, the thiols are more acidic than alcohols and react with aqueous solutions of strong bases to form salts. Like sodium sulfide these salts are hydrolyzed markedly in aqueous solution.

$$RSH + NaOH \rightleftharpoons RSNa + H_2O$$

The heavy metal salts, such as those of lead, mercury, copper, cadmium, and silver, are insoluble in water. The ease of formation of insoluble mercury salts gave rise to the name *mercaptan* (L. *mercurium captans,* mercury seizing). Reaction of alkyl halides with alcoholic sodium sulfide yields the *alkyl sulfides* and with sodium disulfide, the *alkyl disulfides.*

Sulfides are analogs of ethers

$$2\ RX + Na_2S \longrightarrow R{-}S{-}R + 2\ NaX$$
An alkyl sulfide

$$2\ RX + Na_2S_2 \longrightarrow R{-}S{-}S{-}R + 2\ NaX$$
An alkyl disulfide

The disulfides also result from the oxidation of mercaptans with sodium hypoiodite.

$$2\ RSH + NaOI \longrightarrow R{-}S{-}S{-}R + H_2O + NaI$$

Sulfides do not show any of the chemical properties of ethers, nor do disulfides behave like peroxides.

Some thiols, sulfides, and a disulfide

Methyl mercaptan is made commercially by passing a mixture of methyl alcohol and hydrogen sulfide over alumina at about 400°.

$$CH_3OH + H_2S \xrightarrow{400°} CH_3SH + H_2O$$

It is used chiefly for the synthesis of methionine (p. 198). **n-Butyl mercaptan** has been isolated as a component of the malodorous secretion of skunks. **n-Dodecyl mercaptan** is used to regulate the chain length in the manufacture of SBR synthetic rubber (p. 237).

Methyl sulfide is made commercially by heating the spent liquor from the manufacture of kraft pulp (p. 192) with sodium sulfide. It is used as an odorant for natural gas and to make methyl sulfoxide. **Mustard gas** (*β-chloroethyl sulfide*) is one of the more powerful vesicants used in chemical warfare. It is not a gas but a heavy oily liquid boiling at 217°. It can be made by reaction of ethylene and sulfur monochloride.

$$2 \ CH_2{=}CH_2 + S_2Cl_2 \longrightarrow ClCH_2CH_2SCH_2CH_2Cl + S$$

Oil of garlic is a complex mixture of which the chief component appears to be allyl disulfide, $(CH_2{=}CHCH_2)_2S_2$.

Tetrahydrothiophene is a heterocyclic sulfide that can be made from tetramethylene chloride; it resembles alkyl sulfides. *Heterocyclic sulfides*

$$\begin{array}{c} CH_2CH_2Cl \\ | \\ CH_2CH_2Cl \end{array} + Na_2S \longrightarrow \begin{array}{c} H_2C{-\!-\!-}CH_2 \\ | \qquad | \\ H_2C \qquad CH_2 \\ \diagdown_{\ S}\diagup \end{array} + 2 \ NaCl$$

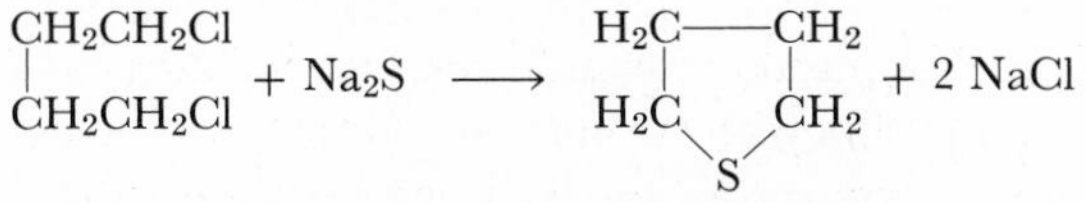

Tetrahydrothiophene

Thiophene, the compound with two conjugated double bonds, resembles benzene even more strikingly than does furan (p. 83). Furan, being an ether, is susceptible to carbon-oxygen scission by strong acids, but thiophene can be halogenated, nitrated, and sulfonated, and undergoes the Friedel-Crafts reaction just as does benzene. *Thiophene an aromatic compound*

2-Chlorothiophene
(2-thienylchloride)

2-Thienyl methyl
ketone

2-Nitrothiophene

Thiophene

2-Thiophenesulfonic
acid

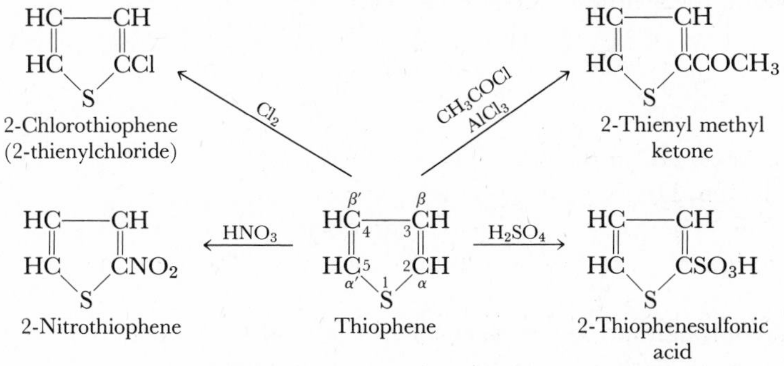

SUMMARY

Alcohols

1. The simplest oxygenated organic compounds are alcohols, phenols, and ethers. Alcohols have an alkyl group, and phenols an aryl group, replacing one of the hydrogens of the water molecule. If both hydrogens of the water molecule are replaced by alkyl or aryl groups, the resulting products are called ethers.
2. The common names of alcohols are formed by naming the alkyl group and adding *alcohol* as a separate word. In the Geneva system, the ending is *ol*. Phenols either have special names ending in *ol* or are named as derivatives of phenol. Ethers usually are named by adding *ether* as a separate word to the names of the alkyl or aryl groups attached to oxygen.
3. Alcohols and phenols undergo proton bonding. Hence they have higher boiling points and are more soluble in water than hydrocarbons of the same molecular weight. Alcohols having less than four carbon atoms and *t*-butyl alcohol are miscible with water, whereas the simplest phenol is not because it has six carbon atoms. However, phenol is somewhat more soluble than cyclohexanol because of the higher electron density of the aromatic ring.

4. The most important commercial monohydric alcohols are methanol and ethanol. Some methanol is obtained by the destructive distillation of wood, but most of it is synthesized from carbon monoxide and hydrogen. Its chief uses are as a solvent, as an antifreeze, and for the synthesis of formaldehyde and other organic chemicals.

   Ethanol is made by the fermentation of hydrolyzed starch, or of black-strap molasses, or by synthesis from ethylene and water. Industrial alcohol is used chiefly as a solvent and for the synthesis of acetaldehyde and other organic chemicals. Other alcohols such as *i*-propyl and *t*-butyl alcohols are made by the hydration of the corresponding alkenes.

5. Some reactions of alcohols are: (1) the formation of complexes with metallic salts, such as calcium chloride, or of oxonium salts with strong acids because of the unshared electrons on oxygen; (2) the replacement of the hydrogen of the hydroxyl by reactive metals such as sodium; (3) the replacement of the hydroxyl group by halogen to give alkyl halides, or by the anion of oxygenated acids to give alkyl esters; (4) oxidation (dehydrogenation) to give aldehydes and ketones.

6. Of the alcohols containing more than one hydroxyl group (polyhydric alcohols), ethylene glycol, propylene glycol, and glycerol are the most important. Ethylene glycol is used chiefly as a nonvolatile antifreeze, and glycerol as a humectant. Both are important intermediates in the synthesis of polyester resins and fibers.

Phenols

7. Phenols, in contrast to alcohols, are sufficiently acidic to form sodium salts with strong bases in aqueous solution. Hence water-insoluble phenols dissolve in dilute solutions of sodium hydroxide. They are weaker acids than carbonic acid and are liberated from their salts by passing carbon dioxide into aqueous solutions of the salts.

8. The hydroxyl group of phenols cannot be displaced readily by halogen. Phenols give characteristic color reactions with aqueous ferric chloride and are easily oxidized, especially in alkaline solutions. Phenols undergo sulfonation, nitration, and halogenation of the nucleus more easily than benzene, the new group entering chiefly at the *ortho* and *para* positions.

9. Phenol itself is synthesized from benzene by several different processes. About half of the total production is used to make phenol-formaldehyde plastics and resins. The remainder is used to synthesize other chemicals.

10. Important polyhydric phenols are pyrocatechol, resorcinol, hydroquinone, pyrogallol, and phloroglucinol.

Ethers

11. Ether molecules cannot proton bond with each other. Hence ethers are not associated liquids and have nearly normal boiling points. On the other hand they can proton bond with water molecules, and ethers with fewer than four carbon atoms are soluble in water. Ethers and alcohols usually are soluble in each other, as are ethers and alkanes.

12. The most general method for preparing ethers is by the Williamson synthesis, although the sulfuric acid process is suitable for lower ethers.

EXERCISES

Alcohols

1. Write condensed structural formulas for all of the alcohols having the molecular formula $C_5H_{12}O$ and state whether each is a primary, secondary, or tertiary alcohol.
2. Write structural formulas for (a) n-octyl alcohol; (b) t-butyl alcohol; (c) i-propyl alcohol; (d) 3-methyl-3-hexanol.
3. (a) Predict the order of increasing solubility in water of the following compounds: n-butyl alcohol, t-butyl alcohol, n-pentane, n-octyl alcohol, n-amyl alcohol, benzene.
   (b) Predict the order of increasing boiling point for these compounds.
4. Give equations for the reactions involved in the commercial synthesis of (a) methanol; (b) ethanol; (c) 2-propanol; (d) 2-methyl-2-propanol.
5. Give equations for the reaction of (a) ethyl alcohol with metallic sodium; (b) s-butyl alcohol with hydrogen bromide; (c) n-heptyl alcohol with nitric acid.
6. Give structural formulas and names for all of the stable saturated dihydric and trihydric alcohols having three or less carbon atoms.
7. What simple tests could be applied to distinguish between n-hexane, 2-hexene, and 1-butanol?
8. (a) What is the advantage of ethylene glycol over methanol as a radiator antifreeze?
   (b) What roughly would be the relative amounts of the two compounds that would be required to produce the same lowering of the freezing point of water?

Phenols

9. Give equations or statements describing the behavior of phenol and of cyclohexanol toward the following reagents: (a) aqueous sodium hydroxide; (b) hydrogen bromide; (c) metallic sodium; (d) aqueous ferric chloride.
10. Give equations for the bromination, nitration, and sulfonation of phenol.
11. Give structural formulas for the toxic compounds isolated from poison ivy.
12. Arrange the following compounds in order of increasing acidity: phenol, 1-hexanol, n-pentane, 2,4,6-trinitrophenol.
13. How do phenols differ in structure from naphthols?
14. What is meant by the statement that an antiseptic has a phenol coefficient of 5?
15. Write the structural formula for p-cresyl phosphate.

Ethers

16. Write structural formulas for all of the ethers having the molecular formula $C_5H_{12}O$. What other group of compounds has the same molecular formula?
17. What simple chemical tests could be used to distinguish between n-propyl ether, n-propyl alcohol, and toluene?
18. Write the equation for the reaction of phenol with methyl sulfate in the presence of sodium hydroxide to give methyl phenyl ether.
19. What is formed by the action of air on ethers and why is the product dangerous?

Sulfur Compounds

20. Write general structural formulas for the sulfur analogs of alcohols and ethers. What names are given to each class?
21. Give equations or statements describing the behavior of ethyl alcohol, ethyl mercaptan, ethyl ether, and ethyl sulfide toward each of the following reagents: (a) metallic sodium; (b) aqueous mercuric acetate; (c) concentrated hydrochloric acid at room temperature.
22. Account for the difference in properties of tetramethylene sulfide and thiophene.

CHAPTER 9

HALOGEN
COMPOUNDS

Nomenclature; two
systems

Alkyl halides are important intermediates for the synthesis of other compounds. They are named as if they were salts of halogen acids, that is, by naming the alkyl group and adding *halide* as a separate word. For example, C_2H_5Br is *ethyl bromide* and $(CH_3)_2CHCH_2I$ is *i-butyl iodide*. They may be considered also as halogen derivatives of saturated hydrocarbons. Thus ethyl bromide may be called *bromoethane* and *i*-butyl iodide may be called *1-iodo-2-methylpropane*. Aryl halides usually are named in this way (p. 45).

Preparation differs for
alkyl and aryl halides

Alkyl halides can be made by the reaction of alcohols with halogen acids (p. 69) and aryl halides by direct halogenation of the aromatic nucleus (p. 46). In the latter reactions, some further substitution takes place to give a mixture of *ortho* and *para* isomers with very little *meta*.

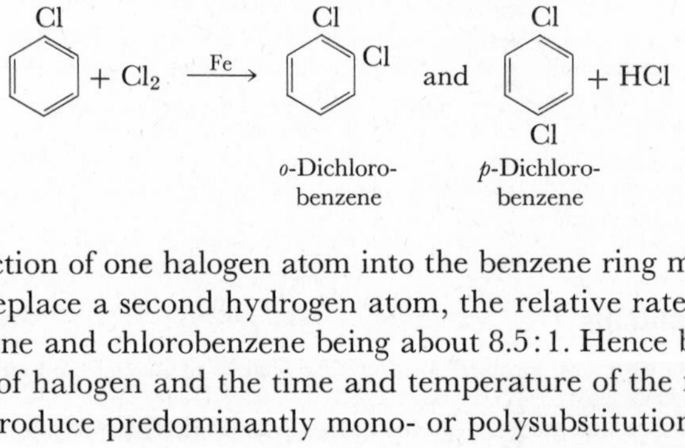

o-Dichloro-
benzene

p-Dichloro-
benzene

Ring halogenation

The introduction of one halogen atom into the benzene ring makes it more difficult to replace a second hydrogen atom, the relative rates of substitution of benzene and chlorobenzene being about 8.5:1. Hence by regulating the amount of halogen and the time and temperature of the reaction, it is possible to produce predominantly mono- or polysubstitution products as desired.

Other aromatic compounds halogenate in a similar manner. For example, toluene on chlorination or bromination in the presence of ferric chloride or ferric bromide yields a mixture of *o*- and *p*-chloro- or bromotoluenes.

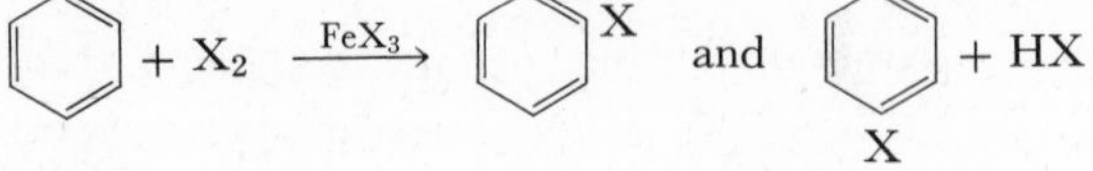

Side-chain
halogenation

If a mixture of toluene vapor and halogen is exposed to light of short wavelength, halogenation takes place in the side chain more rapidly than substitution in the nucleus or than addition to the double bonds. Here the rates of replacement of a second and third hydrogen atom by halogen differ little from the rate of replacement of the first hydrogen atom, and it is more difficult to control the relative amounts of mono-, di-, and trisubstitution products.

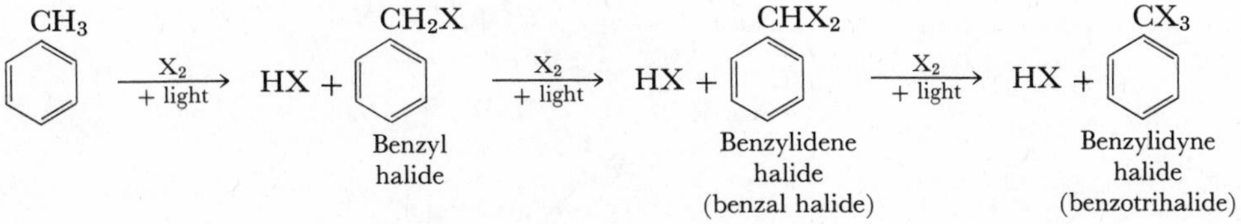

Benzyl halide

Benzylidene halide (benzal halide)

Benzylidyne halide (benzotrihalide)

Benzene can add three moles of chlorine in the presence of light of short wavelength, which provides the necessary activation energy.

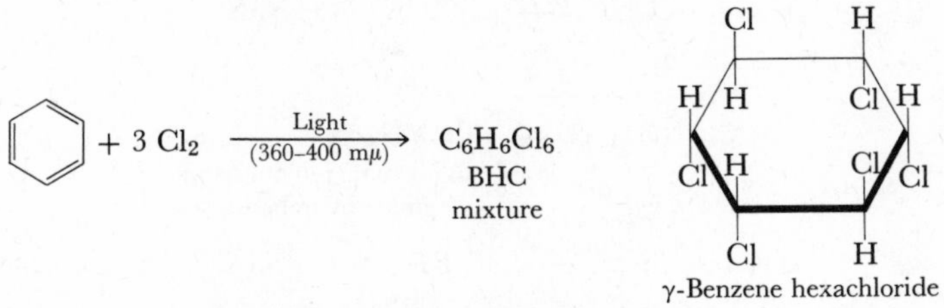

Addition of halogen to double bonds

γ-Benzene hexachloride

The production of the hexachlorides was reported first by Faraday in 1825 in his paper on the isolation of benzene. Nine stereoisomers (p. 153) of benzene hexachloride are possible. The mixture of isomers has become of considerable commercial importance because of the discovery of its insecticidal properties in 1943. It is called **BHC** or **666,** abbreviations of its name or of the formula $C_6H_6Cl_6$. The insecticidal property is due solely to the γ isomer, which makes up only 18 per cent of the mixed halides. The insecticidal products are sold on the basis of the content of the γ isomer, which has been given the names **gammexane** and **lindane** (after van der Linden, who established the existence of the first four isomers in 1912). The mixture of isomers must be used at the proper dilution, because it leaves a persistent musty odor if the concentration is too high. Pure γ isomer is reported to be free of the musty odor.

Benzene hexachloride an insecticide

In physical properties the halides resemble the hydrocarbons. They are insoluble in water and are good solvents for many organic compounds. The boiling points of the chlorides are of the same order of magnitude as those of hydrocarbons of the same molecular weight, whereas bromides boil about 60° lower than chlorides, and iodides 70° lower than bromides, again comparing compounds of the same molecular weight.

Physical properties resemble those of hydrocarbons

Halides are more dense than hydrocarbons. The densities of the compounds considered so far increase in the order hydrocarbons < alcohols < chlorides < bromides < iodides, if compounds with the same number of carbon atoms are compared. The density of hydrocarbons increases with increasing number of carbon atoms because of the increasing van der Waals forces, but, because carbon atoms are less dense than elements of higher atomic number, increasing the size of the hydrocarbon portion of halides causes a decrease in density.

Chemical properties of
alkyl halides

The halogen of alkyl halides is fairly reactive and can be replaced by many other groups. Some of the more important reactions for primary and secondary halides are illustrated by the following equations.

$$RX + AgOH \longrightarrow ROH + AgX \qquad (1)$$
(or aqueous NaOH)   An alcohol   (or NaX)

$$RX + NaOR \longrightarrow ROR + NaX \qquad (2)$$
An ether

$$RX + NaSH \longrightarrow RSH + NaX \qquad (3)$$
A mercaptan
(thio alcohol
or alkanethiol)

$$2 RX + Na_2S \longrightarrow R_2S + 2 NaX \qquad (4)$$
An alkyl
sulfide

$$RX + NaCN \longrightarrow RCN + NaX \qquad (5)$$
An alkyl
cyanide

$$RX + NH_3 \longrightarrow RNH_3{}^+X^- \qquad (6)$$
An alkylammonium halide
(amine hydrohalide)

$$2 RX + 2 Na \longrightarrow RR + 2 NaX \text{ (Wurtz synthesis)} \qquad (10)$$
An alkane

Similarity to halogen
acids

The reagents that react with an alkyl halide are metals or salts of weak acids. These same reagents react with halogen acids. The reactions for the most part are identical in both cases except that a hydrogen atom of the acid takes the part of an alkyl group in the alkyl halide. For example, silver hydroxide and halogen acid give water and silver halide, sodium sulfide gives hydrogen sulfide, sodium cyanide gives hydrogen cyanide, ammonia gives ammonium halide, and sodium gives hydrogen. The principal difference is that the reactions with alkyl halides are slow, whereas those with halogen acids are rapid.

Alkyl iodides react more rapidly than bromides, and bromides than chlorides. Because bromides are cheaper than iodides and usually are sufficiently reactive, they are used most frequently in the laboratory.

Aryl halides usually
unreactive

Unlike the alkyl halides, the simple aryl halides are very unreactive. No observable reaction takes place with sodium hydroxide, silver salts, sodium alkoxide, sodium cyanide, sodium sulfide, or ammonia under the conditions that bring about displacement reactions with the alkyl halides. The reactivity may, however, be increased greatly by the presence of electron-attracting groups in the *ortho* and *para* positions. For example, the chlorine in 2,4,6-trinitrochlorobenzene is highly reactive. Halogen in the side chain of an aromatic hydrocarbon behaves like an alkyl halide. If the halogen is on the carbon atom adjacent to the ring, as in benzyl halides, its reactivity is even greater than that of saturated primary alkyl halides.

Important halogen
compounds

A few of the simple halides are of industrial importance. **Methyl chloride,** b.p. $-24°$, is made by heating methyl alcohol with hydrochloric acid. It is formed also as one product of the reaction of chlorine with methane (p. 91). Its principal uses are as a refrigerant in mechanical refrigerators, as a solvent at low temperatures, and as a methylating agent in the preparation of tetramethyllead (p. 51), silicones (p. 239), and other organic compounds. **Methyl bromide,** b.p. 4.5°, is made from methyl alcohol and hydrogen bromide. It is highly toxic and is used as a poison gas for rodent control. It is toxic to other forms of life also and is used as a soil and grain fumigant. Because of its high toxicity to human beings, it should be used only with proper precautions to prevent inhalation of the vapors. **Ethyl chloride,** b.p. 13°, is made either from ethyl alcohol and hydrochloric acid in the presence of zinc chloride, by passing an equimolar mixture of ethylene and hydrogen chloride into a solution of anhydrous aluminum chloride in liquid ethyl chloride, or by the reaction of a mixture of ethane and ethylene with chlorine whereby the hydrogen chloride formed by the substitution of ethane is added to the ethylene.

$$CH_3CH_3 + Cl_2 \longrightarrow CH_3CH_2Cl + HCl$$
$$H_2C{=}CH_2 + HCl \longrightarrow CH_3CH_2Cl$$

It is used as a quickly-acting general anesthetic for minor operations. Its chief use is for the preparation of tetraethyllead (p. 50) by reaction with sodium-lead alloy.

$$4\ C_2H_5Cl + Na_4Pb \longrightarrow Pb(C_2H_5)_4 + 4\ NaCl$$

Chlorobenzene is an intermediate for the production of phenol (p. 77) and of aniline (p. 130).

Some of the polyhalogenated alkanes are important as solvents. They usually are made by special methods. The reaction of chlorine with methane, either thermally or in the presence of ultraviolet light, yields **methylene chloride,** b.p. 41°, **chloroform,** b.p. 61°, and **carbon tetrachloride,** b.p. 77°, as well as **methyl chloride.**

Polyhalogenated alkanes

$$CH_4 + Cl_2 \xrightarrow[\text{light}]{\text{Heat or}} CH_3Cl + HCl$$
$$\text{Methyl chloride}$$

$$CH_3Cl + Cl_2 \longrightarrow CH_2Cl_2 + HCl$$
$$\text{Methylene chloride}$$

$$CH_2Cl_2 + Cl_2 \longrightarrow CHCl_3 + HCl$$
$$\text{Chloroform}$$

$$CHCl_3 + Cl_2 \longrightarrow CCl_4 + HCl$$
$$\text{Carbon tetrachloride}$$

Carbon tetrachloride is made also by the reaction of carbon disulfide with chlorine.

$$CS_2 + 2\ Cl_2 \longrightarrow CCl_4 + 2\ S$$

Reaction of carbon tetrachloride with hydrogen fluoride in the presence of antimony pentafluoride gives **dichlorodifluoromethane** (*Freon-12*), b.p. −29°.

Fluorine compounds

$$CCl_4 + 2\ HF \xrightarrow{\text{SbF}_5} CCl_2F_2 + 2\ HCl$$
$$\text{Dichlorodifluoromethane}$$

It is used as a refrigerant for commercial refrigerators and air-conditioning equipment, and as a solvent-propellant for aerosol spray preparations. **Chlorodifluoromethane** (*Freon-22*), b.p. 41°, is made by a similar process from chloroform and is an intermediate in the preparation of **tetrafluoroethylene,** the monomer from which Teflon is made (p. 234). **1,2-Dichloro-1,1,2,2-tetrafluoroethane** (*Freon-114*), b.p. 3.8°, is made from hexachloroethane (p. 38) and is the common refrigerant for household refrigerators.

Addition of chlorine to ethylene gives **ethylene chloride,** b.p. 84°, and addition of bromine gives **ethylene bromide.** Both are used in *Ethyl Fluid,* the antiknock additive for gasoline (p. 51). Ethylene chloride also is a useful solvent. Other important chlorinated ethanes are derived from acetylene (p. 38).

Chlorinated solvents toxic

All of the chlorinated hydrocarbons are highly toxic. Prolonged exposure to their vapors causes fatty degeneration of the liver, and recent warnings have been given against their use in the home as cleaning fluids. Saturated acyclic fluorinated compounds having two fluorine atoms on the same carbon atom usually are exceptions to this rule.

SUMMARY

1. Alkyl halides may be prepared by the reaction of alcohols with halogen acids, and aryl halides by direct halogenation of an aromatic nucleus. Addition of three moles of halogen to the aromatic nucleus and replacement of hydrogen in a side chain by halogen also can take place.
2. The liquid halides are nonassociated and have normal boiling points. They are insoluble in water and the bromides, iodides, and polychlorides usually are heavier than water.
3. Primary and secondary alkyl halides react with the salts of weak acids to give products in which the halogen has been replaced by the acid radical. Aryl halides usually are very unreactive. Aralkyl halides, however, in which the halogen is on a carbon atom adjacent to the ring, are more reactive than saturated primary alkyl halides.
4. Many polyhalogenated alkanes, such as methylene chloride, chloroform, carbon tetrachloride, and ethylene chloride, are important solvents and also are used as refrigerants, as aerosol propellants, and as intermediates for the synthesis of other compounds.

EXERCISES

1. Arrange the following compounds in the order of increasing density: *n*-hexyl bromide, ethyl ether, ethyl iodide, *n*-pentane, *n*-butyl bromide, *n*-butyl chloride.
2. Give structural formulas for: (a) all of the dibromopentanes that can be prepared readily from alkenes; (b) all of the monochlorinated toluenes.
3. How could one readily distinguish by chemical reactions between benzene, *n*-hexane, bromobenzene, and benzyl bromide?
4. Give the structural formula and name of a halogenated hydrocarbon that is used as: (a) an insecticide; (b) a solvent; (c) a refrigerant; (d) an intermediate for the production of phenol; (e) a larvicide.

CHAPTER 10

ALDEHYDES
AND KETONES

Just as a double bond may exist between two carbon atoms, a double bond may join a carbon atom to an oxygen atom. This functional group, $C{=}O$, is known as a **carbonyl group.** Here all of the electrons about oxygen are paired and, as indicated in (*a*), the oxygen has a complete octet.

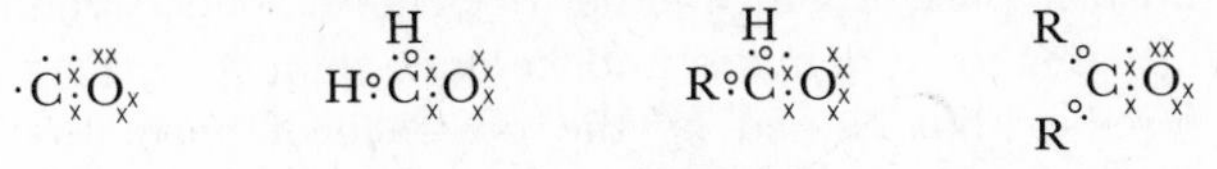

Carbon-oxygen double bond

(*a*)　　　(*b*)　　　(*c*)　　　(*d*)

Carbon, however, still has two unpaired electrons, which it may share with other atoms or groups. If both are shared with hydrogen atoms as in (*b*), or if one is shared with hydrogen and the other with an alkyl or aryl group as in (*c*), the compound is called an *aldehyde*. If both electrons are shared with alkyl or aryl groups, or with one alkyl and one aryl group as in (*d*), the compound is called a *ketone*.

The **common names** of the first four normal aldehydes are formaldehyde, acetaldehyde, propionaldehyde, and butyraldehyde. They are derived from the common names of the acids formed on oxidation (p. 106).

Nomenclature of aldehydes

Branched-chain aldehydes may be named **as derivatives of acetaldehyde;** thus $C_2H_5CH(CH_3)CHO$ may be called *methylethylacetaldehyde*. In the **Geneva system** the aldehydes are named by dropping the *e* of the hydrocarbon corresponding to the longest chain containing the aldehyde group and adding *al*. The compound having the above formula would be called *2-methylbutanal*. The position of the aldehyde group is not indicated because it always is at the end of the chain, and its carbon atom is numbered one.

The first ketone must have three carbon atoms. It is called *acetone*, because it was prepared first from acetic acid. Other ketones usually are named by stating the groups attached to the carbonyl group and adding the separate word *ketone*. For example $CH_3COC_2H_5$ is *methyl ethyl ketone*. The name is written as three separate words since the compound is not a substitution product of a substance *ketone*. In the **Geneva system** the ending is *one* and the position of the carbonyl group must be indicated by a number, unless the name is unambiguous without the number. Thus

Nomenclature of ketones

methyl ethyl ketone may be called simply *butanone,* but ethyl ketone, $CH_3CH_2COCH_2CH_3$, must be called *3-pentanone* to distinguish it from methyl *n*-propyl ketone, $CH_3COCH_2CH_2CH_3$, which is *2-pentanone.* Side chains are named and numbered as usual.

If it is necessary to designate a carbonyl function when another functional group is present, the doubly-bound oxygen is called *oxo.* Thus $CH_3COCH_2CH_2CH_2OH$ is *4-oxo-1-pentanol.* Generically, however, it is called a keto alcohol or ketol rather than an oxo alcohol.

Boil between ethers and alcohols

The aldehydes and ketones resemble the ethers in their solubility characteristics and volatility, but aldehydes and ketones boil somewhat higher than ethers having the same number of carbon atoms. For example methyl ether boils at $-24°$ and acetaldehyde at $+20°$; methyl ethyl ether boils at 6°, whereas propionaldehyde boils at 49° and acetone at 56°.

Thus far two sources of van der Waals forces have been considered, the London forces resulting from the polarizability of the molecule (p. 21), and proton bonding (p. 61). Neither of these attractive forces can account for the fact that aldehydes and ketones boil higher than ethers of approximately the same molecular weight, because the polarizabilities should be nearly the same, and proton bonding is not possible. Hence a third attractive force must be present which either does not exist between ether molecules or is greater for aldehydes and ketones than for ethers. This third

Have permanent dipoles

attractive force is that caused by the presence of **permanent electrical dipoles** in the molecules.

In atoms the center of positive charge and the center of negative charge coincide; that is, the probability of finding an electron at any point about the nucleus is the same as that of finding it at the same distance away from the nucleus on the opposite side. The same situation exists in diatomic molecules made up of like atoms, for example hydrogen or chlorine molecules, or in symmetrical polyatomic molecules such as methane and carbon tetrachloride. However, when unlike atoms are bonded to give an unsymmetrical molecule, the centers of positive and negative charge in the molecule ordinarily do not coincide, and the molecule has a positive and a negative end; that is, it is an electrical dipole. This dipole is a permanent one, in contrast to the dipoles resulting from the transient polarizability of the molecule. Whenever such an unequal distribution of charge occurs, an electrical moment, known as the *dipole moment,* exists. This moment is the product of the difference in charge between the ends of the dipole by the distance between the centers of charge and is designated by the symbol μ. The usual magnitude of the moment is of the order of 10^{-18} electrostatic

Unit of measurement for dipole moment

units $\times$ cm., and this quantity is known as a *debye unit,* or simply a *debye* (after P. Debye, who first measured electric moments), and is given the symbol D. Thus methyl ether has a moment of 1.3 D and methyl ethyl ether one of 1.2 D. The moments of acetaldehyde, propionaldehyde, and acetone are respectively 2.7 D, 2.7 D, and 2.8 D. These permanent dipoles add to those caused by the polarizability of the molecule and increase the attractive forces between the molecules. Thus the higher dipole moments of the carbonyl compounds as compared to those for ethers can account for the higher boiling points of the carbonyl compounds. The attractive forces caused by dipoles are proportional to the square of the dipole moment rather than directly proportional. Hence their effect rapidly increases with increasing magnitude.

Preparation and addition reactions

Aldehydes and ketones have two fewer hydrogen atoms than the corresponding primary and secondary alcohols and can be made by the oxidation or dehydrogenation of alcohols (p. 69). In general their reactions involve addition to the double bond of the carbonyl group. Thus catalytic hydrogenation converts aldehydes into primary alcohols and ketones into secondary alcohols.

$$\overset{\overset{\displaystyle H}{|}}{RC}{=}O + H_2 \xrightarrow{\text{Pt}} RCH_2OH$$

$$R_2C{=}O + H_2 \xrightarrow{\text{Pt}} R_2CHOH$$

Halogens do not add to the carbonyl group to give stable compounds. On the other hand the polarity of the carbon-oxygen double bond increases its reactivity and permits the addition of numerous reagents that do not add to isolated carbon-carbon double bonds. For example hydrogen cyanide adds to aldehydes to give fairly stable products called **aldehyde cyanohydrins.**

Cyanohydrins

$$CH_3CH{=}O + HCN \longrightarrow \underset{\underset{\displaystyle OH}{|}}{CH_3CH}{-}CN$$

Acetaldehyde cyanohydrin

Hydroxy and amino derivatives of ammonia add to give 1-hydroxy-1-amino derivatives which spontaneously lose water. The products of reaction with hydroxylamine are called **oximes,** and those with derivatives of hydrazine are called **hydrazones.**

Oximes and hydrazones

$$CH_3CH{=}O + H_2NOH \longrightarrow \left[\underset{\underset{\displaystyle OH}{|}}{CH_3CH}{-}NHOH\right] \longrightarrow H_2O + CH_3CH{=}NOH$$

Hydroxylamine   Acetaldoxime

$$(CH_3)_2C{=}O + H_2N{-}NHC_6H_5 \longrightarrow \left[\underset{\underset{\displaystyle OH}{|}}{(CH_3)_2C}{-}NH{-}NHC_6H_5\right] \longrightarrow$$

Phenylhydrazine

$$H_2O + (CH_3)_2C{=}N{-}NHC_6H_5$$

Acetone
phenylhydrazone

Aldol addition

An important type of reaction of aldehydes and ketones is known as **aldol addition.** In this reaction a hydrogen α to the carbonyl group of one molecule adds to the oxygen of the carbonyl of a second molecule, and carbon adds to carbon. The reaction is reversible and is catalyzed by either dilute acids or bases.

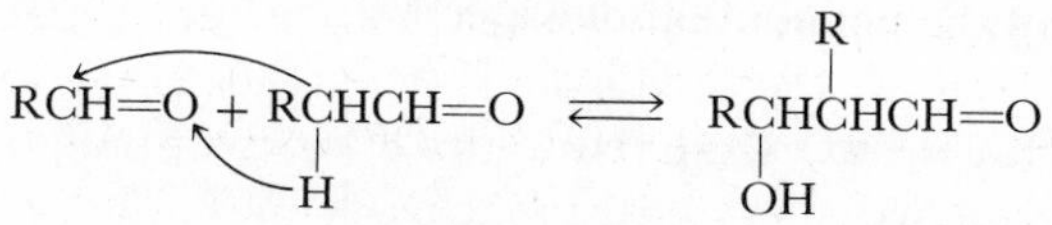

$$RCH{=}O + \underset{\underset{\displaystyle H}{|}}{RCHCH}{=}O \rightleftarrows \underset{\underset{\displaystyle OH}{|}}{R\overset{\overset{\displaystyle R}{|}}{CHCH}CH}{=}O$$

Aldehydes oxidize easily

Although the name of the reaction is derived from the fact that aldehydes give a product having both an aldehyde and an alcohol function, the same type of reaction also takes place between ketones and between aldehydes and ketones.

The hydrogen attached to the carbonyl group in aldehydes can be oxidized readily to a hydroxyl group to give products known as *carboxylic acids* (p. 102), whereas ketones cannot be oxidized without breaking a carbon-carbon bond. It is possible to choose oxidizing agents that attack aldehydes and not ketones, and to use the reaction as a distinguishing test. Some mild oxidizing agents used for this purpose are: Fehling solution, an alkaline solution of a cupric complex with sodium tartrate (p. 170); Benedict solution, a cupric complex with sodium citrate (p. 171); and Tollens reagent, an ammoniacal solution of silver hydroxide. All behave like solutions of the metallic hydroxides. With Fehling and Benedict solutions, the copper is reduced to the cuprous state, which does not form a stable complex with tartrate or citrate ion and precipitates as cuprous oxide.

Reduce Fehling, Benedict, and Tollens reagents

$$RCHO + 2\ Cu(OH)_2 + NaOH \longrightarrow RCOO^-Na^+ + Cu_2O\downarrow + 3\ H_2O$$

If the precipitation of cuprous oxide takes place in the presence of protective colloids such as those present in urine, it is finely divided and yellow, but if formed in the absence of protective colloids, it has a larger particle size and is red. With Tollens reagent, metallic silver is the reduction product.

$$RCHO + 2\ Ag(NH_3)_2OH \longrightarrow RCOO^-NH_4^+ + 2\ Ag\downarrow + H_2O + 3\ NH_3$$

If the vessel in which the latter reaction takes place is clean and the rate of deposition slow enough, the silver deposits as a coherent silver mirror; otherwise it is a gray to black finely-divided precipitate.

Tollens reagent should be freshly prepared and discarded immediately after use. On standing, silver imide, Ag_2NH, is formed along with some silver amide, $AgNH_2$, and silver nitride, Ag_3N, all of which are violently explosive.

Individual aldehydes and ketones

Formaldehyde is made by the oxidation of methanol with air using silver gauze as a catalyst at 635° (p. 70). The formaldehyde and excess methanol are absorbed in water, and the solution is concentrated to 37 per cent formaldehyde. This solution is called **formalin.**

Actually no detectable amount of formaldehyde is present in this solution. When formaldehyde comes in contact with water, water adds to the carbonyl group to give the nonvolatile **methylene glycol.**

$$HCH{=}O + HOH \rightleftharpoons HOCH_2OH$$
Methylene glycol

As the solution is concentrated, condensation of methylene glycol molecules takes place with the elimination of water.

$$HOCH_2OH + HOCH_2OH \rightleftharpoons H_2O + HOCH_2{-}O{-}CH_2OH \xrightarrow{HOCH_2OH}$$

$$HOCH_2{-}O{-}CH_2{-}O{-}CH_2OH \xrightarrow{etc.} HO(CH_2O)_xH$$

In a 37 per cent solution of formaldehyde, X has an average value of three. *Polymerization of*
If a formalin solution is concentrated further under reduced pressure, con- *formaldehyde*
densation continues and a solid residue known as **paraformaldehyde** is
obtained, for which X has an average value of 30. Compounds having
repeating units in their structure are called *polymers* (Gr. *polys,* many, and
meros, part). The process by which polymers are formed is known as *poly-*
merization. The simple molecule which gives rise to the polymer is called a
monomer and intermediate molecules made from two, three, or four molecules of monomer are called *dimers, trimers,* or *tetramers.*

Ordinary formalin contains 7 to 10 per cent methanol in summer and
10 to 15 per cent in winter to prevent separation of polymer. Formalin free
of methanol also is transported for industrial use but must be kept warm
(*ca.* 30°) to prevent precipitation of polymer. Although formaldehyde can
be liquefied readily (b.p. −21°), it cannot be handled safely in this form
because it polymerizes explosively even at temperatures just above its freezing point (−118°), and no effective stabilizers are known.

A *specific test for formaldehyde* is the production of a violet color with casein *Test for formaldehyde*
of milk in the presence of ferric chloride and concentrated sulfuric acid.
The test is sensitive to one part of formaldehyde in 200,000 parts of milk.
This test was important in the enforcement of the law against the addition
of formaldehyde as a preservative. It can be used as a general test for formaldehyde simply by adding to milk the material to be tested and then
applying the test.

Acetaldehyde is made commercially by the hydration of acetylene
(p. 37) and by the oxidation of ethyl alcohol with air over a silver catalyst.
Since 1945 large amounts have been produced by the controlled air-
oxidation of the propane-butane mixture from natural gas. The chief importance of acetaldehyde is its use as an intermediate for the synthesis of
other organic compounds, especially acetic acid (p. 106) and acetic anhydride (p. 108).

In the presence of a trace of mineral acid, acetaldehyde gives the cyclic
trimer, known as **paraldehyde.**

$$3\ CH_3CH{=}O \xrightarrow{\text{[H}^+\text{]}} CH_3CH \overset{\text{O}}{\diagup\diagdown} CHCH_3$$

Trimer and tetramer
of acetaldehyde

$$\text{Paraldehyde}$$

It is a stable liquid, b.p. 125°, which is depolymerized readily by heating
with acids; hence it is a convenient source of acetaldehyde. Paraldehyde
first was used medicinally as a sleep-producer (soporific) in 1882. It still is
considered to be very efficient and one of the least toxic hypnotics. The
chief objections to its use are that it is a liquid with a burning disagreeable
taste, and that, because it is eliminated largely through the lungs, a patient's
breath may smell of paraldehyde for as long as twenty-four hours after
administration. **Metaldehyde,** a cyclic tetramer, is formed when acetaldehyde is treated with traces of acids or sulfur dioxide below 0°.

$$4\ CH_3CHO \xrightarrow[\text{at}\ -20°]{Ca(NO_3)_2,\ HBr}$$

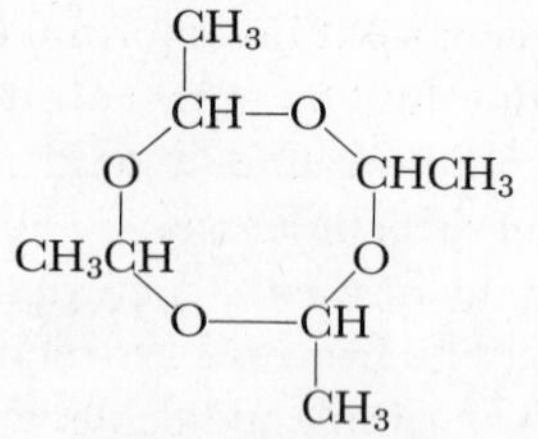

Metaldehyde

Metaldehyde a solid fuel; use in snail baits

Because it is a solid and has a fairly high vapor pressure in spite of its high melting point (m.p. 246°, sublimes below 150°), it is used as a solid fuel for heating liquids or foods under unusual conditions when other fuels are not available or not convenient. Large quantities are used also in garden baits, the vapors being attractive and yet highly toxic to slugs and snails.

Acetaldehyde reacts with three moles of formaldehyde by aldol addition (p. 95) to give tri(hydroxymethyl)acetaldehyde. This product immediately is reduced by excess formaldehyde to tetra-(hydroxymethyl-)methane (**pentaerythritol**).

Pentaerythritol a tetrahydric alcohol

$$CH_3CHO + 3HCH{=}O \xrightarrow{Ca(OH)_2} [(HOCH_2)_3CH{=}O]$$

$$2\ [(HOCH_2)_3CH{=}O] + 2\ HCH{=}O + Ca(OH)_2 \longrightarrow 2\ (HOCH_2)_3CCH_2OH + Ca^{++}(^-OCHO)_2$$

Pentaerythritol   Calcium formate

Pentaerythritol is used to make the explosive **pentaerythritol nitrate** (*PETN*), $C(CH_2ONO_2)_4$, and as a polyhydric alcohol in the manufacture of alkyd resins (p. 239).

Acetaldehyde reacts with three moles of chlorine to give *trichloroacetaldehyde,* commonly called **chloral.**

Chloral and DDT

$$CH_3CHO\ +\ 3\ Cl_2 \rightarrow Cl_3CCHO\ +\ 3\ HCl$$

Trichloroacetaldehyde (chloral)

Reaction of chloral with chlorobenzene in the presence of concentrated sulfuric acid gives *1,1-bis(p-chlorophenyl)-2,2,2-trichloroethane,* an important insecticide known as **DDT.**

$$Cl_3CCHO + 2\ C_6H_5Cl \xrightarrow{H_2SO_4} Cl_3CCH(C_6H_4Cl\text{-}p)_2 + H_2O$$

DDT

Benzaldehyde from amygdalin and by synthesis

Benzaldehyde, C_6H_5CHO, is the simplest aromatic aldehyde. It is one of the products of hydrolysis of the cyanogenetic glycoside (p. 183), *amygdalin* (Gr. *amygdalon,* almond), which is present in the seeds of members of the prune family. It once was called *oil of bitter almonds.*

$$\underset{\underset{\text{Amygdalin}}{OC_{12}H_{21}O_{10}}}{C_6H_5CHCN} \xrightarrow{H_2O} 2\ \underset{\text{Glucose}}{C_6H_{12}O_6} + \underset{\text{Benzaldehyde}}{C_6H_5CHO} + HCN$$

Benzaldehyde is prepared commercially by the hydrolysis of benzylidene chloride, one of the products of the side-chain chlorination of toluene (p. 89).

$$C_6H_5CHCl_2 + H_2O \longrightarrow C_6H_5CHO + 2\ HCl$$

It is used to some extent in almond and cherry flavoring agents, and in the formulation of perfumes, but chiefly for the synthesis of other organic compounds.

Furfural, a heterocyclic aldehyde, is made by heating agricultural wastes, such as oat hulls, corn cobs, or straw, with a dilute mineral acid. Hydrolysis of the pentosans (p. 193) gives pentoses, which are dehydrated to furfural.

Furfural is source of furan derivatives

$$(C_5H_8O_4)_x + x\ H_2O \longrightarrow x\ C_5H_{10}O_5$$
Pentosans   Pentoses

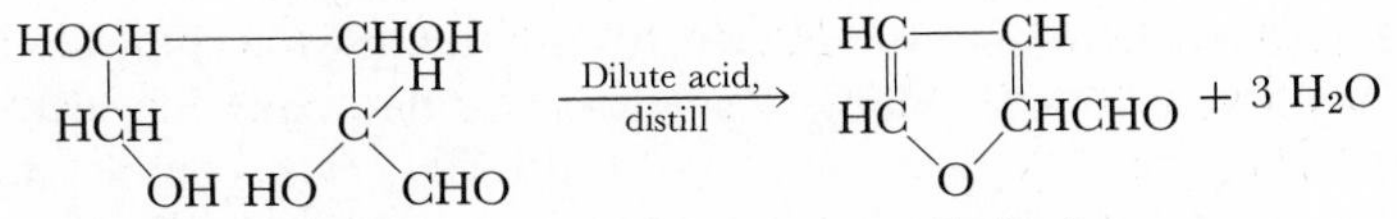

A pentose   Furfural

Estimation of the amount of furfural formed in this reaction (p. 184) is the basis for the determination of pentoses in agricultural products. Furfural resembles benzaldehyde in all of its chemical properties; it is the starting point for the synthesis of most derivatives of furan (p. 83).

Cinnamaldehyde, $C_6H_5CH=CHCHO$, is the main component of cassia oil and oil of cinnamon, the volatile oils of the bark of *Cinnamomium cassia* and *Cinnamomium ceylonicum.*

Cinnamon and vanilla flavors

Vanillin is the principal odorous component of vanilla beans, the long podlike capsules of a tropical climbing orchid, *Vanilla planifolia.* After salt, pepper, and vinegar, it probably is the most widely used flavoring material. Besides being used to produce a desired odor or flavor of vanilla, it has a pronounced effect in masking undesirable odors. For example, one part in 2000 will mask the undesirable odor of fresh paint. The masking and neutralizing of the odors of articles manufactured from rubber, textiles, and plastics is an important phase of the perfumer's art.

Numerous processes have been developed for the synthesis of vanillin. For many years the cheapest synthetic method started with eugenol from natural oil of cloves. The eugenol was isomerized to isoeugenol, in which the double bond is conjugated with the benzene ring, and the side chain then was oxidized with permanganate under controlled conditions.

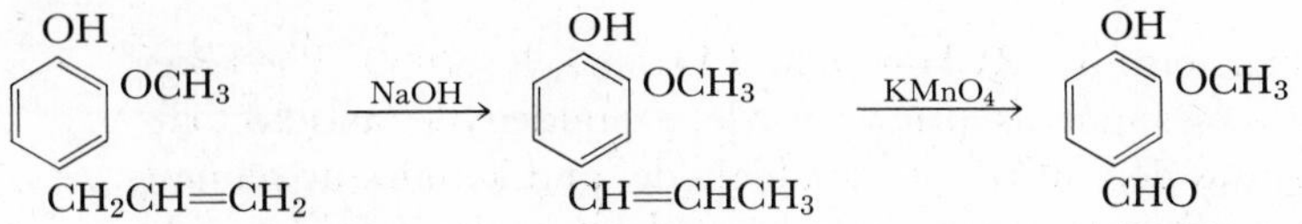

Currently vanillin is made by oxidizing alkaline solutions of lignin sulfonates from waste sulfite liquors (p. 192) with air. **Ethavan** is the trade name of a synthetic product containing an ethoxyl group in place of the methoxyl group. It has 3.5 times the flavoring power of vanillin.

Acetone is technically important

Acetone is by far the most important ketone. It is produced chiefly by the dehydrogenation of *i*-propyl alcohol. More recently a process has been reported in which the uncatalyzed oxidation of isopropyl alcohol with air yields acetone and hydrogen peroxide as the major products.

$$(CH_3)_2CHOH + O_2 \xrightarrow[30 \text{ sec.}]{460°} (CH_3)_2CO + H_2O_2$$

Since 1954 acetone has been obtained as a coproduct of the synthesis of phenol (p. 77) and *p*-cresol (p. 78).

About half of the acetone produced is used as a solvent, especially for cellulose acetate (p. 193), cellulose nitrate (p. 193), and acetylene (p. 38). The other half is used for the synthesis of other organic chemicals.

Methyl ethyl ketone is made by the dehydrogenation of *s*-butyl alcohol and by the oxidation of butane (p. 107). It is known technically by the initials MEK and is used chiefly as a solvent for dewaxing lubricating oils (p. 51).

Cyclohexanone can be made readily by the oxidation of cyclohexanol (p. 66). In 1926 it was shown that **muscone** from the secretion of the musk deer and **civetone** from the secretion of the civet cat are fifteen- and seventeen-membered ring compounds respectively.

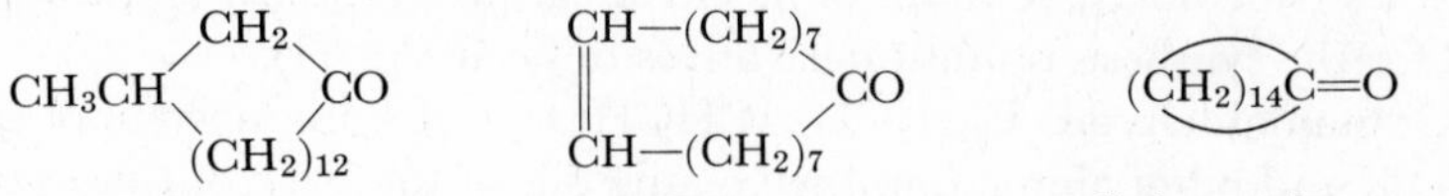

        Muscone   Civetone   Cyclopentadecanone

Cyclic and aromatic ketones in perfumery

Cyclopentadecanone, known as **Exaltone,** is manufactured commercially for use in perfumery in place of the natural musks.

Acetophenone is methyl phenyl ketone and **benzophenone** is phenyl ketone. Both have some use in perfumery and are valuable intermediates for organic synthesis. They have been made from benzene by the Friedel-Crafts reaction (p. 47).

        Acetophenone   Benzophenone

SUMMARY

1. Aldehydes have the general formula, $RCH=O$, and ketones, $R_2C=O$. The lower members have common names such as formaldehyde, acetaldehyde, and acetone. Aldehydes also are named as derivatives of acetaldehyde, and ketones by naming the groups attached to the carbonyl group and adding the separate word *ketone*. In the Geneva system the ending for aldehydes is *al* and for ketones, *one*.

2. Aldehyde or ketone molecules cannot form hydrogen bonds with each other, but they boil somewhat higher than ethers of similar molecular weights, because aldehydes and ketones have larger dipole moments. The solubility characteristics are similar to those of ethers.

3. Aldehydes and ketones result from the oxidation or dehydrogenation of primary and secondary alcohols respectively. Catalytic or chemical reduction of aldehydes and ketones adds two hydrogens to the carbonyl group and converts them into primary and secondary alcohols.

4. Aldehydes are oxidized much more readily than ketones. Thus aldehydes react with mild oxidizing reagents such as Fehling solution, Benedict solution, or Tollens reagent, whereas ketones do not.

5. Aliphatic aldehydes undergo polymerization readily; ketones do not.

6. Formaldehyde, acetaldehyde, and benzaldehyde are the commonest aldehydes. Acetone, methyl ethyl ketone, and acetophenone are the commonest ketones.

EXERCISES

1. Write structural formulas for: (a) propionaldehyde; (b) methyl ethyl ketone; (c) i-butyraldehyde; (d) p-chlorobenzaldehyde; (e) 3-pentanone; (f) 2-methylbutanal.
2. Give reactions for the preparation of acetaldehyde from: (a) ethyl alcohol; (b) acetylene.
3. Give the names and formulas of two aromatic aldehydes used as flavoring agents.
4. Give equations for the following reactions: (a) methyl ethyl ketone with hydroxylamine; (b) benzaldehyde with phenylhydrazine; (c) catalytic reduction of benzophenone; (d) acetone with hydrogen cyanide; (e) stepwise addition of acetaldehyde to formaldehyde to give tri(hydroxymethyl)acetaldehyde.
5. How could one distinguish by chemical reactions between: (a) benzophenone and phenyl ether; (b) acetophenone and phenylacetaldehyde?

CHAPTER 11

ACIDS AND THEIR DERIVATIVES

CARBOXYLIC ACIDS

If a hydroxyl group is bonded to a carbonyl group, the resulting group,

Structure of carboxyl group

$$\overset{\overset{\textstyle O}{\|}}{-C}-OH,$$ is called a *carboxyl group*. Compounds that contain the carboxyl group are called *carboxylic acids*.

The straight-chain or normal carboxylic acids were isolated first from natural sources, particularly by the hydrolysis of fats and waxes from animals and plants (Chapter 12). Hence they frequently are called *fatty acids*. Because little was known about their structure, they were given common names indicating their source. These names and the derivations of the names together with some physical properties are given in Table 6.

Common names for normal acids

Geneva names are given for the odd-carbon acids above C_{10} rather than common names. The reason is that only acids with an even number of carbon atoms had been found in fats, the odd-carbon acids having been prepared synthetically by hydrolysis of the nitriles. The name *margaric* appears to be an exception. However it has been shown that the material isolated from fats and thought to be a C_{17} acid actually is a mixture of palmitic and stearic acids. When the true C_{17} normal acid was synthesized, the common name was retained. The presence of small amounts of normal odd-carbon acids in natural fats has been reported only recently. Thus tri-, penta-, and heptadecanoic acids have been obtained from butter fat. Heptadecanoic acid has been isolated also from mutton fat and from shark liver oil. Branched-chain acids with a methyl group on the second or third carbon from the far end of the chain also have been isolated. The total amount of odd-carbon and branched-chain acids may amount to as much as 2 per cent of the total fatty acids.

Branched-chain acids

As with other homologous series, those compounds having an isopropyl group at the end of a normal hydrocarbon chain may be named by adding the prefix *iso* to the common name, for example $(CH_3)_2CHCOOH$, isobutyric acid, or $(CH_3)_2CHCH_2CH_2CH_2CH_2CH_2CH_2COOH$, isocapric acid. If the methyl branch occurs at any other portion of the chain, the designation *iso* may not be used. Acids with a methyl branch on the third carbon from the end of the chain have been called *anteiso* acids.

TABLE 6.   COMMON NAMES OF NORMAL CARBOXYLIC ACIDS

NO. OF CARBON ATOMS	NAME OF ACID	DERIVATION OF NAME	BOILING POINT	MELTING POINT	DENSITY 20°/4°
1	Formic	L. *formica,* ant	100.7	8.4	1.220
2	Acetic	L. *acetum,* vinegar	118.2	16.6	1.049
3	Propionic	Gr. *proto,* first; *pion,* fat	141.4	−20.8	0.993
4	Butyric	L. *butyrum,* butter	164.1	−5.5	0.958
5	Valeric	valerian root (L. *valere,* to be strong)	186.4	−34.5	0.939
6	Caproic	L. *caper,* goat	205.4	−3.9	0.936
7	Enanthic	Gr. *oenanthe,* vine blossom	223.0	−7.5	0.918
8	Caprylic	L. *caper,* goat	239.3	16.3	0.909
9	Pelargonic	Pelargonium	253.0	12.0	
10	Capric	L. *caper,* goat	268.7	31.3	
11	Undecanoic		280	28.5	
12	Lauric	laurel		43.2	
13	Tridecanoic			41.6	
14	Myristic	Myristica (nutmeg)		54.4	
15	Pentadecanoic			52.3	
16	Palmitic	palm oil		62.8	
17	Margaric	Gr. *margaron,* pearl		61.2	
18	Stearic	Gr. *stear,* tallow		69.6	
19	Nonadecanoic			68.7	
20	Arachidic	Arachis (peanut)		75.4	
21	Heneicosanoic			74.3	
22	Behenic	behen oil		79.9	
23	Tricosanoic			79.1	
24	Tetracosanoic			84.2	
25	Pentacosanoic			83.5	
26	Cerotic	L. *cera,* wax		87.7	

Branched-chain acids may be named also as **derivatives of normal acids.** Acetic acid frequently is chosen as the parent compound, and derivatives are named as compounds in which the hydrogen atoms of the methyl group are replaced by other groups.

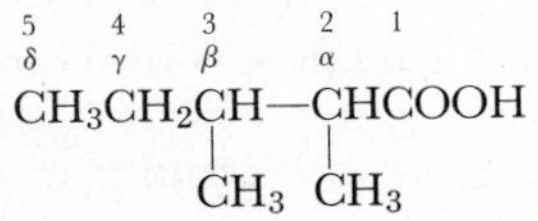

$$\overset{\overset{5}{\delta}}{CH_3}\overset{\overset{4}{\gamma}}{CH_2}\overset{\overset{3}{\beta}}{CH}-\overset{\overset{2}{\alpha}}{CH}\overset{1}{COOH}$$
$$\underset{CH_3}{|}\quad\underset{CH_3}{|}$$

This compound may be called methyl-*s*-butylacetic acid. It also may be considered to be derived from valeric acid and called α,β-dimethylvaleric acid or 2,3-dimethylvaleric acid. When Greek letters are used to designate the positions of substituents, the α carbon atom of the chain is the carbon atom adjacent to the functional group. When numerals are used, the carbon atom of the carboxyl group is numbered 1.

In the **Geneva system** the final *e* is dropped from the name of the hydrocarbon having the same number of carbon atoms as the longest chain containing the carboxyl group, and *oic acid* is added. The carbon atom of the carboxyl group always is numbered 1 when numbering the atoms of

Systematic nomenclature

Physical properties;
high boiling points

the longest chain. For example $CH_3CH_2CH(CH_3)CH(CH_3)COOH$ is called 2,3-dimethylpentanoic acid.

The **boiling points** of carboxylic acids (Table 6) rise more or less uniformly with increase in molecular weight. The increase for those listed averages about 18° per additional methylene group, the same as for the alcohols. The magnitude of the boiling points, however, is even more abnormal than for the alcohols. Ethyl alcohol boils at 78°, but formic acid having the same molecular weight boils at 101°; *n*-propyl alcohol boils at 98°, but acetic acid boils at 118°. The explanation of the abnormal boiling points of the acids is the same as that for the alcohols, namely association

Double molecules

by proton bonds, but the acids are able to form double molecules which are more stable than the association complexes formed by the alcohols.

$$R-C \begin{matrix} O:H-O \\ \\ O-H:O \end{matrix} C-R$$

It has been shown by vapor density measurements that the double molecules of acetic acid persist even in the vapor state. Hence it is not surprising that the boiling point of acetic acid (118°, mol. wt. $= 60 \times 2 = 120$) is of the same order of magnitude as *n*-octane (126°, mol. wt. 114).

Alternation in
melting points

An interesting characteristic of the normal carboxylic acids is the alternation in **melting points.** Acids with an even number of carbon atoms always melt at a higher temperature than the next higher member of the series (Fig. 17). X-ray diffraction has shown that in the solid state the car-

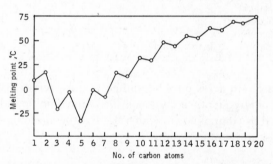

Figure 17. Melting points of normal carboxylic acids.

bon atoms of the hydrocarbon chain assume an extended zigzag arrangement in which the carboxyl groups of the odd carbon acids are on the same side of the chain as the terminal methyl groups, whereas those of the even carbon acids are on the opposite side of the chain (see p. 23). Although all of the acids are double molecules, the arrangement of those with an even number of carbon atoms gives a more symmetrical molecule and a more stable crystal lattice.

More soluble in water
than alcohols

Because of partial ionization in water, carboxylic acids are somewhat more heavily hydrated than alcohols and hence show somewhat greater **solubility** in water. In general they have about the same solubility in water as the alcohol with one less carbon atom. For example *n*-butyric acid is miscible with water as is *n*-propyl alcohol, whereas *n*-butyl alcohol dissolves only to the extent of about 1 volume in 11 volumes of water. Monocarboxylic acids usually are soluble in other organic solvents.

The carboxylic acids that are sufficiently soluble in water to give an appreciable concentration of hydronium ion have a sour taste. The lower *Odor and taste* members have a sharp acrid odor, and the acids from butyric through caprylic have a disagreeable odor. The odor of rancid butter and strong cheese is due to volatile aldehydes, ketones, and acids, and caproic acid gets its name from the fact that it is present in the skin secretions of goats. The higher acids are practically odorless because of their low volatility.

Although the hydrogen of the hydroxyl group in water or alcohol *Chemical properties;* molecules does not ionize appreciably, that in carboxylic acids does. Oxy- *ionization in water* gen, with its greater positive nuclear charge, has a greater attraction for electrons than does carbon or hydrogen; hence, when attached to a carbon atom bearing hydroxyl, it increases the ease with which the proton can be removed from the hydroxyl group. Compounds that transfer protons to bases more readily than does water usually are called acids.

Phenols also show acidic properties, but the simple phenols are weaker *Comparison* than carbonic acid (p. 74). Carboxylic acids are stronger than carbonic *with phenols* acid. Hence carboxylic acids not only form salts with strong bases, such as sodium hydroxide, but also liberate carbon dioxide from carbonates and bicarbonates.

$$RCOOH + NaOH \longrightarrow RCOO^{-+}Na + H_2O$$
$$2\ RCOOH + Na_2CO_3 \longrightarrow 2\ RCOO^{-+}Na + CO_2 + H_2O$$
$$RCOOH + NaHCO_3 \longrightarrow RCOO^{-+}Na + CO_2 + H_2O$$

However, most carboxylic acids are weaker than mineral acids and are liberated from their salts by mineral acids.

$$RCOO^{-+}Na + HCl \longrightarrow RCOOH + NaCl$$

The neutralization of an acid by a standard solution of a base is the *Analysis by titration* customary procedure for estimating acids. When a weak acid is neutralized by a strong base, the equivalence point is on the alkaline side because of hydrolysis of the salt. Therefore an indicator changing color at the proper acidity is necessary. For carboxylic acids, phenolphthalein usually is satisfactory. The equivalent weight of an acid as determined by neutralization with a standard base is known as the **neutralization equivalent** of the acid.

Because salts are completely ionized, and ions are more heavily hydrated than neutral molecules, the alkali metal salts of carboxylic acids are *Solubility of salts* much more soluble than the acids themselves. For example, whereas water solubility of the free normal acids approaches that of the saturated hydrocarbons above C_5, the sodium salts are very soluble up to C_{10} and form colloidal solutions from C_{10} to C_{18}. This fact is used to separate acids from water-insoluble compounds such as alcohols or hydrocarbons. Extraction of the mixture with dilute alkali causes the acid to go into the aqueous layer as the salt. The aqueous layer then can be separated and the free acid liberated from its salt by the addition of a mineral acid. It is necessary to add at least the calculated amount of mineral acid, or if the amount of salt present is unknown, to add mineral acid until a universal indicator, such as Hydrion paper, shows that a pH of 1 or 2 has been reached. Merely making the solution acid to litmus does not free the carboxylic acid completely from its salt, because a mixture of the salt and organic acid is acid to litmus.

Salts are nonvolatile

Another result of the ionic nature of salts is that they are nonvolatile. The nonvolatility of salts permits volatile acids to be recovered from aqueous solutions or separated from other volatile substances by converting into salts and evaporating to dryness.

Individual acids

Formic acid is made by adding a mineral acid to sodium formate. The salt is made by a special process from carbon monoxide and caustic soda.

$$CO + NaOH \xrightarrow[\text{6–10 atm.}]{200°} HCOO^{-+}Na$$

This reaction was one of the earliest used commercially for the synthesis of an organic compound from carbon and salt as the raw materials. Like other compounds containing the aldehyde group (p. 96), formic acid is a mild reducing agent.

Formic acid
a reducing agent

$$HCOOH + [O] \longrightarrow [HOCOOH] \longrightarrow CO_2 + H_2O$$

Stronger than
acetic acid

Because formic acid is approximately ten times as strong an acid as its homologs, it is used when an acid stronger than acetic acid, but not so strong as a mineral acid, is desired. It is used also for the manufacture of its esters and salts. Sodium formate is used to make formic acid and oxalic acid (p. 113), and as a reducing agent.

Acetic acid is by far the most important organic acid from the standpoint of quantity used. It appears in the market largely as *glacial acetic acid* of about 99.5 per cent purity, so-called because on cold days it freezes to an ice-like solid. The melting point of pure acetic acid is 16.7°.

Vinegar

Several methods for the preparation of acetic acid are in use. It is the chief component of **vinegar.** The alcohol in fermented fruit juices or fermented malt (beer) in the presence of various species of *Acetobacter* and air is oxidized to acetic acid.

$$CH_3CH_2OH + O_2 \text{ (air)} \xrightarrow{Acetobacter} CH_3COOH + H_2O$$

Barrel process and
quick process

In the *barrel process* the fruit juice is contained in barrels exposed to air, and the bacteria form a slimy film on the surface known as *mother of vinegar.* Since the alcohol must come in contact with the oxygen and bacteria by diffusion processes, oxidation is slow, and an acetic acid content of 4 to 5 per cent is reached only after several months. In the *quick process* a vat is filled with shavings or other porous material which is inoculated with the microorganism. A 12 to 15 per cent alcohol solution containing nutrient salts for the growth of the bacteria is allowed to trickle over the shavings while a controlled amount of warm air is forced up through the shavings. In this way a vinegar with an acetic acid content of 8 to 10 per cent may be obtained, which is diluted to 4 to 5 per cent for use. Vinegar produced by fermentation is used almost exclusively as a preservative and condiment, its value for this purpose being enhanced by flavors present in the cider, wine, or malt.

By oxidation of
acetaldehyde

In the United States, prior to 1952, most of the synthetic acetic acid was made by the oxidation of acetaldehyde (p. 97). Acetaldehyde absorbs oxygen from the air rapidly to form peroxyacetic acid, a peroxide (p. 111), which in the presence of manganous or cobalt acetate reacts with more acetaldehyde to give acetic acid.

$$CH_3\overset{\overset{O}{\|}}{C}H + O_2 \longrightarrow CH_3\overset{\overset{O}{\|}}{C}-O-OH$$
Peroxyacetic acid

$$CH_3\overset{\overset{O}{\|}}{C}-O-OH + CH_3CHO \xrightarrow[\text{Co(OCOCH}_3)_2]{\text{Mn(OCOCH}_3)_2 \text{ or}} 2\ CH_3COOH$$

Using 99 to 99.8 per cent acetaldehyde, 96 per cent acetic acid is obtained, which may be rectified readily to 99.5 per cent.

Since 1952 increasing amounts of acetic acid have been made by the air oxidation of butane in the liquid phase. A mixture of air and a large excess of butane is passed into acetic acid containing dissolved manganese and cobalt acetates maintained at 165° under 300 p.s.i. The rate of flow of gases is such that the nitrogen and unreacted butane carry off the products as fast as they are formed. The oxygenated products, chiefly acetic acid and methyl ethyl ketone (p. 100), are washed out with water and separated by fractional distillation. Methyl ethyl ketone in excess of demand is recycled. *By oxidation of butane*

$$CH_3CH_2CH_2CH_3 + O_2 \longrightarrow CH_3CH_2COCH_3 + H_2O$$
Methyl ethyl ketone

$$2\ CH_3CH_2COCH_3 + 3\ O_2 \longrightarrow 4\ CH_3COOH$$

Acetic acid is used where a cheap organic acid is required; for the preparation of metallic salts, acetic anhydride (p. 108), and esters (p. 110); in the manufacture of cellulose acetate (p. 193) and white lead; as a precipitating agent for casein from milk, and for rubber or synthetic rubber from their aqueous emulsions (p. 236); and for numerous other purposes. **Sodium acetate** is used to reduce the acidity of mineral acids. **Lead acetate,** known as **sugar of lead,** and **basic lead acetate,** $Pb(OH)(OCOCH_3)$, are used to prepare other lead salts. **Verdigris** is the basic copper acetate, $Cu(OH)_2 \cdot 2\ Cu(OCOCH_3)_2$, and **Paris green** is a mixed cupric acetate-arsenite. **Aluminum acetate** is used to impregnate cotton cloth or fibers with aluminum hydroxide prior to dyeing, a process known as *mordanting* (p. 209). *Salts of acetic acid*

Propionic acid and **butyric acid** may be made by the oxidation of the corresponding alcohols or aldehydes, or by special fermentation processes from starch. They are used in the manufacture of cellulose acetate-propionates and acetate-butyrates (p. 193). **Calcium propionate** is used in bread to prevent molding and ropiness. *Other acids*

When chlorine is passed into acetic acid containing a small amount of phosphorus trichloride, one or more of the hydrogens of the methyl group is replaced by chlorine (*Hell-Volhard-Zelinsky reaction*). The monosubstitution product is called **chloroacetic acid.** *Hell-Volhard-Zelinsky reaction*

$$CH_3COOH + Cl_2 \xrightarrow{PCl_3} ClCH_2COOH + HCl$$
Chloroacetic acid

The chlorine behaves like that in an alkyl chloride, and the sodium salt reacts with the sodium salt of 2,4-dichlorophenol to give the sodium salt of **2,4-dichlorophenoxyacetic acid,** commonly called **2,4-D.**

$$Cl\text{—}C_6H_3(Cl)\text{—}ONa + ClCH_2COONa \longrightarrow Cl\text{—}C_6H_3(Cl)\text{—}OCH_2COONa + NaCl$$

2,4-D

Weed killer

It is highly toxic to broad-leaved plants and is widely used as a weed killer.

Acids from petroleum

The term **naphthenic acids** is applied to the mixture of carboxylic acids obtained from the alkali washes of petroleum fractions. Judging from the pure compounds that have been isolated, naphthenic acids are complex mixtures of normal and branched aliphatic acids, alkyl derivatives of cyclopentane- and cyclohexanecarboxylic acids, and cyclopentyl and cyclohexyl derivatives of aliphatic acids. The crude naphthenic acids are available in large amounts and are used chiefly in the form of metallic salts, which are soluble in oils and organic solvents. The copper salts are used in wood preservatives and the lead, manganese, zinc, and iron salts as driers (oxidation catalysts) for paints and varnishes (p. 123).

Aromatic acids by oxidation of side chains

Because of the activating effect of the benzene nucleus and the resistance of the ring itself to oxidation, aromatic acids frequently can be made readily by the oxidation of side chains. Thus oxidation of toluene yields **benzoic acid.**

$$C_6H_5\text{—}CH_3 \xrightarrow[\text{or KMnO}_4]{Na_2Cr_2O_7 + H_2SO_4,} C_6H_5\text{—}COOH + H_2O$$

Benzoic acid

CH₂COOH — α-Naphthylacetic acid

Benzoic acid a food preservative

Benzoic acid is made also by the partial decarboxylation of phthalic acid (p. 114). About 80 per cent of the production is used as a food preservative in the form of sodium benzoate. Because only free benzoic acid is effective in inhibiting the growth of microorganisms, the pH of the food must be less than 4.5.

Plant hormones

Certain chemicals present in plants accelerate the growth of cells and are known as **auxins.** Many synthetic compounds have similar properties and are used by nurserymen to increase the ease of rooting of cuttings and by orchardists to prevent premature bud formation and premature dropping of fruit. One of the more widely used substances for this purpose is **α-naphthylacetic acid.**

Acid anhydrides

Acetic anhydride, $CH_3\overset{\|}{\underset{O}{C}}\text{—}O\text{—}\overset{\|}{\underset{O}{C}}CH_3$, is an important derivative of acetic acid, and is representative of the class of compounds known as *acid anhydrides*. One commercial process for its manufacture involves the addition of acetic acid to ketene, which has twin or cumulative double bonds, that is, two double bonds not separated by single bonds.

Acetic anhydride from ketene

$$CH_3COOH + CH_2\text{=}C\text{=}O \longrightarrow CH_3\overset{\|}{\underset{O}{C}}\text{—}O\text{—}\overset{\|}{\underset{O}{C}}CH_3$$

Ketene   Acetic anhydride

The ketene is made by the decomposition of acetic acid over aluminum phosphate at 600° to 700°.

$$CH_3COOH \longrightarrow CH_2{=}C{=}O + H_2O$$

Anhydrides hydrolyze easily to two moles of acid.

$$(CH_3CO)_2O + H_2O \longrightarrow 2\,CH_3COOH$$

They react similarly with alcohols to give one mole of ester and one mole of acid.

$$(CH_3CO)_2O + C_2H_5OH \longrightarrow CH_3COOC_2H_5 + CH_3COOH$$
$$\text{Ethyl acetate}$$

Reactions of anhydrides

The replacement of hydrogen by the acyl group, RCO—, is called *acylation*. Hence one may refer to the above reaction as the *acetylation* of ethyl alcohol. Acetic anhydride is used chiefly in the manufacture of cellulose acetate (p. 193).

The reaction of carboxylic acids with phosphorus trichloride yields *acyl chlorides*.

Acyl chlorides

$$3\,CH_3COOH + PCl_3 \longrightarrow 3\,CH_3COCl + P(OH)_3$$
$$\text{Acetyl chloride}$$

Compounds having an alkyl or aryl group instead of the acidic hydrogen of a carboxyl group are known as *carboxylic esters*. They may be made by the reaction of a carboxylic acid with an alcohol in the presence of a strong acid as catalyst.

Esters of carboxylic acids

$$RCOOH + HOR' \underset{}{\overset{[H^+]}{\rightleftarrows}} \overset{\displaystyle O}{\underset{\displaystyle }{R{-}\overset{\|}{C}{-}OR'}} + H_2O$$

by direct esterification

When one mole of acetic acid and one mole of ethyl alcohol are allowed to react, equilibrium is reached when two-thirds of a mole of ethyl acetate has been formed, because the reaction is reversible; that is, ethyl acetate and water react under the same conditions to give acetic acid and ethyl alcohol.

Esters result also from the reaction of alcohols with acid anhydrides. For example, as noted above, acetic anhydride and ethyl alcohol react to give ethyl acetate and acetic acid. This type of reaction goes to completion.

from alcohols and acid anhydrides

Esters are named as if they were alkyl salts of the organic acids, because the early investigators assumed that esterification is analogous to neutralization. Thus $CH_3COOC_2H_5$ is ethyl acetate or ethyl ethanoate. It is necessary to be careful to recognize the portion of the molecule derived from the acid and that from the alcohol, particularly in condensed structural formulas. For example both $(CH_3)_2CHOCOCH_2CH_3$ and $CH_3CH_2COOCH(CH_3)_2$ are *i*-propyl propionate and not ethyl *i*-butyrate. No difficulty should be encountered if it is remembered that the oxygen of a carbonyl group usually follows immediately the carbon atom to which it is attached and that the alkyl group from the alcohol portion of the ester is joined to an oxygen atom. If it is necessary to name esters as substitution products, the ester group is called an *alkoxycarbonyl* group. For example $COOCH_3$ is the methoxycarbonyl group.

Esters named as salts

The esters have normal boiling points, but their solubility in water is less than would be expected from the amount of oxygen present. Ethyl acetate with four carbon atoms and two oxygen atoms dissolves to about the

Boiling points and solubility in water

same extent as *n*-butyl alcohol, which has four carbon atoms and one oxygen atom. The volatile esters have pleasant odors that usually are described as fruity.

Ease of C—O bond scission

The reactions of the esters depend for the most part on the scission of a carbon-oxygen bond. The ease of scission and the type of catalysis possible depend on the groups attached to the carbon atoms joined by the oxygen atom. Ethers, R—O—R, having two alkyl groups joined by oxygen are hydrolyzed least readily, and the hydrolysis is subject only to acid catalysis. Esters, RCO—O—R, in which one acyl and one alkyl group are linked through oxygen, are hydrolyzed more readily, and both acids and bases catalyze the reaction. Anhydrides, RCO—O—COR, have two acyl groups joined by oxygen and are most easily hydrolyzed, water alone bringing about the reaction.

Hydrolysis or saponification

Esters may be split by water (*hydrolyzed*) in the presence of either acidic or basic catalysts.

$$RCOOR' + HOH \underset{}{\overset{[H^+]}{\rightleftharpoons}} RCOOH + HOR'$$

$$RCOOR' + HOH \underset{}{\overset{[OH^-]}{\rightleftharpoons}} RCOOH + HOR'$$

$$\downarrow [OH^-]$$

$$[RCOO^-] + HOH$$

Alkaline hydrolysis frequently is referred to as **saponification,** because it is the type of reaction used in the preparation of soaps (p. 123). The acid-catalyzed reaction is exactly the reverse of acid-catalyzed esterification, and either results in the same equilibrium. The base-catalyzed hydrolysis goes to completion and requires one equivalent of alkali for each equivalent of ester, because the acid formed in the base-catalyzed equilibrium reacts irreversibly with the catalyst to form a salt and water. The over-all reaction becomes

$$RCOOR' + NaOH \longrightarrow [RCOO^-]Na^+ + R'OH$$

Analysis of esters

Because this reaction goes to completion, alkaline saponification is used as a quantitative procedure for the estimation of esters. A weighed sample of the unknown is refluxed with an excess of a standardized aqueous or alcoholic solution of alkali, and the excess base at the end of the reaction is titrated with standard acid using a suitable indicator, usually phenolphthalein (p. 212). The equivalent weight as determined by saponification is called the **saponification equivalent** of the ester.

Esters as solvents

By far the most important general use for esters of aliphatic acids is as solvents, especially for cellulose nitrate in the formulation of lacquers (p. 193). For this purpose **ethyl acetate** and **butyl acetate** are used to the greatest extent.

as fumigant; as plastics

Ethyl formate is used as a fumigant and larvicide for grains and food products. Higher boiling esters are used as softening agents (plasticizers) for resins and plastics (p. 230), and a number of the resins and plastics are themselves esters, such as poly(methyl methacrylate) poly(vinyl acetate) Dacron (p. 238), cellulose acetate (p. 193), and alkyd resins (p. 239).

Some of the volatile esters have specific fruit odors. For example, the   *Odor of esters*
odors of *i*-amyl acetate, *i*-amyl valerate, butyl butyrate, and *i*-butyl propionate resemble the odors of banana, apple, pineapple, and rum respectively. Hence they are used to a limited extent in synthetic flavors or
perfumes. Natural odors and flavors are the result of complex mixtures of
organic compounds. Very careful blending of synthetic compounds is nec-

TABLE 7.   COMPOSITION OF THE VOLATILE OIL OF THE PINEAPPLE   *Pineapple flavor*

WINTER FRUIT		SUMMER FRUIT	
CONSTITUENT	MG. PER KG.	CONSTITUENT	MG. PER KG.
Total volatile oil	15.6	Total volatile oil	190.0
Ethyl acetate	2.91	Ethyl acetate	119.6
Ethyl alcohol	0.0	Ethyl alcohol	60.5
Acetaldehyde	0.61	Acetaldehyde	1.35
Methyl *n*-valerate	0.49	Ethyl acrylate	0.77
Methyl *i*-valerate	0.60	Ethyl *i*-valerate	0.39
Methyl *i*-caproate	1.40	Ethyl *n*-caproate	0.77
Methyl caprylate	0.75		

essary to imitate the natural product. Table 7 summarizes the results of a
careful analysis of the substances responsible for the odor and flavor of the
pineapple. Both the amount of volatile oil and its components vary with
the time of the year at which the fruit is harvested. The bouquet of fine
wines has been ascribed to esters produced by the slow esterification of
organic acids during the aging process.

The active principles of **pyrethrum,** the commercially important insec-   *Insecticidal esters*
ticide derived from the flower heads of *Chrysanthemum cinerariaefolium,* and
a few other varieties, are four esters of cyclopropanecarboxylic acids with
cyclopentyl alcohols, called *pyrethrin I, pyrethrin II, cinerin I,* and *cinerin II.*
The relative toxicity to houseflies is $100:23:71:18$.

Pyrethrin I

Pyrethrin II

Cinerin I

Cinerin II

PEROXY ACIDS AND ACYL PEROXIDES

When carboxylic acids are allowed to react with 30 to 90 per cent
aqueous hydrogen peroxide in the presence of a mineral acid, a reaction   *Peroxy acids from*
analogous to the esterification of an alcohol takes place. The product is an   *hydrogen peroxide*
acyl hydroperoxide, also called a **per acid** or a **peroxy acid.**

$$CH_3COOH + H_2O_2 \underset{}{\overset{H_2SO_4}{\rightleftharpoons}} \overset{\displaystyle O}{\overset{\|}{CH_3C}}-O-OH + H_2O$$

Peroxyacetic acid
(peracetic acid)

This reaction is reversible and peroxy acids slowly hydrolyze in aqueous solution to the carboxylic acid and hydrogen peroxide.

as epoxidizing agents

The most important reaction of the peroxy acids is the formation of epoxides from unsaturated compounds (*epoxidation*).

$$RCH{=}CHR + RCOO_2H \longrightarrow \underset{O}{RCH{-}CHR} + RCOOH$$

In the presence of a strong acid, the monoacylated glycol is formed.

$$\underset{O}{RCH{-}CHR} + RCOOH \overset{[H^+]}{\longrightarrow} \underset{OCOR}{RCHCHOHR}$$

Acyl peroxides

Acyl peroxides are obtained by the reaction of an excess of acid anhydride or acyl chloride with alkaline solutions of hydrogen peroxide.

$$2\,(CH_3CO)_2O + Na_2O_2 \longrightarrow \overset{\displaystyle O}{\overset{\|}{CH_3C}}-O-O-\overset{\displaystyle O}{\overset{\|}{CCH_3}} + 2\,NaOCOCH_3$$

Acetyl peroxide

$$2\,C_6H_5COCl + Na_2O_2 \longrightarrow \overset{\displaystyle O}{\overset{\|}{C_6H_5C}}-O-O-\overset{\displaystyle O}{\overset{\|}{CC_6H_5}} + 2\,NaCl$$

Benzoyl peroxide

Violent explosions of **acetyl peroxide** have been reported, and extreme care should be taken when it is prepared or used. **Benzoyl peroxide** is considerably more stable. The chief use for the acyl peroxides is as catalysts for polymerization reactions (p. 233) and as bleaching agents for flour, oils, fats, and waxes.

as catalysts and bleaching agents

POLYCARBOXYLIC ACIDS

α,ω-Dicarboxylic acids

Of the polycarboxylic acids, the dicarboxylic acids having the carboxyl groups at each end of a chain or attached to a benzene nucleus are encountered most frequently, and some are of considerable importance. **Oxalic acid, HOOC—COOH,** having two carboxyl groups directly joined, was known at an early date. The presence of its potassium acid salt in the sorrels (various species of *Rumex* and *Oxalis;* Gr. *oxys,* sharp or acid) was observed at the beginning of the seventeenth century. It is present in many other plants, such as spinach, rhubarb, sweet potatoes, cabbage, grapes, and tomatoes. When these fruits and vegetables are eaten, microscopic star-shaped crystals of the insoluble calcium oxalate may appear in the urine. Commercially it is manufactured by heating sodium formate (p. 106) and liberating the free acid from the sodium salt with sulfuric acid.

$$2\,HCOONa \overset{400°}{\longrightarrow} H_2 + NaOOCCOONa \overset{H_2SO_4}{\longrightarrow} HOOCCOOH$$

The remaining α,ω-dicarboxylic acids may be represented by the general formula $HOOC(CH_2)_xCOOH$. The names of some of the unbranched acids are malonic ($x = 1$), succinic ($x = 2$), glutaric ($x = 3$), adipic ($x = 4$), pimelic ($x = 5$), suberic ($x = 6$), azelaic ($x = 7$), and sebacic ($x = 8$).

The dicarboxylic acids, like all polyfunctional compounds, have certain characteristic behaviors depending on the relative positions of the functional groups. When **oxalic acid** is heated slowly to 150°, it sublimes unchanged, but rapid heating to a higher temperature decomposes it into carbon dioxide and formic acid, and the latter decomposes further into carbon monoxide and water.

Characteristic reactions

$x = 0$, decomposes to CO_2, CO, and H_2O

$$HOOCCOOH \xrightarrow{\text{Heat}} CO_2 + HCOOH \longrightarrow CO + H_2O$$

These reactions are brought about better by warming with concentrated sulfuric acid. **Malonic acid** and substituted malonic acids, when heated above the melting point, lose carbon dioxide to give the monocarboxylic acid.

$x = 1$, decomposes to CO_2 and acid

$$HOOCCH_2COOH \xrightarrow{\text{Heat}} CO_2 + CH_3COOH$$

Succinic and **glutaric** acids and their substitution products lose water when heated to give the stable five- and six-membered cyclic anhydrides.

$x = 2$, or 3, gives cyclic anhydride

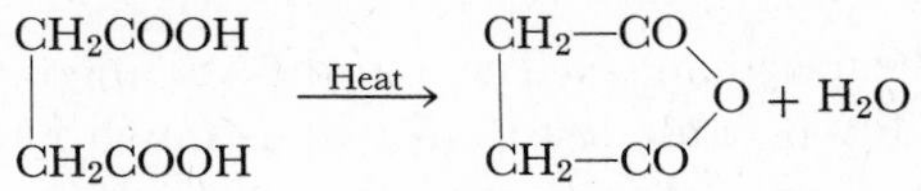

Succinic anhydride

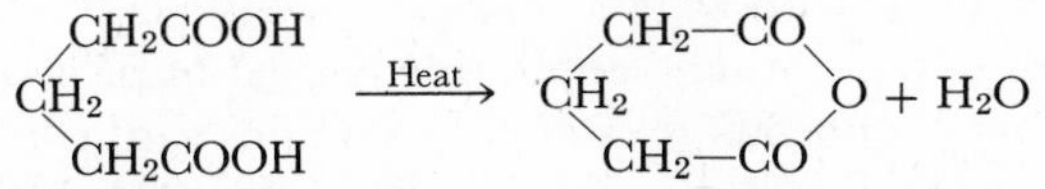

Glutaric anhydride

Adipic acids and acids having the carboxyl groups more widely separated do not give cyclic anhydrides. When heated with dehydrating agents they give linear polymeric anhydrides.

$$(x + 1)\,HOOC(CH_2)_4COOH + x\,(CH_3CO)_2O \xrightarrow{\text{Heat}}$$
$$HOOC(CH_2)_4[COOCO(CH_2)_4]_xCOOH + 2x\,CH_3COOH$$
Polyadipic anhydride

When adipic acids are heated, especially in the presence of a small amount of barium hydroxide, five-membered cyclic ketones are formed.

$x = 4$ or 5, gives cyclic ketone

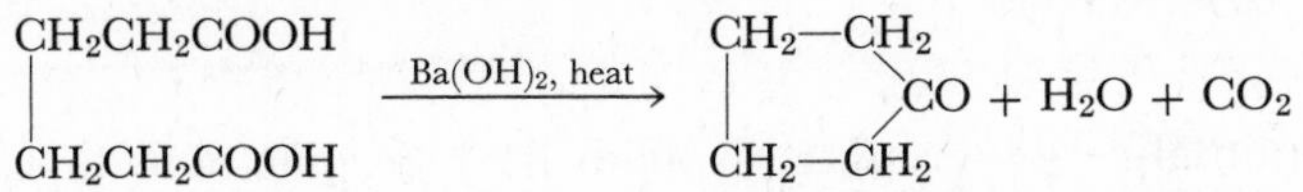

Adipic acid   Cyclopentanone

Pimelic acids on similar treatment yield six-membered cyclic ketones.

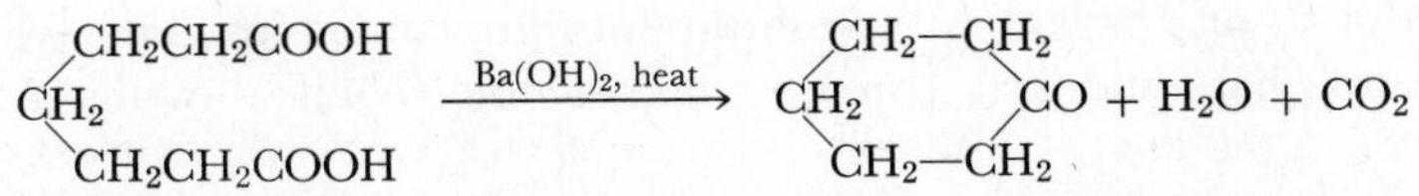

Pimelic acid   Cyclohexanone

Aromatic dicarboxylic acids

The *o*-, *m*-, and *p*-benzenedicarboxylic acids are known as *phthalic,* *isophthalic,* and *terephthalic acids.* **Phthalic acid** when heated above 180° rapidly loses water to form the volatile cyclic anhydride.

Phthalic acid gives cyclic anhydride

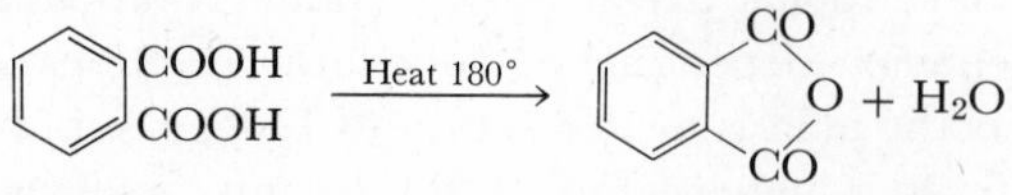

         Phthalic acid   Phthalic anhydride

Made from o-xylene or naphthalene

Hence in the usual methods for synthesizing phthalic acid, namely the high temperature oxidation of *o*-xylene or naphthalene (p. 52), it is the anhydride that is obtained.

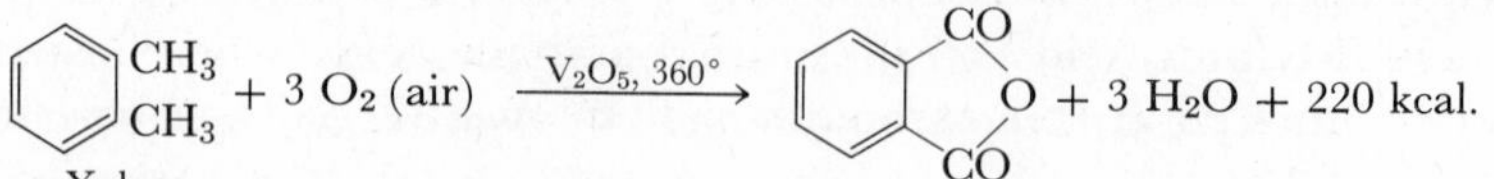

   o-Xylene

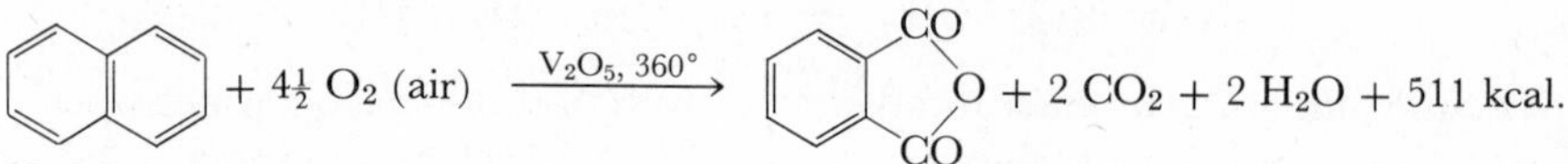

  Naphthalene

Naphthalene is cheaper than *o*-xylene, but the oxidation of *o*-xylene is controlled more readily because less than half as much heat is evolved per mole of anhydride formed. For most purposes for which it is used, the anhydride is preferable to the acid. If the acid is desired, it is necessary only to heat the anhydride with water.

Esters are plasticizers

About half of the phthalic anhydride is used to produce the **methyl, ethyl, butyl,** and **higher alkyl esters** of phthalic acid, which are used as plasticizers of synthetic polymers, especially poly(vinyl chloride). Production of the esters in millions of pounds in 1960 was as follows: methyl, 3; ethyl, 16; butyl, 19; 2-ethylhexyl, 123. **Methyl phthalate** (dimethyl phthalate, DMP) is an effective insect repellent. Most of the remainder of the phthalic anhydride is used for the manufacture of alkyd and polyester resins (pp. 238, 239), although a considerable quantity is used for the manufacture of anthraquinone and its derivatives, which are intermediates for the synthesis of anthraquinone dyes (p. 210). Smaller amounts are used for miscellaneous purposes such as the manufacture of phenolphthalein (p. 212) and benzoic acid.

Used to make resins, anthraquinones, and benzoic acid

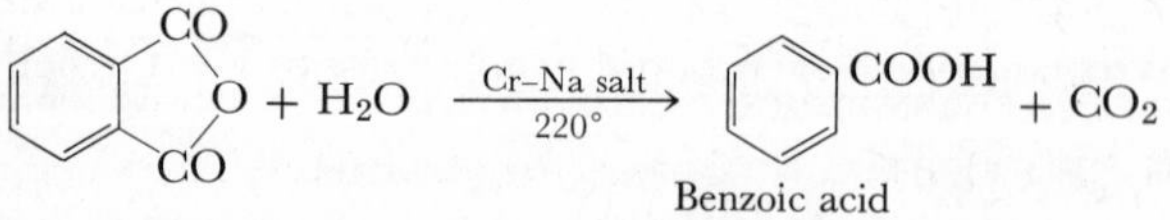

                                         Benzoic acid

Isophthalic and terephthalic acids

Isophthalic and **terephthalic acids** have become of technical importance only since 1950. They cannot be made by the same process used for phthalic anhydride because normal bond lengths and bond angles do not permit the formation of volatile monomeric anhydrides. Usually the oxidation of *m*- or *p*-xylene is brought about in several steps. The xylene in the liquid phase and in the presence of a soluble cobalt or manganese salt

Do not give monomeric anhydrides

s oxidized by air to the toluic acid. The toluic acid is converted to the methyl ester, which is oxidized to the methyl hydrogen phthalate. The latter s isolated as the dimethyl ester.

$$C_6H_4(CH_3)_2 \xrightarrow[140°]{O_2, \text{ Co or Mn salt}} C_6H_4(CH_3)COOH \xrightarrow[[H^+]]{CH_3OH}$$

m- or *p*-Xylene   *m*- or *p*-Toluic acid

Made by oxidation of m- and p-xylene

$$C_6H_4(CH_3)COOCH_3 \xrightarrow[\text{salt}]{O_2, \text{ Co or Mn}} C_6H_4(COOH)COOCH_3 \xrightarrow[[H^+]]{CH_3OH} C_6H_4(COOCH_3)_2$$

Methyl *m*- or *p*-toluate   Methyl hydrogen iso- or terephthalate   Methyl iso- or terephthalate

For most purposes methyl isophthalate and methyl terephthalate are preferable to the free acids, although the latter can be obtained by hydrolysis. Isophthalic acid is used in the manufacture of alkyd resins (p. 239) and terephthalic acid in the production of polyester fibers (p. 238).

Used for alkyd resins and polyester fibers

SULFONIC ACIDS

Only the aromatic sulfonic acids are important. They usually are made by direct sulfonation of the aromatic nucleus (p. 46). Unlike the carboxylic acids, the sulfonic acids are as strong as mineral acids. They are soluble in water and are nonvolatile.

Sulfonic acids are strong acids

The free sulfonic acids find very little use. Because they are strong acids and have a much weaker oxidizing action than sulfuric acid, they frequently are used as acid catalysts. An important use of the sodium sulfonates is for the manufacture of phenols by fusion with sodium hydroxide (p. 77). The sodium sulfonate group usually is present in direct dyes (p. 209), its function being to confer water solubility on the dyestuff. Sodium salts of alkylated aromatic sulfonic acids are important synthetic detergents. Because their calcium, magnesium, and iron salts are soluble in water, they are as effective in hard water as in soft water (cf. p. 124). In one process of manufacture, benzene is alkylated with tetrapropylene (p. 232) and the product is sulfonated and converted to the sodium salt.

Used to make phenols and synthetic detergents

$$C_{10}H_{21}CH{=}CH_2 + \underset{}{\bigcirc} \xrightarrow{HF} \underset{CH_3CHC_{10}H_{21}}{\bigcirc} \xrightarrow[\text{or } SO_3]{H_2SO_4} \underset{C_{12}H_{25}}{\overset{SO_3H}{\bigcirc}} \xrightarrow{Na_2CO_3} \underset{C_{12}H_{25}}{\overset{SO_3Na}{\bigcirc}}$$

The sulfonyl chlorides are obtained readily by direct *chlorosulfonation*. Thus toluene yields a mixture of *o*- and **p-toluenesulfonyl chlorides** (*tosyl chlorides*).

Sulfonyl halides made by chlorosulfonation

$$\underset{}{\overset{CH_3}{\bigcirc}} + 2 \text{ HOSO}_2\text{Cl} \longrightarrow \underset{}{\overset{CH_3}{\bigcirc}}{SO_2Cl} \quad \text{and} \quad \underset{SO_2Cl}{\overset{CH_3}{\bigcirc}} + H_2SO_4 + HCl$$

o-Toluenesulfonyl chloride   *p*-Toluenesulfonyl chloride

Saccharin a sweetening agent from toluene

Saccharin, discovered by Remsen (1846–1927), professor of chemistry at Johns Hopkins University, is the imide of the mixed anhydride of o-carboxybenzenesulfonic acid. It usually is stated to have a sweetness from 550 to 750 times that of cane sugar. Relative sweetness, however, depends on the method of determination and on the individual (p. 186). For most tastes a $\frac{1}{2}$ grain (0.03 gram) tablet replaces a heaping teaspoon (10 grams) of sucrose, indicating a sweetening power about 300 times that of sucrose. Saccharin has no food value and is used only when it is desirable to reduce the consumption of sugar. Saccharin has been made from o-toluene-sulfonyl chloride by a series of reactions.

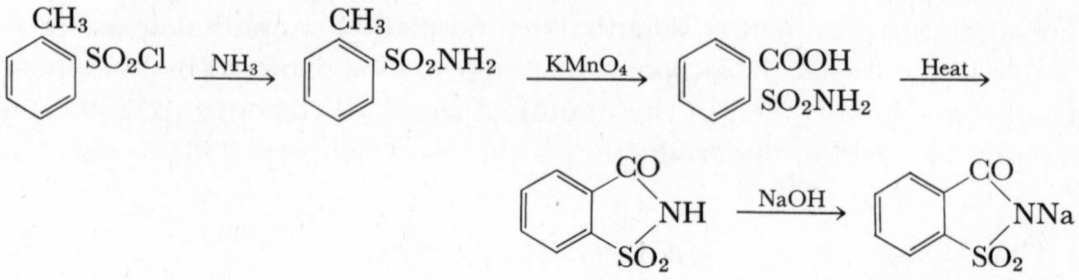

Saccharin   Saccharin soluble
                             (sodium salt)

The imide is converted to the sodium salt to increase the solubility in water.

SUMMARY

1. Carboxylic acids contain the functional group —COOH. The electron attracting properties of the carbonyl are greater than those of a phenyl group. Thus, although phenols are weaker acids than carbonic acid, carboxylic acids are stronger than carbonic acid.

2. Carboxylic acids react with bases in aqueous solution to give nonvolatile salts. If the organic acid is insoluble in water and contains fewer than ten carbon atoms, it dissolves in dilute aqueous solutions of ammonia or alkali metal hydroxides or carbonates, because these salts are more soluble than the free acid. Acids having ten to eighteen carbon atoms give colloidal solutions. Above eighteen carbon atoms the salts are only slightly soluble.

3. The normal carboxylic acids are called fatty acids, because those having an even number of carbon atoms are obtained by the hydrolysis of fats. Their common names are derived from the natural source of the acid. In the Geneva system, the ending is *oic acid.*

4. The most important acyclic acid is acetic acid. It is produced in the form of vinegar by the enzymic-catalyzed oxidation of ethyl alcohol by air. Commercially acetic acid is made by the oxidation of acetaldehyde or by the controlled oxidation of butane by air.

5. Acetic acid may be used to prepare esters that are valuable solvents. Most of it is used in the manufacture of cellulose acetate by way of acetic anhydride.

6. Direct esterification of an alcohol by an acid requires a strong acid as catalyst and is a reversible reaction. Hydrolysis of an ester is catalyzed either by an acid or a base. The acid-catalyzed reaction is reversible, but the base-catalyzed reaction goes to completion because the base reacts irreversibly with the acid formed.

7. Aromatic carboxylic acids can be made by the oxidation of carbon side chains. Thus oxidation of toluene yields benzoic acid.

8. Dicarboxylic acids of the general formula $HOOC(CH_2)_xCOOH$ have different properties depending on the value of x. Oxalic acid ($x = 0$) decomposes when heated with concentrated sulfuric acid into carbon dioxide, carbon monoxide and water. Malonic acids ($x = 1$) when heated above their melting points lose carbon dioxide to give a monocarboxylic acid. Succinic and glutaric acids ($x = 2$ and $x = 3$) when heated lose water to give five- and six-membered cyclic anhydrides. Adipic and pimelic acids ($x = 4$ and $x = 5$) when heated with barium hydroxide give five- and six-membered cyclic ketones.

9. The o-, m-, and p-benzenedicarboxylic acids are known as phthalic, isophthalic, and terephthalic acids and are made by the oxidation of carbon side chains in the appropriate positions. Only phthalic acid yields a volatile cyclic anhydride, because only when the carboxyl groups are in the *ortho* positions can a ring be formed that will accommodate the normal bond lengths and bond angles.

EXERCISES

1. Write condensed structural formulas for: (a) the saturated acyclic carboxylic acids having six carbon atoms; (b) the saturated cyclic carboxylic acids having six carbon atoms.

2. Using accepted structural theory, write formulas for all of the possible compounds having the molecular formula $C_2H_4O_2$.

3. Arrange the following compounds in the order of increasing acidity: caproic acid, phenol, benzenesulfonic acid, 1-hexanol, benzoic acid, toluene.

4. Predict the order of increasing boiling point for the following compounds: propionaldehyde, n-propyl alcohol, propionic acid, n-butane, methyl ethyl ether, acetic acid.

5. Devise a procedure for separating n-amyl alcohol from n-valeric acid without resorting to distillation.

6. Write structural formulas for: (a) α-methylbutyric acid; (b) 2-ethyl-3-methylpentanoic acid; (c) s-butyl i-caproate; (d) i-propyl 2,4-dichlorophenoxyacetate.

7. Arrange the following compounds in the order of increasing ease of hydrolysis: acetic anhydride, ethyl ether, ethyl acetate.

8. (a) Complete saponification of 5 g. of an ester requires 1.54 g. of sodium hydroxide. What is the equivalent weight of the ester?

(b) Removal of the alcohol formed on saponification, and acidification of the residual liquid yields an acid, 1 g. of which requires 0.455 g. of sodium hydroxide for complete neutralization. What is the equivalent weight of the acid?

(c) Assuming that the acid contains one carboxyl group and that the alcohol with which it was esterified contains one hydroxyl group, what are the possible structures of the original ester?

9. Of the following carboxylic acids, which will readily: (a) lose carbon dioxide; (b) form a cyclic anhydride; (c) form a cyclic ketone; (d) undergo none of these reactions:

$(C_2H_5)_2CHCOOH$, $HOOCCH_2CH(CH_3)COOH$, $(CH_3)_2C(COOH)_2$,

$HOOC(CH_2)_4COOH$?

CHAPTER 12

WAXES, FATS, AND OILS

Classification

Waxes, fats, and oils are naturally occurring esters of higher straight chain carboxylic acids. They usually are classified on a mixed basis, including source, physical properties, and chemical properties.

$$
\text{Waxes}
\begin{cases}
\text{Vegetable} \\
\text{Animal}
\end{cases}
$$

$$
\text{Fats}
\begin{cases}
\text{Vegetable} \\
\text{Animal}
\end{cases}
$$

$$
\text{Oils}
\begin{cases}
\text{Vegetable}
\begin{cases}
\text{Nondrying} \\
\text{Semidrying} \\
\text{Drying}
\end{cases} \\[2ex]
\text{Animal}
\begin{cases}
\text{Terrestrial} \\
\text{Marine}
\end{cases}
\end{cases}
$$

WAXES

Definition

A physical definition of a wax might be that it is anything with a waxy feel and a melting point above body temperature and below the boiling point of water. Thus the term paraffin wax is used for a mixture of solid hydrocarbons, beeswax for a mixture of esters, and Carbowax for a synthetic polyether. Chemically, however, waxes are defined as *esters of long-chain monohydric* (one hydroxyl group) *alcohols with long-chain fat acids* (Table 6, p. 103). Hence they have the general formula of a simple ester, RCOOR′. Actually the natural waxes are mixtures of esters and frequently contain hydrocarbons as well.

Plant and animal waxes are esters

Carnauba wax is the most valuable of the vegetable waxes. It occurs as a coating on the leaves of a Brazilian palm, *Corypha cerifera*, from which it is removed by shredding and beating the leaves. It consists of a mixture of the esters of the normal alcohols and normal fat acids having even numbers of carbon atoms from eighteen to thirty. In addition a considerable quantity of esterified C_{18} to C_{30} ω-hydroxy acids and smaller amounts of esters of α,ω-dihydroxyalkanes are present. Because of its high melting

Hardness of waxes

point of 80°–87°, its hardness, and its imperviousness to water, carnauba wax is a valuable ingredient of automobile and floor polishes and carbon

118

paper coatings. **Beeswax** is the material from which the bee builds the cells of the honeycomb. Its composition resembles that of carnauba wax, except that the esters on hydrolysis yield chiefly C_{26} and C_{28} acids and alcohols; hence it has the lower melting point of $60°$–$82°$. **Spermaceti** is obtained from the head of the sperm whale (*Cetaceae*). It is chiefly cetyl palmitate, $C_{15}H_{31}COOC_{16}H_{33}$, and melts at $42°$–$47°$. **Degras** or **wool grease** is a complex mixture of waxes, alcohols, and free fat acids recovered from the scouring of wool. Wool grease has the unusual property of forming a stable semisolid emulsion containing up to 80 per cent water. A purified product known as **lanolin** or **lanum** finds use as a base for salves and ointments in which it is desired to incorporate both water-soluble and fat-soluble substances.

FATS AND OILS

The constitution of fats and oils was investigated systematically first by the French chemist Chevreul (1876–1889). They are *esters of higher fat acids and the trihydric alcohol, glycerol,* $HOCH_2CHOHCH_2OH$. Esters of glycerol frequently are called *glycerides.* They have the general formula $RCOOCH_2CHCH_2OCOR'$. The difference between fats and oils is merely

|
OCOR″

that fats are solid or semisolid at room temperature, whereas oils are liquids. Vegetable fats and oils usually occur in the fruits and seeds of plants and are extracted (*1*) by cold pressing in hydraulic presses or continuous expellers, (*2*) by hot pressing, and (*3*) by solvent extraction. Cold pressing gives the blandest product and is used for producing the highest grade food oils, such as olive, cottonseed, and peanut oils. Hot pressing gives a higher yield, but larger quantities of undesirable components are expressed, and the oil has a stronger odor and flavor. Solvent extraction gives the highest recovery, and in recent years the process has been so improved that even food oils may be prepared which are free from undesirable odors and flavors. Animal fats are recovered by heating fatty tissue to a high temperature (dry-rendering) or by treating with steam or hot water and separating the liberated fat.

Since all fats and oils are esters of glycerol, their differences must be due to the acids with which the glycerol is esterified. These acids are both saturated and unsaturated. Of the saturated acids the most important are **lauric acid,** $CH_3(CH_2)_{10}COOH$, **palmitic acid,** $CH_3(CH_2)_{14}COOH$, and **stearic acid,** $CH_3(CH_2)_{16}COOH$. The most important unsaturated acids have eighteen carbon atoms, and one double bond usually is at the middle of the chain. If other double bonds are present they lie further removed from the carboxyl group. **Oleic acid,** $CH_3(CH_2)_7CH{=}CH(CH_2)_7COOH$, has only one double bond; **linoleic acid (linolic acid),** $CH_3(CH_2)_4CH{=}CHCH_2CH{=}CH(CH_2)_7COOH$, has two double bonds separated by one methylene group; **linolenic acid,** $CH_3CH_2CH{=}CHCH_2CH{=}CHCH_2CH{=}CH(CH_2)_7COOH$, has three double bonds each separated by methylene groups; **eleostearic acid,** $CH_3(CH_2)_3CH{=}CH{-}CH{=}CH{-}CH{=}CH(CH_2)_7COOH$, also has three double bonds, but they are conjugated.

Fats and oils are esters of glycerol

Obtained by pressing or solvent extraction

Yield saturated and unsaturated acids

One double bond at middle of 18-carbon chain

Ricinoleic acid, $CH_3(CH_2)_5CHOHCH_2CH=CH(CH_2)_7COOH$, is 12-hydroxyoleic acid. Of all the fat acids palmitic acid is the most abundant, and oleic acid is the most widely distributed.

Fats and oils are chiefly mixed glycerides and not a mixture of simple glycerides. The different fat acids appear to be distributed randomly except that the amount of any particular glyceride does not exceed the amount that can remain fluid *in vivo*. Simple glycerides occur in quantity only if more than two thirds of the acyl groups are of one kind. The approximate relative amounts of the different acids obtained by the hydrolysis of fats are given in Table 8.

Oils are more highly unsaturated than fats

In the acids obtained from fats, saturated acids predominate, but in those from oils, unsaturated acids predominate. In other words unsaturation lowers the melting point. Another factor which lowers the melting point

TABLE 8. SAPONIFICATION AND IODINE VALUES OF FATS AND OILS AND THE COMPOSITION OF THE FAT ACIDS OBTAINED BY HYDROLYSIS

FAT OR OIL		SAPONIFICATION VALUE	IODINE VALUE	COMPOSITION OF FAT ACIDS (PER CENT)					
				MYRISTIC	PALMITIC	STEARIC	OLEIC	LINOLEIC	OTHER COMPONENTS
VEGETABLE FATS	Coconut	250–60	8–10	17–20	4–10	1–5	2–10	0–2	a
	Palm	196–210	48–58	1–3	34–43	3–6	38–40	5–11	
ANIMAL FATS	Butter	216–35	26–45	7–9	23–26	10–13	30–40	4–5	b
	Lard	193–200	46–66	1–2	28–30	12–18	41–48	6–7	c
	Tallow	190–200	31–47	2–3	24–32	14–32	35–48	2–4	
VEGETABLE OILS — NONDRYING	Castor	176–87	81–90		0–1		0–9	3–7	d
	Olive	185–200	74–94	0–1	5–15	1–4	69–84	4–12	
	Peanut	185–95	83–98		6–9	2–6	50–70	13–26	e
VEGETABLE OILS — SEMI-DRYING	Corn	188–93	116–30	0–2	7–11	3–4	43–49	34–42	
	Cottonseed	191–6	103–15	0–2	19–24	1–2	23–33	40–48	
VEGETABLE OILS — DRYING	Soybean	189–94	124–36	0–1	6–10	2–4	21–29	50–59	f
	Sunflower	190–2	122–36		10–13		21–39	51–68	
	Safflower	186–94	130–50		5–10		14–21	73–78	
	Linseed	189–96	170–204		4–7	2–5	9–38	3–43	g
	Tung	189–95	160–80		2–6		4–16	0–1	h
ANIMAL OILS — TERRESTRIAL	Lard	190–95	46–70		22–26	15–17	45–55	8–10	
	Neat's-foot	192–7	67–73		17–18	2–3	74–77		
ANIMAL OILS — MARINE	Whale	188–94	110–50	4–6	11–18	2–4	33–38		i
	Fish (sardine)	185–95	120–90	6–8	10–16	1–2			j

(a) 5–10 caprylic, 5–11 capric, and 45–51 lauric acids.
(b) 3–4 butyric, 1–2 caproic, 1 caprylic, 2–3 capric, and 2–3 lauric acids; 5 C_{16} unsaturated acid.
(c) 2 C_{20} and C_{22} unsaturated fat acids.
(d) 80–92 ricinoleic acid.
(e) 2–5 arachidic and 1–5 tetracosanoic acids.

(f) 4–8 linolenic acid.
(g) 25–58 linolenic acid.
(h) 74–91 eleostearic acid.
(i) 13–18 C_{16}, 11–20 C_{20}, and 6–11 C_{22} unsaturated acids.
(j) 6–15 C_{16}, 24–30 C_{18}, 19–26 C_{20}, and 12–19 C_{22} unsaturated acids.

is molecular weight. The acids from low-melting fats such as coconut oil, palm oil, and butter contain relatively small amounts of unsaturated acids but considerable amounts of lower fat acids. Although classified as fats because they are solid in temperate zones, coconut oil and palm oil were called oils because they are liquids in the tropics where they are produced.

The characteristic chemical features of the fats are the ester linkages and the unsaturation. As esters they may be hydrolyzed in the presence of acids, enzymes, or alkali to free fat acids or their salts, and glycerol.

Hydrolysis of fats

$$
\begin{array}{c}
\text{RCOOCH}_2 \\
| \\
\text{R'COOCH} + 3\,\text{H}_2\text{O} \\
| \\
\text{R''COOCH}_2
\end{array}
\xrightarrow[\text{enzymes}]{[\text{H}^+] \text{ or}}
\begin{array}{cc}
\text{RCOOH} & \text{CH}_2\text{OH} \\
 & | \\
\text{R'COOH} + & \text{CHOH} \\
 & | \\
\text{R''COOH} & \text{CH}_2\text{OH} \\
 & \text{Glycerol}
\end{array}
$$

$$
+ 3\,\text{M}^+\text{OH}^- \longrightarrow
\begin{array}{cc}
[\text{RCOO}^-]\text{M}^+ & \text{CH}_2\text{OH} \\
 & | \\
[\text{R'COO}^-]\text{M}^+ + & \text{CHOH} \\
 & | \\
[\text{R''COO}^-]\text{M}^+ & \text{CH}_2\text{OH}
\end{array}
$$

Because the fat acids differ in molecular weight, and because substances that do not react with alkali, such as hydrocarbons and alcohols of high molecular weight, may be present, different fats require different amounts of alkali for saponification. Hence the amount of alkali required to saponify a given weight of fat may be used as a characteristic of the particular fat. An arbitrary unit known technically as the **saponification value** is used, which is the *number of milligrams of potassium hydroxide required to saponify one gram of fat*. Table 8 shows that the fats containing chiefly C_{18} acids have almost identical saponification values, and the determination is useful only to identify or detect the presence of coconut oil and butter fat, or to determine whether these fats have been adulterated with others having a lower saponification value, or with mineral oils or greases.

Analysis by saponification

The extent of unsaturation likewise is characteristic of a fat and may be determined by the amount of halogen which the fat can add. Iodine does not ordinarily form stable addition products with the double bond (p. 32), and chlorine or bromine replace hydrogen as well as add to the double bonds. In practice, standardized solutions of iodine monochloride (*Wijs solution*) or of iodine monobromide (*Hanus solution*) in glacial acetic acid are used. However, the Wijs or Hanus solution is standardized by adding potassium iodide and titrating the liberated iodine with standard thiosulfate solution. The amount of reagent remaining after reaction with a fat is determined in the same way. *The difference expressed in terms of grams of iodine* (as if iodine had added) *per 100 grams of fat* is known as the **iodine value** of the fat. The increase in iodine value with increasing amounts of unsaturated acids is apparent in Table 8.

Analysis by addition of halogen

The **hydrogenation of oils** is carried out technically on a large scale by bubbling hydrogen through the oil containing a suspension of finely divided nickel. In this process the double bonds of oleic, linoleic, and linolenic glycerides are hydrogenated and the oils converted into the hard waxy tristearin. By controlling the amount of hydrogen added, any consistency desired may be obtained. People of temperate zones prefer fat to oil for

Conversion of oils to fats

cooking purposes, and fats are more useful than oils as soap stocks. Hence hydrogenation greatly increases the value of an oil.

Rancidity of oils is caused chiefly by oxidation of the unsaturated acids by the oxygen of the air (autoxidation), which gives a complex mixture of volatile aldehydes, ketones, and acids. In some cases rancidity may be caused by microorganisms. Fats that have been freed of odor and undesirable tastes now are stabilized by the addition of substances called *antioxidants* (pp. 78, 224), which inhibit oxidation.

Waste or rags containing unsaturated oils is subject to **spontaneous combustion** if air is not excluded, or if not enough ventilation is possible to prevent a rise in temperature as the oil oxidizes. Any rise in temperature increases the rate of oxidation, and the process is accelerated until the material bursts into flame.

From 25 to 50 per cent of the caloric intake of man consists of fats. When metabolized by the organism to carbon dioxide and water, fats produce about 9.5 kcal. of energy per gram compared to 4 kcal. per gram for carbohydrates or proteins. Fats in their ordinary form cannot be absorbed through the walls of the intestine because of their insolubility in water and their large particle size. In the small intestine they are partially hydrolyzed

in the presence of the enzyme catalyst, **steapsin,** to di- and monoglycerides which, together with the bile, can bring about emulsification. Sufficient reduction in particle size takes place to permit passage through the intestinal walls into the lymph ducts, which discharge the fats into the blood stream as a highly dispersed emulsion. The blood stream transports them to the tissues, where they are burned for energy or stored as fat deposits for future use. From the standpoint of digestion, one fat is as useful as another unless its melting point is so high that when mixed with other fats it does not melt or emulsify with the bile at body temperature, in which case it passes into the feces unchanged. However, either linoleic or linolenic acid must be supplied by the ingested fats to insure a healthy condition of the skin.

The relatively high cost of butter has led to the development of a substitute generally referred to as **oleomargarine.** Selected vegetable or animal fats and oils, which have been highly refined and properly hydrogenated to give the desired melting point and consistency, are emulsified with about 17 per cent by weight of milk cultured with certain microorganisms to give it flavor. An emulsifying agent such as a monoglyceride (p. 124) or a vegetable lecithin (p. 134) usually is added as well. Butter consists of droplets of water suspended in oil (water-in-oil type emulsion). Oleomargarines may be either water-in-oil or oil-in-water types of emulsions depending on the method of manufacture. Diacetyl, $CH_3COCOCH_3$, and methylacetylcarbinol, $CH_3CHOHCOCH_3$, which account for the characteristic taste of butter, also may be added along with vitamins A and D. For many years oleomargarine manufacturers in the United States were not permitted to add color to their product unless an additional Federal tax of ten cents per pound was paid. By changing from imported coconut oil to domestic soybean oil as the raw material, the makers of oleomargarine were able to enlist the aid of soybean growers to oppose the dairy lobby, and this law was repealed in 1950. By 1953 the production of oleomargarine exceeded that of butter.

Glycerides of fat acids containing two or more double bonds absorb *Use as protective* oxygen on exposure to air to give peroxides, which catalyze the polymeri- *coatings* zation of the unsaturated portions (p. 232). As a result the oils become solid or semisolid and are known as *drying oils*. If exposed in thin layers, tough elastic waterproof films are formed. **Paint** is a mixture of drying oil, pig- *Oils as paint vehicles* ment, thinner, and drier. The pigment is an opaque material having a refractive index different from that of the oil film. It provides color and covering power, and protects the oil film from the destructive action of light. The thinner is a volatile solvent, either turpentine (p. 215) or a petroleum fraction called mineral paint spirits. It permits spreading and on evapora- tion leaves a thin even film of oil and pigment that does not run. The drier is a solution of cobalt, manganese, or lead salts of organic acids, usually naphthenic acids from petroleum (p. 108), which catalyzes the oxidation and polymerization of the oil. The drying oil is known as the *vehicle* because *Dry by polymerization* after polymerization it holds or carries the pigment. Linseed oil is the most widely used drying oil, although a certain amount of tung oil in a paint gives it superior properties, which seem to be due to the conjugation of the unsaturation.

Varnish is a mixture of drying oil, rosin (p. 216), and thinner. The rosin imparts hardness and high gloss to the dried film and may be replaced by other natural or synthetic resins. **Enamels** are pigmented varnishes. **Oil cloth** is made by coating cotton cloth with a mixture of partially oxidized *Oil cloth and linoleum* oil and a pigment, and drying in warm chambers. If the oil is more highly oxidized to a thick viscous mass, mixed with rosin and ground cork or other filler, and rolled into a continuous sheet, **linoleum** is produced.

Wetting agents, emulsifying agents, and **detergents** are compounds that have an oil-soluble portion at one end of the molecule and a water- soluble portion at the other end. The oil-soluble portion usually is a hydro- carbon chain of twelve to eighteen carbon atoms. The water-soluble portion may be the salt of a carboxylic or sulfonic acid (*anionic agents*), a quaternary ammonium salt (*cationic agents,* p. 132), or a polyoxygenated group (hydroxyl or ether oxygen; *nonionic agents,* p. 83).

The alkali metal salts of fat acids having from ten to eighteen carbon atoms are known as **soaps.** They have a long oil-soluble hydrocarbon chain *Soaps as detergents* attached to a water-soluble carboxylate ion and hence act as wetting agents, emulsifying agents, and detergents. Strictly speaking, only such salts should be referred to as soaps. If the hydrocarbon chain of the alkali metal salts is less than ten carbon atoms long, it does not cause emulsification of oil. If more than eighteen carbon atoms are present, the salt is too insolu- ble in water to form a sufficiently concentrated colloidal solution. The alkaline earth and heavy metal salts are insoluble in water and hence use- less as detergents. Hard water, containing calcium, magnesium, and iron *Inadequacy in* ions, precipitates insoluble salts when soap solutions are added, and deter- *hard water* gent action does not take place until these ions are completely removed. Moreover the scum of insoluble salts produced from the soap and inorganic salts may be difficult to remove from the article being washed. The insolu- ble salts have other uses, however (p. 124), and frequently are called soaps.

In recent years numerous synthetic compounds have become available *Synthetic detergents and* which meet the general structural requirements for a detergent or emulsi- *emulsifying agents*

Useful in hard water

fying agent, namely a water-soluble portion and an oil-soluble portion. The chief advantage of these products over the salts of fat acids is that their alkaline earth and iron salts are soluble in water or that they do not form salts. Hence such detergents are not precipitated by hard water. Since 1930 the catalytic reduction of fat acids or the sodium-alcohol reduction of fats, especially coconut oil, has been used to produce mixtures of higher alcohols, which can be sulfated to produce detergents.

$$RCOOH + 2\,H_2 \xrightarrow{Cu-Cr} RCH_2OH + H_2O$$

$$\text{or} \quad RCOOR' + 4\,Na + 3\,R''OH \longrightarrow RCH_2OH + R'ONa + 3\,R''ONa$$

$$\text{then} \quad RCH_2OH + H_2SO_4 \longrightarrow RCH_2OSO_3H \xrightarrow{NaOH} RCH_2OSO_3Na$$

Sulfonic acids
as detergents

The number of synthetic surface-active agents has increased enormously in recent years. Between 500 and 600 are available commercially. The most widely used synthetic detergents have been the sodium salts of alkylated aromatic sulfonic acids (p. 115). The use of products containing synthetic detergents has increased rapidly. By 1960 the quantity of synthetic detergents produced in the United States was three times that of soaps.

Monoglycerides in foods
and cosmetics

In contrast to the triglycerides, monoglycerides have free hydroxyl groups that act as water-solubilizing groups, and hence they become emulsifying agents. They have found extensive use particularly in the manufacture of oleomargarine and in other food industries, and in the preparation of cosmetic creams. They are mixtures prepared either by the partial esterification of glycerol with free fat acids or by the glycerolysis of fats.

Numerous other uses

Free fat acids are used as softening agents for rubber. Commercial stearic acid is a mixture of stearic and palmitic acids used in the manufacture of candles, cosmetics, and shaving soaps. The aluminum, calcium, lead, and lithium soaps when heated with petroleum oils form a gel and are used to thicken oils in the manufacture of lubricating greases (p. 51). Magnesium and zinc stearates are used in face powders and dusting powders, and as lubricants to prevent sticking in the molding of plastics. Fat acid chains are incorporated into the molecules of antiseptics, drugs, dyes, resins, and plastics to modify their solubility and setting characteristics.

SUMMARY

1. Natural waxes are composed chiefly of esters of long-chain normal monocarboxylic acids with long-chain monohydric alcohols. Fats and oils are esters of monocarboxylic acids with the trihydric alcohol, glycerol.
2. Fats are solids at room temperature and oils are liquids. Fats yield a higher proportion of saturated fat acids on hydrolysis, whereas oils yield a higher proportion of unsaturated fat acids. Catalytic hydrogenation of an oil converts it into a fat.
3. The degree of unsaturation of a fat or oil is measured by its iodine value. The average molecular weight of the acids combined with the glycerol is indicated by the saponification value of the fat or oil.
4. Oils having a high content of acid residues containing two or three double bonds are known as drying oils. They absorb oxygen from the air and undergo polymeri-

zation. They are used in the manufacture of paints, varnishes, and enamels, and to make linoleum and oil cloth.

5. Next to their use as food, the chief use of fats and oils is for the manufacture of soap. They are used also as raw materials for the production of certain types of wetting agents and synthetic detergents.

EXERCISES

1. What conclusions may be drawn from the following facts: (a) one oil has a higher iodine value than another; (b) one fat has a higher saponification value than another; (c) the saponification value of an oil is almost zero?

2. Explain the following observations: (a) a deposit forms in a bottle of cooking oil when it is stored in a refrigerator; (b) when water is shaken with a small volume of a soap solution, no foaming results and a precipitate is formed; (c) a dilute solution of a powder sold for cleaning purposes foams when shaken, and foaming is not prevented by adding lime water; (d) by the time a bottle of salad oil has been used completely a sticky semisolid gum has formed around the threads of the cap and bottle.

3. Why does lard melt quietly in a frying pan, whereas butter or oleomargarine sizzles and sputters?

4. Indicate the possible structures for the molecules present in a fat that yields palmitic, stearic, and oleic acids on hydrolysis. (Use the letters P, S, and O as symbols for the three acyl groups.)

5. How could one distinguish: (a) linseed oil from cottonseed oil; (b) butter from oleomargarine; (c) beeswax from a highly hydrogenated cottonseed oil; (d) lard oil from mineral oil?

CHAPTER 13

NITROGEN COMPOUNDS

Structurally the organic oxygen compounds have been considered as derivatives of the water molecule. Similarly many of the organic nitrogen compounds may be considered as ammonia molecules, the hydrogen atoms of which have been replaced by other groups. Because nitrogen has three replaceable hydrogen atoms instead of two as in water, the number of possible combinations is increased. Some of the more common functional groups containing nitrogen are listed in Table 5, p. 55.

AMINES

Nomenclature of amines

Aliphatic amines are alkyl substitution products of ammonia and are named as such, *ammonia* being contracted to *amine*. Thus CH_3NH_2 is methylamine, $(CH_3)_2NH$ is dimethylamine, and $(CH_3)_3N$ is trimethylamine. With mixed amines the alkyl groups frequently are named in the order of increasing complexity, for example $CH_3(C_2H_5)NCH(CH_3)_2$ is methylethyl-*i*-propylamine. Compounds in which the nitrogen atom is united to one carbon atom, RNH_2, are called *primary amines;* to two carbon atoms, R_2NH, *secondary amines;* and to three carbon atoms, R_3N, *tertiary amines. The terms primary, secondary, and tertiary refer here to the condition of the nitrogen atom,* whereas when used with alcohols they referred to the carbon atom to which the hydroxyl group was attached. Thus although tertiary butyl alcohol, $(CH_3)_3COH$, is a tertiary alcohol, because the carbon atom is united to three other carbon atoms, tertiary butylamine, $(CH_3)_3CNH_2$, is a primary amine, because the nitrogen atom is united directly to only one carbon atom. The NH_2 group is called the *amino group,* and primary amines having other functional groups may be named as amino substitution products; for example, $CH_3CHNH_2CH_2CH_2OH$ is 3-amino-1-butanol. The simpler aromatic amines usually have common names. For example aminobenzene is called *aniline,* and the three aminotoluenes are called *o-, m-,* and *p*-toluidines.

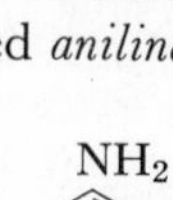

Aniline
(aminobenzene or
phenylamine)

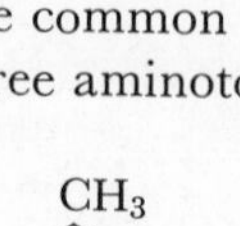

o-Toluidine
(*o*-aminotoluene or
o-tolylamine)

Secondary and tertiary amines are named as derivatives of ammonia or as derivatives of the primary amine. The prefix *N*- indicates that a group is attached to nitrogen and not to another portion of the molecule.

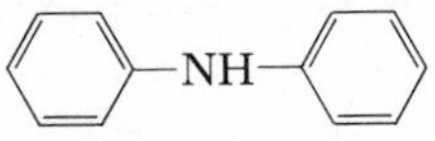

Diphenylamine 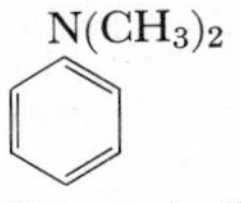   *N,N*-Dimethylaniline

Aliphatic amines may be prepared by the reaction of alkyl halides with ammonia. In this reaction the more basic ammonia molecule displaces chlorine as a chloride ion, the alkyl group attaching itself to the unshared pair of electrons of the ammonia molecule.

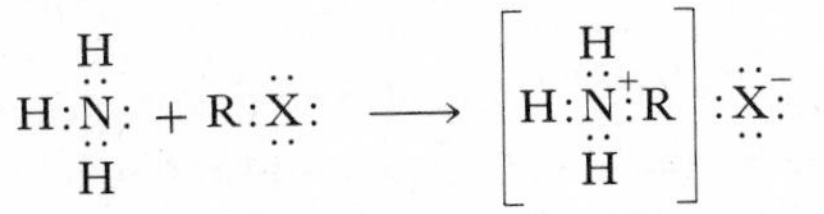

Preparation of aliphatic amines from alkyl halides and ammonia

This initial reaction, however, is followed by a series of secondary reactions. Just as ammonia can be liberated from an ammonium salt by reaction with a stronger base,

$$NH_4Cl + NaOH \longrightarrow NH_3 + H_2O + NaCl$$

the free primary amine can be liberated from the alkylammonium salt.

$$RNH_3X + NaOH \longrightarrow RNH_2 + H_2O + NaX$$

Similarly the excess of ammonia present when the alkyl halide is reacting with ammonia competes with the primary amine for the hydrogen halide. Because ammonia and the amine have about the same basicity, the reaction does not go to completion, but an equilibrium is established.

$$RNH_3X + NH_3 \rightleftharpoons RNH_2 + NH_4X$$

The primary amine thus formed also has an unshared pair of electrons and can react with a molecule of alkyl halide, giving rise to a second pair of reactions to form a secondary amine.

$$RNH_2 + RX \longrightarrow R_2NH_2X$$
$$R_2NH_2X + NH_3 \rightleftharpoons R_2NH + NH_4X$$

Immediately a third pair of reactions is possible, giving a tertiary amine.

$$R_2NH + RX \longrightarrow R_3NHX$$
$$R_3NHX + NH_3 \rightleftharpoons R_3N + NH_4X$$

Finally a single further reaction can take place, giving a quaternary ammonium salt.

$$R_3N + RX \longrightarrow R_4NX$$

The reaction stops at this point, because there is no hydrogen attached to nitrogen in the quaternary ammonium salt (nitrogen united to four carbon atoms), and hence no proton can be transferred to another base.

Preparation of aromatic amines from nitro compounds

In general it is difficult to prepare aromatic amines by this method, because halogen attached to an aromatic nucleus is not sufficiently reactive (p. 90). Technically the operation is carried out at around 200° in the presence of cuprous chloride. Because aromatic nitro compounds are made readily by direct nitration (p. 146), reduction of the nitro compound to the amine is the procedure more commonly used.

$$\text{Nitrobenzene} \quad NO_2 + 3\ H_2 \xrightarrow{\text{Ni}} \quad NH_2 + 2\ H_2O \quad \text{Aniline}$$

Reduction by metals, such as tin or iron, and hydrochloric acid also may be used.

Physical properties

Water, ammonia, and methane have very nearly the same molecular weights, but their boiling points are 100°, −33°, and −161°, respectively. The abnormally high boiling point of water is explained by proton bonding between hydrogen united to oxygen, and the unshared pair of electrons on the oxygen atom (p. 61). Ammonia also forms proton bonds, but its boiling point indicates that it is not so strongly associated as water. The nitrogen atom is nearer the center of the periodic table than oxygen and hence has less attraction for electrons (p. 105). Therefore the hydrogen atoms attached to nitrogen have less tendency to leave nitrogen as protons or to be shared with other atoms than do those joined to oxygen. The decrease in tendency to share a proton accounts for the smaller degree of association.

Primary and secondary amines are associated

Primary and secondary amines also are associated. Methylamine (mol. wt. 31) boils at −7° and dimethylamine (mol. wt. 45) boils at +7°, but trimethylamine (mol. wt. 59) boils at +4°. Thus even though its molecular weight is greater than that of dimethylamine, trimethylamine has the lower boiling point. The explanation is that trimethylamine no longer has a hydrogen atom capable of proton bond formation, and hence it is not associated.

There is nothing, however, to prevent the unshared pair of electrons of tertiary amines from forming proton bonds with water molecules, and all types of amines of low molecular weight are soluble in water. Because amines have a greater tendency to share their unshared pair of electrons than do alcohols, they form stronger proton bonds with water and are somewhat more soluble. For example, *n*-butyl alcohol dissolves in water to the extent of about 8 per cent at room temperature, but *n*-butylamine is miscible with water; and although less than 1 per cent of *n*-amyl alcohol dissolves in water, this degree of insolubility is not reached in the amines until *n*-hexylamine. Like the alcohols and ethers, simple amines are soluble in most organic solvents.

Amines form hydrogen bonds with water

The physical properties of the aromatic amines are about what would be expected. Just as benzene (b.p. 80°) boils at a higher temperature than *n*-hexane (b.p. 69°), so aniline (b.p. 184°) has a higher boiling point than *n*-hexylamine (b.p. 130°). The greater difference in the boiling points of the second pair may be ascribed to the fact that aniline has a higher dipole moment ($\mu = 1.6$) than *n*-hexylamine ($\mu = 1.3$). *N*-methylaniline (b.p. 195°) boils at a higher temperature than aniline, but *N,N*-dimethylaniline (b.p. 193°) boils at a lower temperature than *N*-methylaniline, despite the increase in molecular weight, because proton bonding is not possible for dimethylaniline.

Aniline is somewhat more soluble in water (3.6 g. per 100 g. of water) than *n*-hexylamine (0.4 g. per 100 g. of water). Water dissolves in aniline to the extent of about 5 per cent. Aniline is miscible with benzene but not with *n*-hexane.

As is true for all of the disubstituted benzenes, the *para*-substituted anilines, being the most symmetrical, have the highest melting point. Thus *p*-toluidine is a solid at room temperature, whereas both the *ortho* and *meta* isomers are liquids.

The lower amines have an odor resembling that of ammonia; the odor of trimethylamine is described as "fishy." As the molecular weight increases, the odors become decidedly obnoxious, but they decrease again with increasing molecular weight and decreasing vapor pressure.

Lower amines have fishy odor

The aromatic amines, like the aromatic hydrocarbons and their halogen and nitro derivatives, are highly toxic. The liquids are absorbed readily through the skin, and low concentrations of the vapors produce symptoms of toxicity when inhaled for prolonged periods. Aniline vapors may produce symptoms of poisoning after several hours of exposure to concentrations as low as 7 parts per million. The chloro and nitro nuclear-substituted amines, the *N*-alkylated and acylated amines, and the diamines all are highly toxic. The *N*-phenylamines are considerably less toxic than the *N*-alkyl derivatives. The phenolic hydroxyl group also decreases the toxicity somewhat. Toxicity is greatly reduced by the presence of free carboxylic or sulfonic acid groups in the ring.

Aromatic amines are highly toxic

Amines are the bases in organic chemistry. For many purposes it is sufficient to define an acid as a substance that yields hydrogen ions when dissolved in water, and a base as a substance that yields hydroxide ions when dissolved in water. A more general concept is useful in organic chemistry, because acid-base reactions are carried out in many solvents other than water. Usually an acid is considered to be any substance that can lose a proton, and a base is any substance having an unshared pair of electrons that can combine with a proton. Reaction of an acid with a base consists of the transfer of a proton from one base to another. For example when hydrogen chloride dissolves in water, the proton is transferred from the very weak base, chloride ion, to the stronger base, the water molecule.

Acid-base reactions are proton-transfer reactions

$$H:\overset{..}{\underset{H}{O}}: + H:\overset{..}{\underset{..}{Cl}}: \longrightarrow \left[H:\overset{..}{\underset{H}{O}}^{+}H \right] :\overset{..}{\underset{..}{Cl}}:^{-}$$

Hydronium chloride

If ammonia is added to the water solution of hydrogen chloride, the proton is transferred from the water molecule to the stronger base, the ammonia molecule.

$$[H_3O^+] + :NH_3 \longrightarrow [NH_4{}^+] + H_2O$$

Similarly the hydroxide ion displaces the weaker base, ammonia, from the ammonium ion.

$$[NH_4^+] + \left[\ddot{:}\!\ddot{O}H \right] \longrightarrow NH_3 + H_2O$$

Aliphatic amines stronger than ammonia; aromatic weaker

In general the aliphatic amines are slightly stronger bases than ammonia, whereas aromatic amines, because of the electron-attracting power of the aromatic nucleus, are weaker than ammonia. If strongly electron-attracting groups are in positions *ortho* or *para* to the amino group in an aromatic nucleus, it may lose its basic properties completely, as is true for 2,4,6-trinitroaniline.

Amine salts are nonvolatile

If sufficiently basic, the amines form nonvolatile salts with acids. Water-insoluble amines dissolve in aqueous solutions of acids. Amines are liberated from their salts by stronger bases such as aqueous solutions of sodium hydroxide.

Some important amines

Methylamine, dimethylamine, and **trimethylamine** occur in herring brine and are distributed widely in other natural products, probably as the result of the decomposition or metabolism of other nitrogenous compounds. They are manufactured commercially by passing a mixture of methyl alcohol and ammonia over heated alumina.

$$CH_3OH + NH_3 \xrightarrow[400°]{Al_2O_3} \underset{+\;H_2O}{CH_3NH_2} \xrightarrow{CH_3OH} \underset{+\;H_2O}{(CH_3)_2NH} \xrightarrow{CH_3OH} \underset{+\;H_2O}{(CH_3)_3N}$$

Although all three amines are obtained in the commercial synthesis, dimethylamine is the most important. The three chief uses are for the preparation of dimethylamine salts of 2,4-D and 2,4,5-T used as herbicides (p. 107), of ultra accelerators for rubber vulcanization (p. 236), and of dimethylformamide (p. 137) used as a solvent in the spinning of acrylic fibers (p. 235). Originally dimethylamine was used chiefly as a dehairing agent for kid hides. The total quantity used for this latter purpose has remained about constant, but it now accounts for only about 2 per cent of production. There are numerous minor uses for methylamine, but most of it is recycled. The chief use for trimethylamine is for the manufacture of choline chloride (p. 132) used in animal feeds.

Aniline is by far the most important amine from the technical viewpoint. It is one of the products of the thermal decomposition of indigo and was called *aniline* from *anil,* the Spanish word for indigo. It is made both by the reduction of nitrobenzene and by the ammonolysis of chlorobenzene (p. 128). Aniline is used almost exclusively as an intermediate in the production of other compounds. About 65 per cent of the total production is used in the manufacture of rubber accelerators and antioxidants (p. 78), about 15 per cent for dyes and dye intermediates, and about 10 per cent for drug manufacture.

α-**Naphthylamine** is made by the reduction of *α*-nitronaphthalene with iron and water (p. 128). *β*-**Naphthylamine** is made by the ammonolysis of *β*-naphthol. This reaction, which is slow in the benzene series, can be brought about easily in the naphthalene series by aqueous ammonia and ammonium sulfite, and is known as the **Bucherer reaction.**

β-Naphthylamine

Heterocyclic nitrogen compounds

Pyrrolidine is a heterocyclic amine made by the catalytic reduction of **pyrrole.**

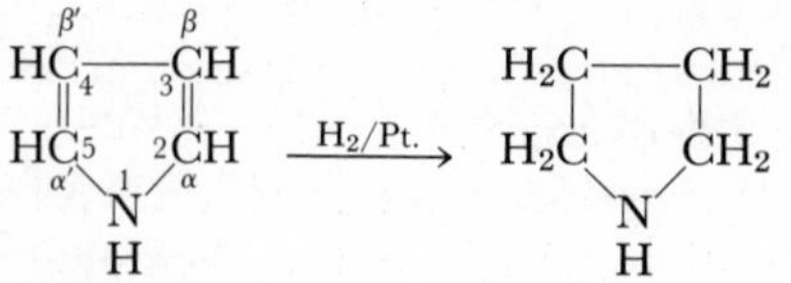

Pyrrole Pyrrolidine

Pyrrolidine has the properties of a typical aliphatic secondary amine, whereas pyrrole is not basic. In pyrrole, as in furan and in thiophene (p. 85), the electrons of the unshared pair on the hetero atom interact with the electrons of the double bonds to confer aromatic properties on the molecule. At the same time this pair no longer is available for bonding with a proton. In fact the withdrawal of the electrons from nitrogen permits the hydrogen atom to leave more readily as a proton, and pyrrole is weakly acidic.

Pyridine, present in coal tar, is the most important of the simple heterocyclic compounds. It has a structure analogous to that of benzene, but it is basic because it still has an unshared pair of electrons on nitrogen. Although it is a considerably weaker base than the aliphatic amines, it is somewhat stronger than aniline. Not only are the double bonds of pyridine unreactive; it also is much more resistant to substitution reactions than benzene. **Piperidine,** the reduction product of pyridine, is a typical alicyclic amine.

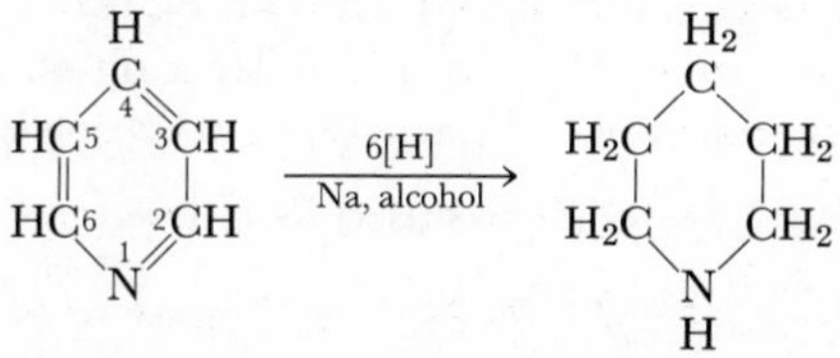

Pyridine Piperidine

QUATERNARY AMMONIUM SALTS

Quaternary ammonium salts and hydroxides resemble alkali metal salts and hydroxides

The final product of the reaction of ammonia or of an amine with an alkyl halide is a quaternary ammonium salt (p. 127). The properties of these salts are quite unlike those of the amine salts, because the nitrogen no longer carries a hydrogen atom. They do not dissociate into amine and acid on heating, and strong alkalies have no effect on them. When a solution of a quaternary ammonium halide is shaken with silver hydroxide, the insoluble silver halide precipitates, leaving the quaternary ammonium hydroxide in solution.

$$[R_4N^+]X^- + AgOH \longrightarrow [R_4N^+]OH^- + AgX$$

The quaternary ammonium hydroxide dissociates completely into its ions in aqueous solution, and hence it has the same basic strength in water as sodium or potassium hydroxide. For example glass is etched by solutions of quaternary ammonium hydroxides just as it is by solutions of sodium hydroxide.

Choline ion and acetylcholine ion have remarkable biological activity

Choline chloride is trimethyl-(2-hydroxyethyl)ammonium chloride, $[(CH_3)_3\overset{+}{N}CH_2CH_2OH]Cl^-$. Its quaternary ammonium ion, commonly called **choline,** is an extremely important factor in biological processes and must be supplied by the diet of the animal organism. It has been shown to be a factor which (*1*) is necessary for growth, (*2*) affects fat transport and carbohydrate metabolism, (*3*) is involved in protein metabolism, (*4*) prevents hemorrhagic kidney disintegration, and (*5*) prevents the development of fatty livers in depancreatized dogs. It also is the precursor in the animal organism of acetylcholine ion, $[(CH_3)_3\overset{+}{N}CH_2CH_2OCOCH_3]$, commonly called **acetylcholine,** which is extremely important in controlling the functions of the body. Nerve impulses arriving at a junction between nerve cells and nerve fibers liberate chemicals that permit the transfer of the impulse to the next cell or fiber. These chemicals are acetylcholine, or a mixture of epinephrine and norepinephrine, frequently called *sympathin* (p. 135). The action of acetylcholine is confined to the site where it is liberated, because the blood and neighboring tissues contain an esterase (an enzyme that catalyzes the hydrolysis of esters) that almost immediately converts acetylcholine to the practically inactive choline. If nerve impulses cannot be transmitted along nerve fibers, muscular activity cannot take place; hence some of the most toxic substances known are quaternary salts that can displace acetylcholine at the nerve endings. By preventing the action of acetylcholine, they lead to total muscular relaxion and paralysis.

Medicinally important quaternary salts

Excessive activity of the sympathetic nervous system can lead to high blood pressure and nervous irritability. It can be relieved by blocking the function of the nerve ganglia by the administration of quaternary ammonium salts. **Hexamethonium** (*hexamethylene-bis-triethylammonium bromide*), $[(C_2H_5)_3\overset{+}{N}(CH_2)_6\overset{+}{N}(C_2H_5)_3][B\bar{r}]_2$ is used for this purpose. **Succinylcholine iodide,** $[(CH_3)_3\overset{+}{N}CH_2CH_2OCOCH_2—]_2[I^-]_2$, is used instead of curare (p. 223) as an adjuvant in ether anesthesia.

Quaternary ammonium salts in which one of the alkyl groups attached to nitrogen is a long-chain hydrocarbon group, such as cetyltrimethylammonium chloride, $[C_{16}H_{33}\overset{+}{N}(CH_3)_3]Cl^-$, have properties similar to soaps and are known as *invert soaps* or *cationic detergents,* because the detergent action resides in a positive ion rather than in a negative ion as is the case with ordinary soaps. Many of these invert soaps have high germicidal action.

POLYAMINES, HYDROXYAMINES, AND AMINOPHENOLS

Diaminoalkanes can be prepared by the usual methods for preparing amines. Thus **ethylenediamine** is obtained by the reaction of ethylene chloride with ammonia.

$$ClCH_2CH_2Cl + 4\,NH_3 \longrightarrow H_2NCH_2CH_2NH_2 + 2\,NH_4Cl$$

Complexing agent from ethylenediamine

Reaction of ethylene diamine with sodium chloroacetate in the presence of base gives the sodium salt of **ethylenediaminetetraacetic acid** (*EDTA, Sequestrene, Versene*) $(NaOOCCH_2)_2NCH_2CH_2N(CH_2COONa)_2$.

It is a strong chelating (or complexing) agent for alkaline earth and heavy metal ions. Cyclic compounds in which a ring is closed by an unshared pair of electrons on one atom filling an empty orbital of another atom are known as **chelate compounds** (Gr. *chele,* claw), the ring closure being thought of as having a pincer-like action. The process involved is called **chelation.** The relative positions of four unshared pairs of electrons on the four carboxylate ions and the two pairs on the nitrogen atoms in EDTA is such that stable five-membered chelate rings can be formed with metal ions. Ferric ion, for example, which can hold six pairs of electrons in its valence shell (*coordination number six*), would be expected to use all six pairs of electrons. Usually, however, only four rings form, presumably for steric reasons, and the sixth pair of electrons is supplied by a water molecule.

Chelate compounds and chelation

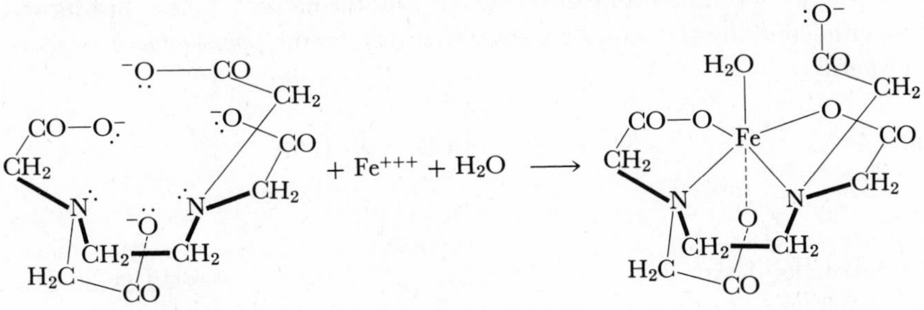

EDTA ion

Ethylenediaminetetraacetic acid and its salts have found important uses in analytical chemistry. Their chief use, however, is to bind traces of alkaline earth and heavy metal ions in a nonionic form, thus preventing undesirable catalytic effects or precipitation by other components of aqueous solutions. The complex with iron is used in agriculture to prevent chlorosis in plants, a disease caused by unavailability of iron in the soil.

Reduction of nitrobenzene with zinc and sodium hydroxide gives **hydrazobenzene** (*α,β-diphenylhydrazine*).

$$2 C_6H_5NO_2 + 5 Zn + 10 NaOH \longrightarrow C_6H_5NHNHC_6H_5 + 5 Na_2ZnO_2 + 4 H_2O$$

When hydrazobenzene is heated with hydrochloric acid, a rearrangement takes place to give **benzidine hydrochloride** (*p,p′-diaminobiphenyl hydrochloride*), an important intermediate for the synthesis of direct dyes for cotton (p. 209).

Benzidine a valuable aromatic diamine

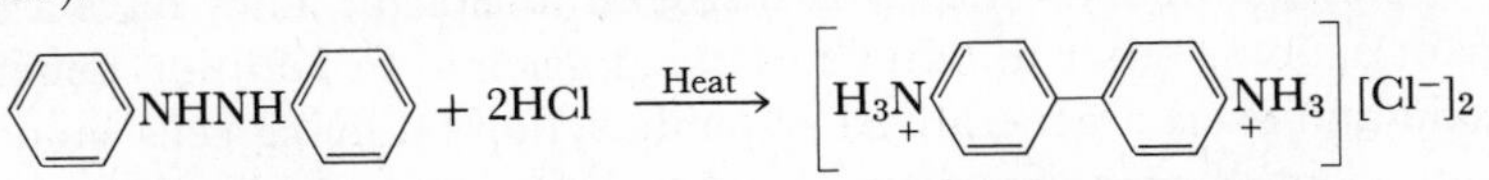

Hydrazobenzene   Benzidine hydrochloride

o-Tolidine (*p,p′-diamino-m,m′-dimethylbiphenyl*) is made similarly from *o*-hydrazotoluene.

Reaction of ethylene oxide (p. 83) with ammonia gives 2-aminoethanol, commonly called **ethanolamine.** A second molecule of ethylene oxide gives bis(2-hydroxyethyl)amine or **diethanolamine,** and a third yields tris(2-hydroxyethyl)amine or **triethanolamine.**

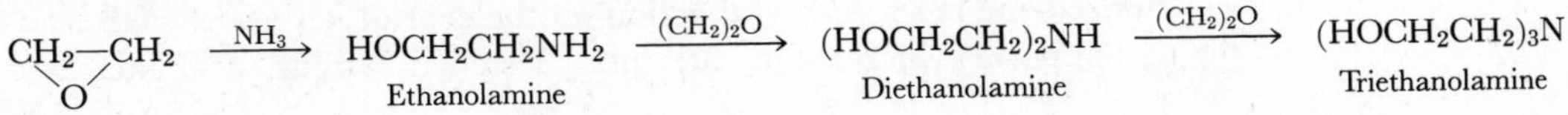

CH₂—CH₂ $\xrightarrow{NH_3}$ $HOCH_2CH_2NH_2$ $\xrightarrow{(CH_2)_2O}$ $(HOCH_2CH_2)_2NH$ $\xrightarrow{(CH_2)_2O}$ $(HOCH_2CH_2)_3N$

Ethanolamine   Diethanolamine   Triethanolamine

Ethanolamine salts as
emulsifying agents

Salts of the ethanolamines with fat acids are soluble in both water and hydrocarbons and are good emulsifying agents. Thus kerosene or paraffin oil containing a small amount of triethanolamine oleate can be mixed with water to give stable emulsions useful as agricultural sprays or as lubricating coolants for high-speed metal-cutting operations. Ethanolamine and diethanolamine are used for the recovery of acidic gases such as carbon dioxide and hydrogen sulfide. The gases are absorbed by the cold amine and are liberated by heating the solution.

Ethanolamine and its trimethylammonium salt, choline (p. 132), constitute a portion of an important class of biological substances known as the *phospholipids*. Thus the **lecithins** are mixed esters of glycerol and choline with fat acids and phosphoric acid. The **cephalins** (or kephalins) are esters of ethanolamine or serine (p. 198) instead of choline. **Sphingogomyelin** contains the unsaturated dihydroxy amine *sphingosine* instead of glycerol.

Phospholipids are
mixed esters

$$CH_2OCOR$$
$$CHOCOR'$$
$$\underset{\underset{O^-}{|}}{CH_2O}-\overset{\overset{O^-}{|}}{\underset{|+}{P}}-OCH_2CH_2\underset{+}{N}(CH_3)_3$$

Lecithins

$$CH_3(CH_2)_{12}CH{=}CHCHOH$$
$$CHNHCOR$$
$$\underset{\underset{O^-}{|}}{CH_2O}-\overset{\overset{O^-}{|}}{\underset{|+}{P}}-OCH_2CH_2\underset{+}{N}(CH_3)_3$$

Sphingomyelin

The phospholipids are components of all animal and vegetable cells and are abundant in the brain, spinal cord, eggs, and soybeans. *Soybean lecithin* is used in large quantities for the stabilization of emulsified food fats such as oleomargarine and mayonnaise.

Reaction of methyldiethanolamine hydrochloride with thionyl chloride or phosphorus trichloride gives **methylbis(2-chloroethyl)amine hydrochloride.**

$$(HOCH_2CH_2)_2NHCH_3{}^{+-}Cl + 2\ SOCl_2 \longrightarrow (ClCH_2CH_2)_2NHCH_3{}^{+-}Cl + 2\ HCl + 2\ SO_2$$

Nitrogen mustards
affect living cells
much like X-rays

The free base is a nitrogen analog of mustard gas (p. 84) and belongs to the class of compounds known as **nitrogen mustards.** They have a local vesicant action similar to that of mustard gas and in addition penetrate the skin and exert a generalized systemic action on living cells similar to the action of X-rays. Exposure to very low concentrations may cause opacity of the cornea.

Sympathomimetic
amines

The name **sympathomimetic amines** has been given to a group of hydroxylated β-phenylethylamines that mimic the action of the sympathetic nervous system. For example they dilate the pupil of the eye (*mydriatic action*), strengthen the heart beat, and increase blood pressure (*pressor activity*). Formulas for only a few of these important compounds are given.

Benzedrine has a powerful action on the central nervous system leading to temporary increase in alertness, lessened fatigue, and increased

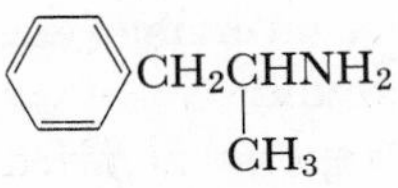

Amphetamine
(Benzedrine)

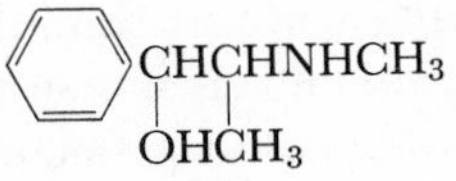

Ephedrine

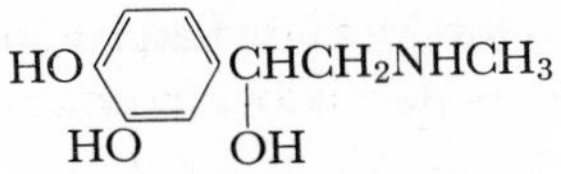

Epinephrine
(Adrenalin)

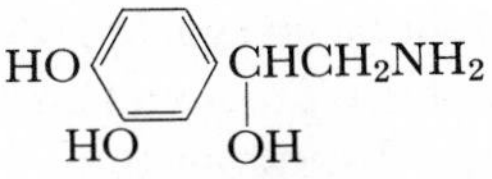

Norepinephrine
(Arterenol)

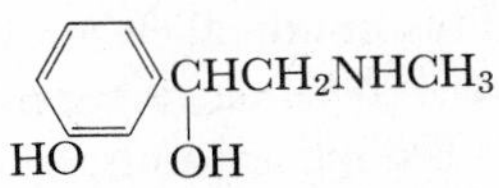

Phenylephrine
(Neo-Synephrine)

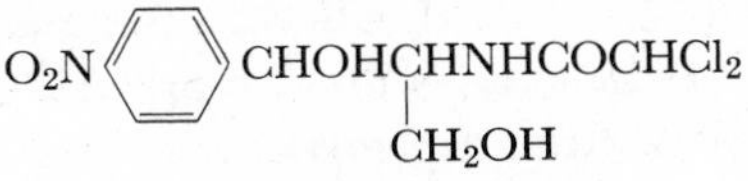

Chloramphenicol
(Chloromycetin)

irritability and sleeplessness. This action is followed by fatigue and mental depression; hence considerable danger lies in promiscuous use of the drug.

The closely related compound **ephedrine** is present in the herb *Ma Huang* (*Ephedra vulgaris*) used medicinally by Chinese physicians for thousands of years. It is administered for the treatment of bronchial asthma, and for a few years was used in nose drops for contracting the capillaries and relieving nasal congestion caused by colds. For the latter purpose it has been replaced largely by other synthetic arylethylamines such as **Neo-Synephrine.**

Epinephrine (*Adrenalin*) and **norepinephrine** (*Arterenol*) are the active principles produced by the adrenal medulla and by the postganglionic nerve endings (p. 132). Epinephrine was the first hormone to be isolated in crystalline form (Abel, 1897) and the first hormone to be synthesized (Stolz, 1904, and Dakin, 1905). Hormones (Gr. *hormaein*, to excite) are chemical substances produced by the cells of one part of an organism and transported by the fluids of the organism to another site where they exert their specific action. Although it was suspected for a long time that the sympathin liberated by nerve endings (p. 132) consisted of two substances, designated as *sympathin E* and *sympathin I,* it was not until after 1948 that it was proved that sympathin I is chiefly epinephrine and sympathin E almost pure norepinephrine, and that ordinary epinephrine from adrenal glands (U.S.P. epinephrine) contains from 12 to 18 per cent of norepinephrine. Epinephrine in very small amounts increases the blood pressure by increasing the force and the rate of the heart beat and by constricting the arteries. This pressor effect is diminished by a dilating action on the peripheral and capillary blood vessels. Norepinephrine has an action similar to epinephrine but lacks the last property; hence it has about 1.5 times the pressor activity of epinephrine. U.S.P. epinephrine is administered with local anesthetics (p. 205) to prolong their action by constricting the blood vessels locally and preventing the anesthetic from being carried away from the site of injection. Epinephrine also is a powerful bronchodilator and is used in the treatment of bronchial asthma. It is about 100 times more effective than norepinephrine for this purpose. Both epinephrine and norepinephrine contain an

Adrenal hormones

asymmetric carbon atom (p. 160), and the naturally occurring $(-)$ forms are around twenty times more active than the $(+)$ forms.

Chloromycetin (*chloramphenicol*), isolated from a species of *Streptomyces*, a soil organism, was the first antibiotic to be synthesized by a practical procedure. It is a relatively simple molecule and contains an aromatic nitro group and a dichloroacetyl group. Neither structural feature had been found previously in a natural product. Chloromycetin is especially effective against typhus and Rocky Mountain fever.

An amino ether antihistaminic

Benadryl, $(C_6H_5)_2CHOCH_2CH_2N(CH_3)_2$, the diphenylmethyl (or benzhydryl) ether of β-dimethylaminoethanol, was one of the first synthetic chemicals to be used widely in the treatment of histamine allergies. It also is one of the more effective preventives and cures for seasickness. It is synthesized from diphenylmethyl bromide and β-dimethylaminoethanol.

$$(C_6H_5)_2CHBr + HOCH_2CH_2N(CH_3)_2 \xrightarrow[140°]{K_2CO_3}$$

$$(C_6H_5)_2CHOCH_2CH_2N(CH_3)_2 + KBr + KHCO_3$$

Amino phenols are photographic developers

Of the aminophenols, **p-aminophenol** (P.A.P.) is the most important because of its use as a photographic developer. It is made by the nitrosation of phenol followed by reduction.

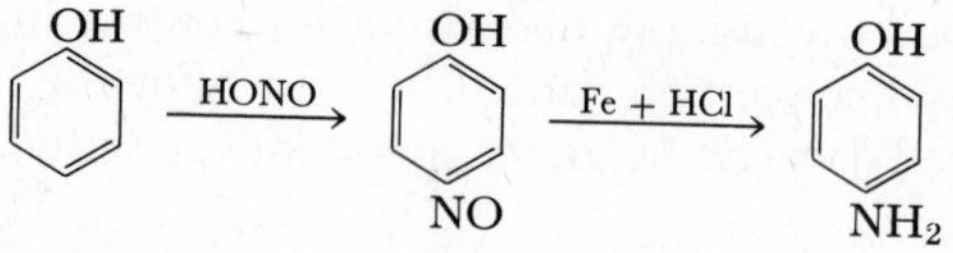

p-Hydroxyphenylglycine (photographer's *Glycine*) is made by the condensation of p-aminophenol with sodium chloroacetate.

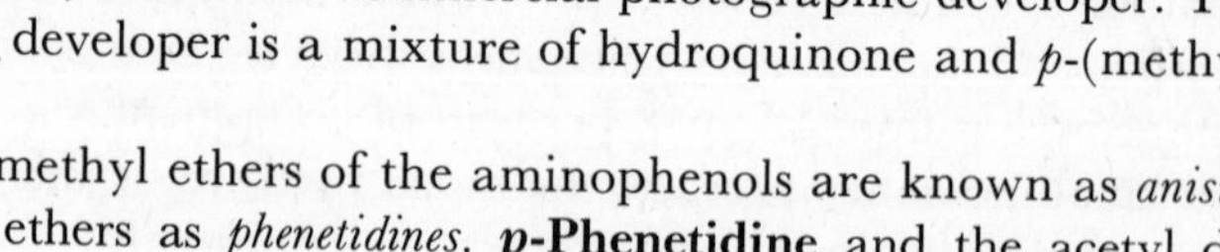

When p-hydroxyphenylglycine is heated in a mixture of cresols, decarboxylation takes place to give **p-(methylamino)phenol.** The sulfate, known as *Metol* or *Elon,* is another commercial photographic developer. The widely used MQ developer is a mixture of hydroquinone and p-(methylamino)-phenol.

Some analgesics

The methyl ethers of the aminophenols are known as *anisidines* and the ethyl ethers as *phenetidines.* **p-Phenetidine** and the acetyl derivative, known as **acetophenetidine** or **phenacetine,** have antipyretic and analgesic action. Although less toxic than acetanilide (p. 138), they also reduce the oxygen-combining power of the blood.

AMIDES

Amides and imides are acyl derivatives of ammonia

The monoacyl derivatives of ammonia, primary amines, and secondary amines, having the general formula $RCONH_2$, $RCONHR$, or $RCONR_2$, are known as *amides.* Diacyl derivatives of ammonia, $(RCO)_2NH$, and of primary amines, $(RCO)_2NR$, also are possible and are called *imides*. Except for cyclic imides (pp. 141, 116) their preparation usually is more difficult, because the first acyl group greatly reduces the basicity of the nitrogen. The preparation of triacylamines is still more difficult.

Amides result when salts of carboxylic acids with ammonia or amines are decomposed by heat. *Preparation*

$$RCOONH_4 \xrightarrow{\text{Heat}} RCONH_2 + H_2O$$

$$RCOONH_3R \xrightarrow{\text{Heat}} RCONHR + H_2O$$

$$RCOONH_2R_2 \xrightarrow{\text{Heat}} RCONR_2 + H_2O$$

Water is removed at the temperature of decomposition, forcing the reaction to completion.

The simple amides are named by replacing *ic acid* or *oic acid* in the *Nomenclature* name of the acid by *amide*. Thus $HCONH_2$ is formamide or methanamide, and $(CH_3)_2CHCONH_2$ is *i*-butyramide or methylpropanamide. Amides derived from amines are named as nitrogen substitution products; for example $CH_3CONHCH_3$ is *N*-methylacetamide, or *N*-methylethanamide.

Most amides containing the $CONH_2$ group are solids. Formamide *Physical properties* melts at 2°. Amides that have hydrogen on nitrogen are associated by proton bonding and have high boiling points. Because they also form proton bonds with hydroxylic solvents and other oxygenated molecules, amides of monocarboxylic acids containing five carbon atoms or less are soluble in water. The liquid amides are excellent solvents for other organic compounds.

In contrast to ammonia and the amines, the amides do not form salts *Amides are* that are stable in aqueous solution; that is, the replacement of a hydrogen *neutral compounds* atom of the ammonia molecule by an acyl group gives a compound that is a weaker base than water. This effect is in harmony with the effect of replacement of a hydrogen atom of a water molecule by an acyl group. The carbonyl group exerts an electron-attracting effect which increases the ease of ionization of the remaining proton of carboxylic acids. In amides it decreases the ability of the nitrogen atom to share its unshared pair. If two hydrogen atoms of ammonia are replaced by acyl groups, the attraction for electrons is sufficient to permit the remaining hydrogen to be removed as a proton by strong bases in aqueous solution. In other words the imides are weak acids. *Imides are weak acids*

$$(RCO)_2NH + NaOH \longrightarrow (RCO)_2N^{-+}Na + H_2O$$

The hydrolysis of amides produces the acid and the amine. Like the *Hydrolysis of amides* hydrolysis of esters, the reaction is catalyzed by both acids and bases. *by acids or bases* However, with esters only the basic catalyst reacts with one of the products, *is irreversible* whereas in the hydrolysis of the amides both the acidic and basic catalyst react with one of the products, thus causing both reactions to go to completion.

$$RCONH_2 + NaOH \longrightarrow RCOONa + NH_3$$
$$RCONH_2 + HCl + H_2O \longrightarrow RCOOH + NH_4Cl$$

Most of the simple aliphatic amides are of little commercial importance. **N, N-Dimethylformamide** and **N, N-dimethylacetamide** are used as

Hydrolysis of thioacetamide gives hydrogen sulfide

solvents for spinning acrylic fibers (p. 235). **Thioacetamide** is being used instead of gaseous hydrogen sulfide in qualitative and quantitative inorganic analysis. It is reasonably stable in neutral aqueous solution, but in the presence of acids or bases, especially on warming, it hydrolyzes to give hydrogen sulfide or sulfide ion.

$$CH_3CSNH_2 + H_2O + HCl \longrightarrow H_2S + CH_3COOH + NH_4Cl$$
$$CH_3CSNH_2 + 3\ NaOH \longrightarrow Na_2S + CH_3COONa + NH_3 + H_2O$$

Thioacetamide is prepared by the reaction of acetamide with phosphorus pentasulfide.

$$CH_3CONH_2 + P_2S_5 \longrightarrow CH_3CSNH_2 + P_2OS_4$$

Acetanilide is N-phenylacetamide

When aniline acetate is heated, **acetanilide** is formed. It was introduced as an antipyretic in 1886 under the name *antifebrine,* and at one time it was used widely for this purpose and as an analgesic. It is highly toxic, however, being similar to aniline in its action, and it has been displaced largely by the relatively safer salicylates (p. 171), especially aspirin which was introduced in 1899. Because acetanilide is cheap, it still is used in some proprietary headache and pain-killing remedies.

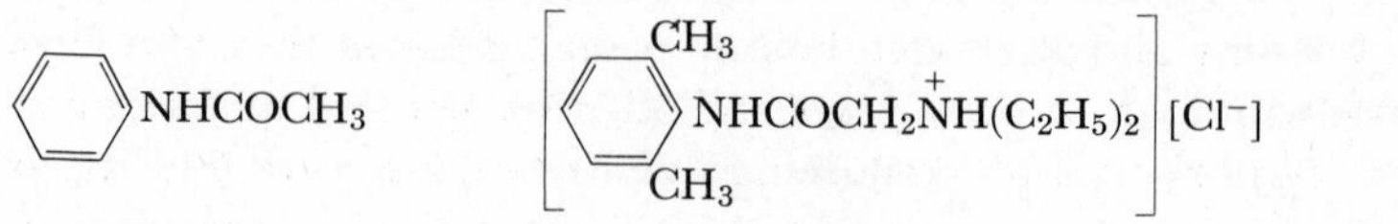

Acetanilide

Xylocaine

A small amount is used as a dye intermediate but most goes into the manufacture of sulfa drugs (p. 143).

Xylocaine, a new type of local anesthetic (p. 205), is the hydrochloride of α-diethylamino-2,6-dimethylacetanilide.

The **amide** of **nicotinic acid** (*pyridine-β-carboxylic acid*) is required in the diet for the production of coenzymes I and II, which are involved in oxidation-reduction reactions in biological systems. The **hydrazide** of **isonicotinic acid** (*isoniazide*) is one of the more effective tuberculostatic drugs.

Nicotinamide
(Niacinamide)

Isonicotinic acid
hydrazide (Isoniazide)

Urea is the diamide of carbonic acid

The most important amide is **urea,** which is the amide of the hypothetical carbamic acid or the diamide of the hypothetical carbonic acid.

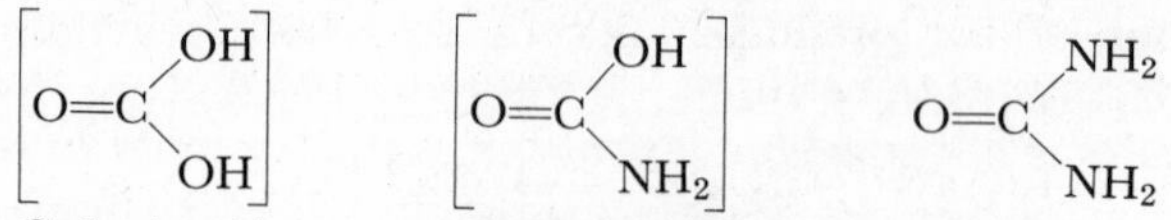

Carbonic acid

Carbamic acid

Urea

It is the chief final product of nitrogen metabolism in mammals, being eliminated in the urine. Adult man excretes about 30 g. of urea in 24 hours.

Urea was one of the first compounds of biological origin to be synthesized in the laboratory. Woehler obtained it by boiling a solution of ammonium cyanate in 1828, the same year in which Hennel prepared ethyl alcohol by the hydrolysis of potassium ethyl sulfate made from ethylene (p. 66).

Synthesis from ammonium cyanate

$$NH_4OCN \rightleftharpoons O=C(NH_2)_2$$

The present commercial synthesis is from dry carbon dioxide and ammonia. Ammonia adds to one of the double bonds of carbon dioxide to yield carbamic acid, which reacts with a second molecule of ammonia to form ammonium carbamate. The general method of preparing an amide by heating an ammonium salt converts the ammonium carbamate into urea.

Synthesis from carbon dioxide and ammonia

$$CO_2 + NH_3 \rightleftharpoons \left[\begin{array}{c} OH \\ | \\ O=C-NH_2 \end{array} \right] \xrightarrow{NH_3} \left[\begin{array}{c} O^- \\ | \\ O=C-NH_2 \end{array} \right] NH_4^+ \xrightarrow{150°}$$

Carbamic acid   Ammonium carbamate

$$O=\overset{\overset{\displaystyle NH_2}{|}}{C}-NH_2 + H_2O$$

Urea

Urea is used as a fertilizer and for the manufacture of urea-formaldehyde plastics (p. 240). A part of the nitrogen required by ruminants for the synthesis of proteins can be supplied by urea, and it is being added to commercial cattle feeds. A small amount is used in the manufacture of pharmaceuticals (p. 141).

Urea has the useful property of forming crystalline **inclusion compounds** with many straight-chain organic compounds having more than four carbon atoms, for example hydrocarbons, alcohols, mercaptans, alkyl halides, ketones, acids, and esters, but not with most branched chain or cyclic compounds. The procedure for preparing these inclusion compounds merely involves mixing saturated methanol solutions of urea and of the compound. A crystalline precipitate forms from which the components can be separated either by extracting the urea with water or the organic compound with ether. The process can be used to improve the octane number of gasoline, to lower the freezing point of fuel for jet planes, and to lower the pour point of lubricating oil by removing the normal hydrocarbons. Thiourea forms inclusion compounds with many branched and cyclic compounds.

Urea forms inclusion compounds

There is no evidence that the straight chain compounds are bound to the urea molecules by other than adsorption forces at the solid surface. The chains merely occupy channels in the urea crystal lattice. The melting point of each compound is that of urea, and the heat of formation is even less than the usual heats of adsorption on solid surfaces. Although each compound has a definite composition, the ratio of urea molecules to straight-chain molecules is not stoichiometrical but is proportional to the number of carbon atoms in the chain. Approximately two-thirds mole of urea is combined for each Ångstrom of chain length. It is of interest that unsaturated compounds included in urea crystals are not subject to autoxidation.

When urea is heated above its melting point it decomposes into ammonia and isocyanic acid.

$$H_2NCONH_2 \longrightarrow NH_3 + HN{=}C{=}O$$
Isocyanic acid

Alcohols and isocyanic acid give the **alkyl carbamates** (*urethans*).

$$HN{=}C{=}O + HOR \longrightarrow H_2NCOOR$$

The simple urethans, such as ethyl carbamate, have mild hypnotic properties. The dicarbamate derived from 2-methyl-2-*n*-propyl-1,3-propanediol is known as **meprobamate** (*Equanil* or *Miltown*) and is one of the more widely used tranquilizing (ataraxic) drugs.

Miltown a carbamate

If urea is heated gently, the isocyanic acid first produced adds a molecule of urea to form **biuret.**

$$HN{=}C{=}O + H_2NCONH_2 \longrightarrow H_2NCONHCONH_2$$
Biuret

Copper complex of biuret

An alkaline solution of biuret gives a violet-pink color when copper sulfate solution is added. The color is due to a chelated (p. 133) coordination complex with cupric ion in which the four water molecules normally coordinated with the cupric ion are displaced by the amino groups. The alkali removes two protons from the coordinated amino groups to give the neutral insoluble complex, and then two more protons to give the water-soluble salt.

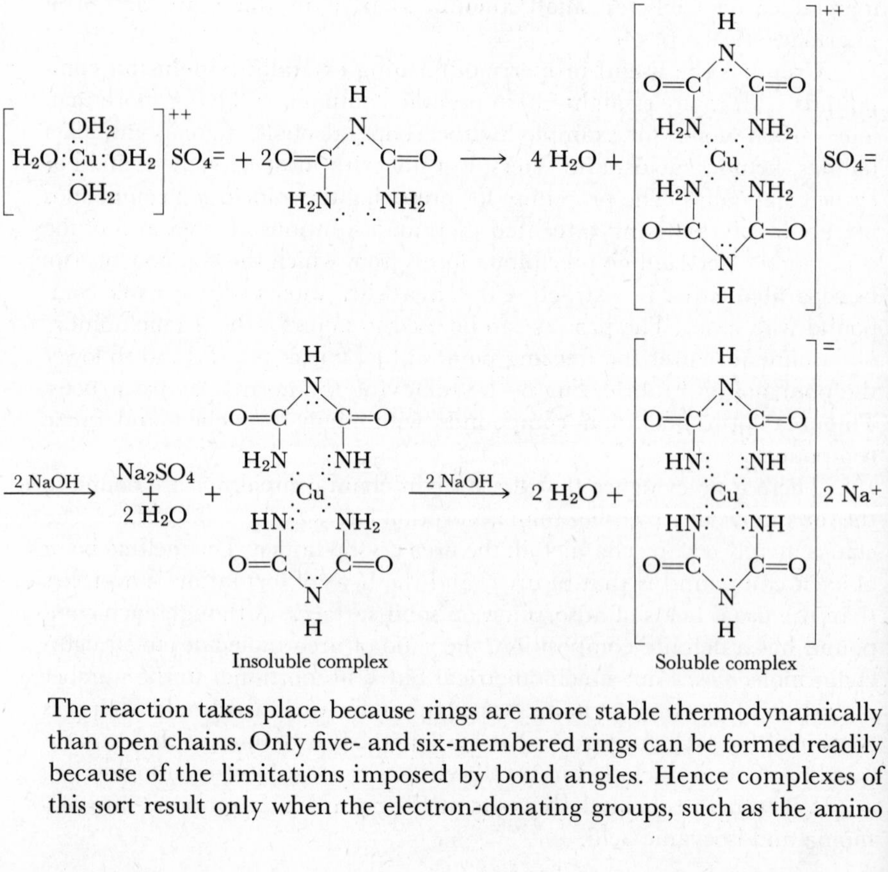

Insoluble complex   Soluble complex

The reaction takes place because rings are more stable thermodynamically than open chains. Only five- and six-membered rings can be formed readily because of the limitations imposed by bond angles. Hence complexes of this sort result only when the electron-donating groups, such as the amino groups, are spaced properly in the molecule. The peptide linkage in proteins can lead to a stable complex with copper in which two five-membered rings are formed, and proteins and peptides give the biuret test (p. 204). Analogous complexes are formed with 1,2- and 1,3-dihydroxy compounds in which the hydroxyl groups are electron-donors. Examples are Fehling and Benedict solutions (p. 170).

The **barbiturates** are cyclic diimides prepared by condensing urea or thiourea with disubstituted malonic esters. They are sufficiently acidic to form stable sodium salts.

$$\begin{array}{c} R \\ R' \end{array} C \begin{array}{c} COOC_2H_5 \\ COOC_2H_5 \end{array} + \begin{array}{c} H_2N \\ H_2N \end{array} CO \xrightarrow{NaOC_2H_5} \begin{array}{c} R \\ R' \end{array} C \begin{array}{c} CO-N\overset{+}{N}\overset{-}{a} \\ CO-NH \end{array} CO + 3\ C_2H_5OH$$

Although these compounds as a class are called barbiturates by the medical profession, the free compounds as well as their sodium salts are used medicinally. The ending commonly used for the free compound is *al,* and *sodium* is added as a separate word to indicate the sodium salt, for example, *barbital* and *barbital sodium.*

The barbiturates have a depressant action on the central nervous system and are valuable sedatives and soporifics. **Barbital** (R and R′ = C_2H_5) was synthesized first in 1882. In 1903 von Mering discovered its sedative properties and called it *Veronal,* because he considered Verona to be the most restful city in the world. Barbital is its nonproprietary name. **Phenobarbital** (R = ethyl, R′ = phenyl) was introduced several years later under the trade name *Luminal.* It has a specific action in preventing epileptic seizures. **Amytal** (R = ethyl, R′ = isoamyl), and **pentobarbital** **(Nembutal)** (R = ethyl, R′ = 1-methylbutyl) act more quickly but have a shorter duration of action than either barbital or phenobarbital. **Seconal** (R = allyl, R′ = 1-methylbutyl) acts still more quickly and for a relatively short period.

Barbiturates used in medicine

Unfortunately the indiscriminate distribution and use of barbiturates and the danger of overdosage make them a hazard to a large portion of the population. A total of 852,000 pounds of barbiturates having a value of $4,500,000 was produced in the United States in 1960. This amount is equivalent to ten 0.2-gram doses per capita.

Pentothal Sodium is a thiobarbiturate that is used for general anesthesia by intravenous injection. The use of barbiturates for general anesthesia requires careful technique, because the anesthetic dose is 50 to 70

$$\begin{array}{c} C_2H_5 \\ CH_3CH_2CH_2\underset{\underset{CH_3}{|}}{CH} \end{array} C \begin{array}{c} CO-N^-Na^+ \\ CO-NH \end{array} CS$$

Pentothal Sodium (*sodium thiopental*)

per cent of the lethal dose. However, their ease of administration and rapid action, and the rapid recovery of the patient, led to their use for major surgical operations in the front battle lines during World War II, and the experience gained has been carried over to civilian practice.

The **aryl isocyanates** are of considerable importance. They are made by the thermal decomposition of aryl carbamyl chlorides, which are prepared from phosgene and the aromatic amine.

$$2\ C_6H_5NH_2 + COCl_2 \longrightarrow C_6H_5NH_3Cl + \underset{\substack{\text{Phenylcarbamyl}\\\text{chloride}}}{C_6H_5NHCOCl} \xrightarrow{\text{Heat}} \underset{\substack{\text{Phenyl}\\\text{isocyanate}}}{C_6H_5N{=}C{=}O} + HCl$$

Isocyanates add water, alcohols, and amines

Like isocyanic acid, the isocyanates readily hydrolyze with water. The final products are the primary amine and carbon dioxide.

$$RN{=}C{=}O + H_2O \longrightarrow [RNHCOOH] \longrightarrow RNH_2 + CO_2$$

Addition of alcohols gives *urethans;* addition of amines gives substituted ureas.

$$RN{=}C{=}O + HOR' \longrightarrow RNHCOOR'$$
$$+ HNHR' \longrightarrow RNHCONHR'$$
$$+ HNR'_2 \longrightarrow RNHCONR'_2$$

Intermediates for urethan polymers

Diisocyanates such as **2,4-tolylene diisocyanate** and **1,5-naphthylene diisocyanate** (so-called *toluene diisocyanate* and *naphthalene diisocyanate*) are made from the corresponding diamines. They are essential intermediates for the production of the urethan rubbers and rigid foams (p. 238).

Calcium cyanamide from coke, lime, and nitrogen

Cyanamide, $H_2NC{\equiv}N$, may be considered as the amide of hydrocyanic acid. Its most important derivative is the calcium salt, **calcium cyanamide,** which is made by passing nitrogen through calcium carbide containing 10 per cent of calcium oxide at about 1100°.

$$CaC_2 + N_2 \xrightarrow{\text{CaO}} CaNCN + C$$

The mixture is brought to reaction temperature by an electrically heated carbon rod, but after the exothermic reaction has been started, the carbon rod may be removed. The cyanamide process was the first important method for the fixation of atmospheric nitrogen, and calcium cyanamide has continued to be an important nitrogen fertilizer. It is used also as a soil fumigant and as a defoliant.

Cyanamide is stable in aqueous solutions of pH $<$ 5 but dimerizes readily to **dicyandiamide** at pH 7–12. Hence dicyandiamide is the product formed when calcium cyanamide is heated with water.

$$CaNCN + 2\ H_2O \longrightarrow Ca(OH)_2 + H_2NCN$$

$$H_2NC{\equiv}N + H_2NC{\equiv}N \longrightarrow \underset{\substack{\\ \overset{\|}{N}H}}{H_2NCNHC{\equiv}N}$$

Dicyandiamide

A source of melamine for melamine resins

When dicyandiamide is heated in the presence of anhydrous ammonia and methyl alcohol, **melamine,** the cyclic trimer of cyanamide, is formed

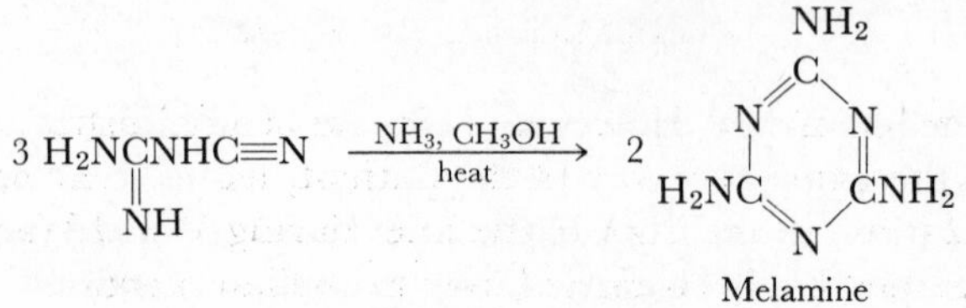

$$3\ \underset{\substack{\\ \overset{\|}{N}H}}{H_2NCNHC{\equiv}N} \xrightarrow[\text{heat}]{NH_3,\ CH_3OH} 2\ \text{Melamine}$$

Melamine

Condensation of melamine with formaldehyde gives the melamine resins (p. 240).

SULFONAMIDES

Amides of sulfonic acids are important only in the aromatic series. *Sulfonamides from* They ordinarily are made by the reaction of amines with sulfonyl chlorides *sulfonyl chlorides* (p. 115) in the presence of a strong base.

$$C_6H_5SO_2Cl + NH_3 + NaOH \longrightarrow C_6H_5SO_2NH_2 + H_2O + NaCl$$

| Benzenesulfonyl chloride | | Benzene-sulfonamide |

The sulfonyl group is a much stronger electron-attracting group than the carbonyl group. The result is that the strength of sulfonic acids is greater than that of carboxylic acids and is comparable to that of mineral acids (p. 115). Likewise, although carboxylic acid amides are neutral, sulfonamides of ammonia and of primary amines are weakly acidic and dissolve in dilute sodium hydroxide.

$$C_6H_5SO_2NH_2 + NaOH \longrightarrow C_6H_5SO_2NH^-Na^+ + H_2O$$

The **sulfa drugs,** which are effective in combating streptococcal infec- *Sulfa drugs* tions, are sulfonamides. *Sulfanilamide* is synthesized from acetanilide by a *are sulfonamides* series of reactions.

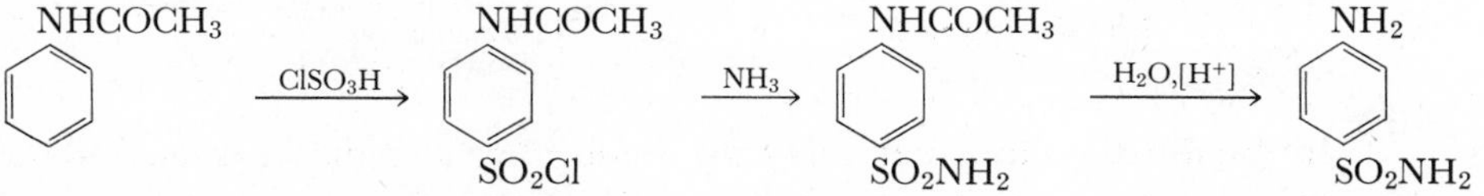

Acetanilide

Sulfanil-amide

Most of the derivatives of sulfanilamide that have proved to be its superior differ from it in structure only in that one of the hydrogen atoms of the sulfonamide group is replaced by a more complex organic group. These derivatives are made by substituting another amine for ammonia in the step in which the sulfonamide is formed. One exception is *marfanil,* in which the nuclear amino group is separated from the benzene ring by a methylene group. It is more effective than the sulfanilamides against anaerobic bacteria, such as the anthrax bacillus, and is used for dusting into open wounds.

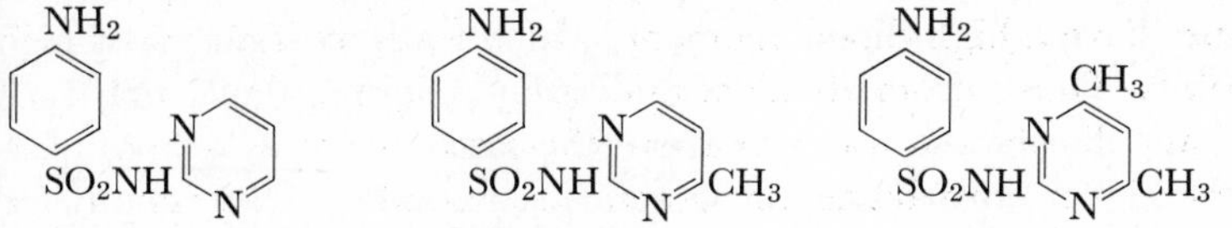

Sulfadiazine

Sulfamerazine

Sulfamethazine

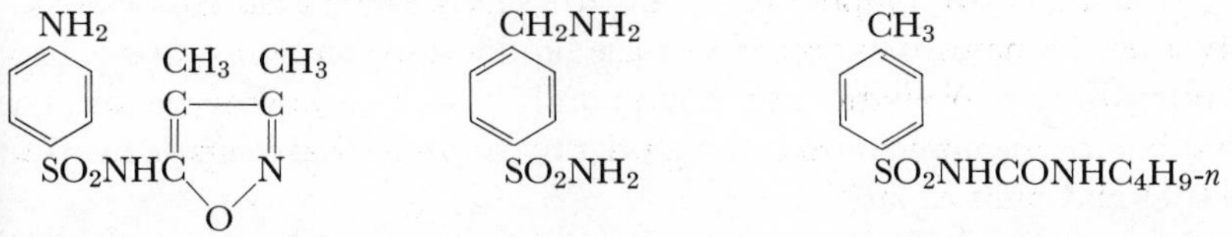

Sulfisoxazole

Marfanil

N-(p-Tolylsulfonyl)-N'-(n-butyl)urea (Orinase)

The disadvantage of the sulfanilamides has been their low solubility in water, which has led to deposition in the kidneys and renal damage. This difficulty has been alleviated by administering a mixture of three different compounds. The combined dose is as effective as an equal amount of any one drug, but the concentration of each is only one third. *Sulfisoxazole* has the advantage that it has a relatively high solubility in urine. Clinical tests reported in 1955 indicated that *p*-aminobenzenesulfonyl and *p*-tolylsulfonyl derivatives of *n*-butylurea are effective orally in lowering the blood sugar in mild cases of diabetes, although some cause serious undesirable side effects.

NITRO COMPOUNDS

Nitro compounds are characterized by the presence of the nitro (NO_2) group, which is linked to a carbon atom through nitrogen. In order to maintain octets of electrons about the nitrogen atom and both oxygen atoms, two of the electrons from the nitrogen are paired with two from one of the oxygen atoms to form a double bond. The result is a nitroso compound (I).

Structure of nitro group

$$R \cdot \overset{\times}{\underset{\cdot\,\times}{N}} \overset{\times}{\underset{\times}{O}} \overset{\times}{\underset{\times}{}}$$

Nitroso compound
I

$$R \cdot \overset{\times\,O\,\times}{\underset{\times O \times}{N^+}} \quad \text{or} \quad R-N \overset{O}{\underset{O}{}} \quad \text{or} \quad R-N^+ \overset{O}{\underset{O^-}{}}$$

Nitro compound
II

In the nitroso compound, all of the atoms have a complete octet, and the only way the nitrogen can combine with another oxygen atom is to supply both electrons of its unshared pair to fill the empty orbital of the oxygen atom as in II. In doing so, the nitrogen has in effect lost an electron, that is, half of the shared pair, while the oxygen has in effect gained an electron. Thus although the bond is a shared pair of electrons, a difference in charge of approximately one electron exists between the two atoms. A bond of this

Semipolar bonds

type is called a **semipolar** or **dative bond** or a **coordinate covalence**. It is represented either by an arrow indicating which atom has supplied the pair of electrons or by a single bond with a plus charge at the donor and a minus charge at the acceptor end.

High dipole moment causes high boiling point

Because of the presence of the semipolar bond in the nitro group, the nitroalkanes have a high dipole moment, which leads to abnormally high boiling points. Thus nitromethane of molecular weight 61 boils at 101.5°. Nitromethane dissolves in water to about the same extent as *n*-butyl alcohol, but the higher nitroalkanes are practically insoluble. They usually are good solvents for other organic compounds.

Aromatic nitro compounds usually are solids, either colorless or yellow. Only a few mononitro hydrocarbons are liquids at room temperature. Like the nitroalkanes, aromatic nitro compounds have high boiling points. The lowest boiling aromatic nitro compound, nitrobenzene, has a dipole moment of 4.0 D and boils at 209°.

Solvents for inorganic salts

Aromatic nitro hydrocarbons are practically insoluble in water. The liquids are good solvents for most organic compounds and fair solvents for many inorganic salts, especially those such as zinc chloride or aluminum chloride that can accept an unshared pair of electrons and form a complex.

$$C_6H_5\overset{+}{N}\overset{\bar{O}}{\diagdown_O} + AlCl_3 \longrightarrow C_6H_5\overset{+}{N}\overset{O:\bar{A}lCl_3}{\diagdown_O}$$

Nitrobenzene strongly absorbs ultraviolet light just beyond the visible. Electronic disturbances, produced by other groups in the molecule or by the approach of other molecules, may shift the absorption band to longer wavelengths, causing the compounds or their solutions to be yellow, orange, or red.

Light absorption and color

Nitro compounds having a sufficiently high vapor pressure have strong characteristic odors. The aromatic nitro compounds are highly toxic substances. Even those compounds with low vapor pressures are dangerous because they are absorbed readily through the skin, particularly from solutions. Symptoms of poisoning are dizziness, headache, irregular pulse, and cyanosis (blue lips and finger tips caused by a change in the hemoglobin of the blood). Prolonged contact or exposure leads to death.

Toxicity

Prior to 1940 the nitroalkanes were largely of theoretical interest. With the advent of the commercial development of vapor phase nitration of propane, however, the lower nitroalkanes were made available and their numerous reactions became of considerable importance.

Nitroalkanes by vapor phase nitration

$$RH + HONO_2 \xrightarrow{420°} RNO_2 + H_2O$$

In the nitration of propane not only 1- and 2-nitropropane are obtained, but nitroethane and nitromethane also are formed by the scission of carbon-carbon bonds. These products are separated by distillation and are available commercially.

The nitro group has a strong attraction for electrons and decreases the electron-density about an atom to which it is attached. Hence hydrogen is removed more readily from a carbon atom attached to a nitro group than from an ordinary alkyl group. In fact the aliphatic nitro compounds that have an α hydrogen atom are stronger acids than water and form water-soluble salts with strong bases in aqueous solution.

Primary and secondary are weak acids

$$RCH_2NO_2 + NaOH \longrightarrow [R\bar{C}HNO_2] Na^+ + H_2O$$

2-Nitropropane, although practically insoluble in water, maintains the acidity of water at pH 4.3. Tertiary aliphatic nitro compounds, R_3CNO_2, and aromatic nitro compounds, in which no hydrogen is united to the carbon atom bearing the nitro group, do not form salts.

Aromatic nitro compounds long have been technically important. They have been used as intermediates for the manufacture of dyes since the discovery of mauve in 1856 by the English chemist, Perkin (1838–1907). Other technical developments have led to their use as explosives and as intermediates for the manufacture of pharmaceuticals and many other aromatic compounds of commercial importance.

The factor contributing most to the widespread use of aromatic nitro compounds is the ease of preparation by direct nitration of aromatic com-

Aromatic nitro compounds by liquid phase nitration

pounds. When benzene is warmed with fuming nitric acid or with a mixture of concentrated nitric acid and sulfuric acid, the chief product is nitrobenzene.

Nitrobenzene

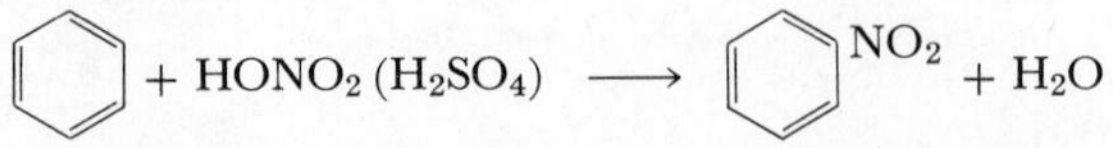

The presence of a nitro group in a benzene ring decreases the rate of substitution of a second hydrogen atom; consequently more concentrated acids and higher temperatures are needed to obtain appreciable quantities of the dinitrated product. When substitution of a second hydrogen takes place, the nitro group enters chiefly at the *meta* position.

m-Dinitrobenzene

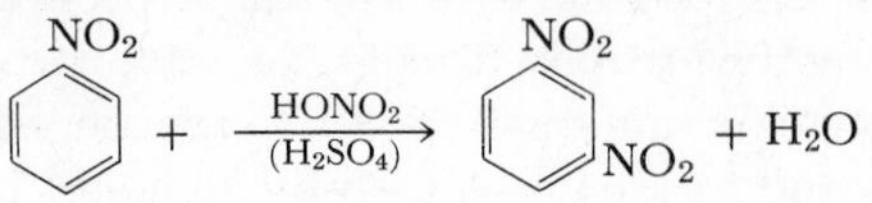

It is very difficult to introduce a third nitro group into benzene by direct nitration.

Toluene nitrates more readily than benzene. The principal products are first a mixture of *o*- and *p*-nitrotoluene, then 2,4-dinitrotoluene, and finally 2,4,6-trinitrotoluene (TNT).

2,4-Dinitrotoluene 2,4,6-Trinitrotoluene

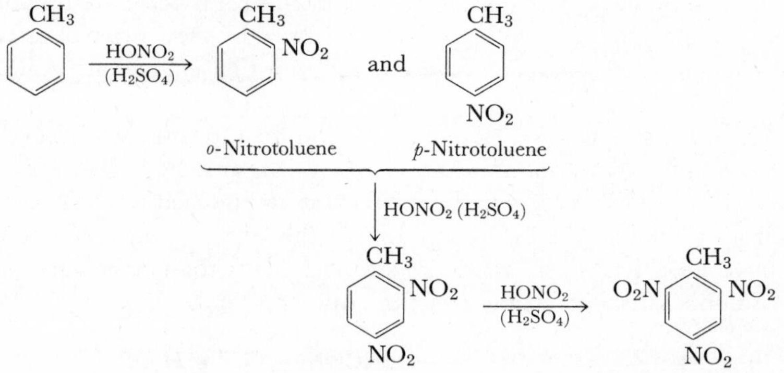

Chloro- and bromobenzene nitrate somewhat less readily than benzene and give chiefly a mixture of the *ortho* and *para* isomers.

o-Nitrochlorobenzene *p*-Nitrochlorobenzene

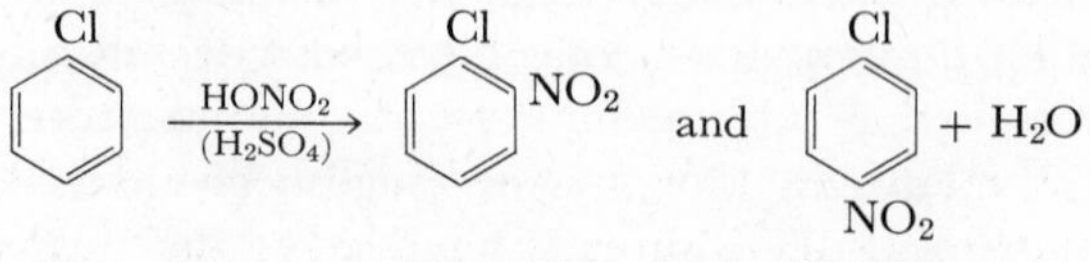

On the other hand, chlorination or bromination of nitrobenzene gives chiefly the *meta* isomer.

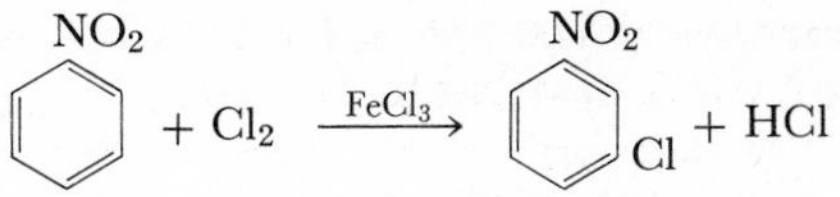

NO₂ benzene ring + Cl₂ —FeCl₃→ NO₂ benzene ring with Cl + HCl

m-Nitrochloro-
benzene

Because iron reduces nitro groups (p. 128), anhydrous ferric halides are the preferred catalysts for the halogenation of nitro compounds.

Two striking facts are evident from the substitution reactions discussed so far: (*1*) in some reactions a substituting group enters chiefly the positions that are *ortho* and *para* to the group already present in the ring as in the halogenation or nitration of toluene and chlorobenzene, and in other reactions it enters chiefly the *meta* position as in the halogenation or nitration of nitrobenzene; (*2*) the substituent already present, for example a methyl group, may make a second hydrogen more readily substituted than a hydrogen atom of benzene, or a substituent such as a halogen atom or a nitro group may make it more difficult to replace a hydrogen atom. *Rules for aromatic substitution*

Many investigations of the products formed in substitution reactions between a variety of reagents and a large number of aromatic compounds have led to the following generalizations:

(*1*) A number of groups, such as halogen (X), nitro (NO₂), sulfonic acid (SO₃H), alkyl (R), and acyl (RCO or ArCO), may be introduced directly into the benzene nucleus, hydrogen being displaced.

(*2*) When a second substituent is introduced into a benzene nucleus, the relative amounts of the *ortho, meta*, and *para* isomers should be 40, 40, and 20 per cent respectively on a statistical basis. Usually this ratio is not obtained. The relative amounts of the isomers depends primarily on the nature of the group already present in the ring, although the nature of the entering group and the conditions of the reaction, such as temperature and concentrations, have some influence.

(*3*) Groups vary greatly in their directing power, from the $[\overset{+}{N}R_3]$ group, which causes substitution almost exclusively in the *meta* position, to the [O⁻] group, which causes substitution almost exclusively in the *ortho* and *para* positions. Other groups fall between these extremes in directing power (Table 9, p. 148). Groups causing the production of more than 60 per cent of the *ortho* and *para* isomers combined are called *ortho,para-directing groups*, and those causing the production of more than 40 per cent of the *meta* isomer are called *meta-directing groups*. *Directing power of groups*

(*4*) *ortho,para*-Directing groups, *with the exception of halogen*, increase the ease with which a second hydrogen can be displaced. Such groups are said to *activate* the ring. *meta*-Directing groups *and halogen* decrease the ease with which a second hydrogen can be displaced; that is, they are *deactivating* groups. *Ease of substitution*

Activation and deactivation are reflections of the rates of substitution compared with benzene. The effect of a group on the relative amounts of the three isomers formed reflects the relative rates of substitution at the unsubstituted positions. When the group already present is activating and *ortho,para*-directing, it increases the rate of substitution over that of benzene, and at the *ortho* and *para* positions more than at the *meta* positions. When

TABLE 9. RELATIVE AMOUNTS OF *meta, ortho,* AND *para* ISOMERS FORMED IN THE NITRATION OF MONOSUBSTITUTED BENZENES

GROUP PRESENT IN RING	ISOMERS FORMED ON NITRATION (PER CENT)			
	meta	*ortho*	*para*	*o + p*
OH*	0	73	27	100
I	trace	34	66	100
Br	trace	42	58	100
Cl	trace	30	70	100
F	trace	12	88	100
$NHCOCH_3$	2	19	79	98
CH_3	4	59	37	96
$CH_2COOC_2H_5$	11	42	47	89
$CH_2CH_2NO_2$	13	35	52	87
CH_2Cl	16	32	52	84
$CHCl_2$	34	23	43	66
$[NH_3{}^+]$	47	1	52	53
CH_2NO_2	48			52
$COCH_3$	55	45	0	45
CCl_3	64	7	29	36
$CONH_2$	70	27	3	30
$COOC_2H_5$	72	24	4	28
SO_3H	72	21	7	28
CHO	72	19	9	28
COOH	80	19	1	20
CN	81	17	2	19
NO_2	93	7	trace	7
SO_2CH_3	99	trace	trace	1
$[N(CH_3)_3{}^+]$	100	0	0	0

*In the absence of nitrous acid.

a group is deactivating and *meta*-directing, it decreases the rate of substitution compared with that for benzene, but decreases the rate less at the *meta* positions than at the *ortho* and *para* positions. Halogen, which is deactivating and *ortho, para*-directing, decreases the rate of substitution over that for benzene, but decreases the rate less at the *ortho* and *para* positions than at the *meta* positions.

Order of directive influence

From Table 9 an approximate order of directive influence of different groups can be obtained. *These results hold quantitatively only for nitration and for the particular conditions of the experiment.*

Nitrobenzene and many other nitro compounds are of importance chiefly because the nitro group can be reduced to the amino group (p. 128).

TNT, an explosive

2,4,6-Trinitrotoluene, commonly known as TNT, is an important military explosive. It is used for filling bombs, shells, and hand grenades either alone or with other explosives. Since it melts at 81° and does not explode until 280°, it can be poured into shells in a liquid state and allowed to solidify. It is relatively insensitive to shock and must be exploded by a detonator. Production in the United States during World War II probably reached a rate of one million tons per year. The first H-bomb exploded is believed to have had a force equivalent to the explosion of around 14 million tons of TNT.

Some of the di- and trinitroalkylbenzenes have a musk-like odor and *Nitro compounds* are used in perfumery. Methoxyl or acetyl groups also may be present. These *in perfumery* compounds are known as **synthetic musks** or **nitro musks,** although they are not related chemically to the true musks, which are cyclic ketones.

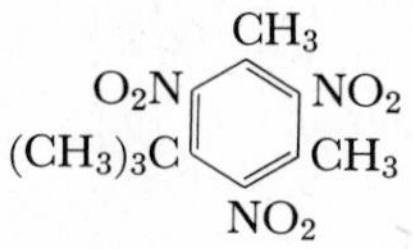

Musk xylene

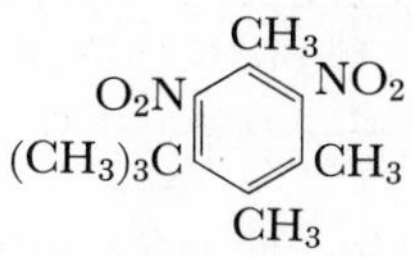

Musk tibetine

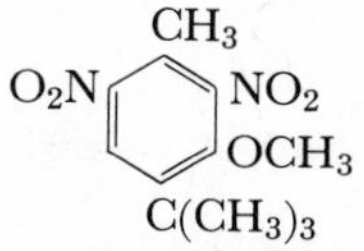

Musk ambrette

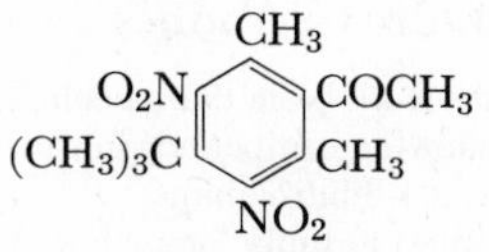

Musk ketone

Nitration of naphthalene yields 95 per cent **α-nitronaphthalene** and only 5 per cent of the β-isomer. It is used to make α-naphthylamine, a dye intermediate (p. 130).

SUMMARY

1. Amines are compounds that have alkyl or aryl groups replacing one or more hydrogen atoms of ammonia. They behave like ammonia in that they form salts with acids. They are the chief basic organic compounds.
2. Amines are classed as primary, secondary, or tertiary according to whether the nitrogen is attached to one, two, or three carbon atoms.
3. Primary and secondary amines are associated liquids. Amines having fewer than six carbon atoms are soluble in water. Amines that are insoluble in water dissolve in dilute acids and are liberated from their salts by strong bases.
4. Aliphatic amines can be made by the reaction of an alkyl halide with ammonia; aromatic amines usually are made by the reduction of nitro compounds.
5. Tertiary amines react with alkyl halides to give quaternary ammonium salts from which the amine no longer can be liberated.
6. Ethylene diamine, the ethanolamines, and the aminophenols are technically important compounds.
7. Amides are acyl derivatives of ammonia, or of primary or secondary amines. The electron-attracting property of the carbonyl group greatly decreases the availability of the unshared pair of electrons on nitrogen; hence the carboxylic acid amides are neutral. The still greater electron-attracting power of the sulfonyl group causes the sulfonamides of ammonia and of primary amines to be weakly acidic.
8. Nitro compounds contain an NO_2 group with nitrogen attached to carbon. The lower nitroalkanes are available by the vapor phase nitration of alkanes. Direct nitration of the aromatic nucleus proceeds more easily making aromatic nitro compounds readily available.
9. Nitro compounds have an abnormally high boiling point because of the high permanent electrical dipole of the nitro group. They are insoluble in water but are

good solvents for organic compounds and frequently dissolve inorganic salts, such as anhydrous zinc chloride or aluminum chloride, that lack a pair of electrons in their valence shell.

10. Highly nitrated compounds are useful explosives, but the nitro compounds are important chiefly because they can be reduced to primary amines.

11. Certain approximate rules enable one to predict the predominant isomers formed when aromatic compounds are nitrated, halogenated, or sulfonated.

EXERCISES

Amines and Hydroxy Amines

1. Why are amines more basic than alcohols?
2. Arrange the following compounds in the order of increasing basicity: aniline, n-hexylamine, n-hexyl alcohol, 2,4-dinitroaniline.
3. Write the structural formula for sphingosine, which is obtained by the hydrolysis of sphingomyelin.
4. How does epinephrine differ from: (a) norepinephrine; (b) Neo-Synephrine?
5. (a) Why are aromatic amine hydrochlorides more stable to oxidation than the free bases?
   (b) Why are o- and p-aminophenol more easily oxidized than m-amino phenol?
   (c) Why is a photographic developer such as p-aminophenol used in alkaline solution?
6. Why can trimethylamine be liberated readily from trimethylammonium chloride by reaction with sodium hydroxide but not from tetramethylammonium chloride?

Amides and Imides

7. How does the acid hydrolysis of amides differ from the acid hydrolysis of esters?
8. Write the reaction for the formation of: (a) acetanilide; (b) isonicotinic hydrazide; (c) 2,4-tolylene diisocyanate.
9. Write the structural formula for: (a) meprobamate; (b) phenobarbital.
10. Group the following compounds into pairs that have roughly the same basicity and arrange the pairs in the order of increasing basicity: diethylamine, acetamide, pyrrolidine, barbital, aniline, benzenesulfonamide, pyridine, 2,4,6-trinitroaniline.

Nitro Compounds

11. Why are aromatic nitro compounds more important than aliphatic nitro compounds?
12. How could one distinguish readily by chemical reactions between 1-nitropropane, nitrobenzene, aniline, and N,N-dimethylformamide?
13. Give the formulas of the chief products that would be expected when one more group is introduced by the following substitution reactions: (a) nitration of bromobenzene; (b) chlorination of nitrobenzene; (c) sulfonation of toluene; (d) light-catalyzed bromination of toluene; (e) sulfonation of o-nitrotoluene; (f) chlorination of naphthalene.

CHAPTER 14

STEREOISOMERISM.
UNSATURATED,
HYDROXY, AND
KETO ACIDS

STEREOISOMERISM

The existence of two or more compounds having the same number and kinds of atoms and the same molecular weight has been called *isomerism*. Isomers have the same *composition* and are represented by the same molecular formulas. The existence of isomeric compounds such as the two butanes, the two propyl alcohols, or ethyl alcohol and methyl ether is explained by the different order in which the atoms are attached. These isomers have different structures, and this type of isomerism is called **structural isomerism.** The order in which atoms are joined together is spoken of as the *constitution* of the compound and is represented by a *structural formula*.

However, isomeric compounds are known which have identical structures. For example, two 1,2-dichloroethylenes, $ClCH{=}CHCl$, are known, as well as two α-hydroxypropionic acids, $CH_3CHOHCOOH$ (*lactic acids*), and three α,β-dihydroxysuccinic acids, $HOOCCHOHCHOHCOOH$ (*tartaric acids*). To explain this type of isomerism it is necessary to postulate a different distribution of the atoms in space, and the phenomenon is known as **stereoisomerism** (Gr. *stereos,* solid). The subject of stereoisomerism may be divided into two parts, *geometrical isomerism* and *optical isomerism.* The space arrangement of the atoms is referred to as the *configuration* of the molecule, and three-dimensional models, perspective drawings, or projections of the space models must be used to illustrate the difference between stereoisomers.

Because of essentially free rotation about single bonds and a certain flexibility of bond angles, the same kinds of molecules, that is, molecules having the same structure and configuration, may assume different shapes in space. The particular shape that a molecule assumes is referred to as its *conformation* (p. 16). The four terms *composition, constitution, configuration,* and *conformation* have definite and distinct meanings. They should not be used interchangeably.

Kinds of isomerism

151

Geometrical or
cis-trans isomerism

Geometrical isomerism is associated with unsaturation or with cyclic compounds. For example, oxides of nitrogen convert oleic acid, m.p. 16°, into elaidic acid, m.p. 44°, an isomer having the same constitution (p. 15) Although only one 1-butene is known, there are two 2-butenes, one boiling at 0.96° and the other at 3.73°. Similarly 1,1-dichloroethylene exists i only a single form, but two forms of 1,2-dichloroethylene are known, on boiling at 48.3° and the other at 60.5°. There is only one cyclohexanol bu there are two 1,4-dihydroxycyclohexanes.

Unsaturated compounds

The explanation of the increased number of isomers in certain unsaturated compounds is that the two doubly-bound carbon atoms and the four atoms or groups joined to them lie in a plane and that free rotation about the double bond is not possible. Hence if the two groups on each carbon atom are different, two isomers can result (Fig. 18). If the two members of

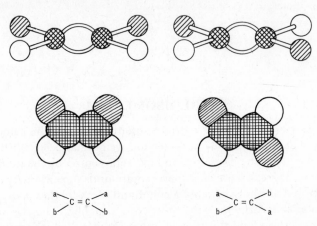

Figure 18.   Representation of *cis* and *trans* forms of geometrical isomers by molecular models and by projection formulas.

either pair of groups are alike, only one compound is possible. Accordingly in one of the 2-butenes the two methyl groups are on the same side of the molecule, and in the other they are on opposite sides. The isomer with like groups on the same side is known as the *cis* form, whereas that in which like groups are on opposite sides is known as the *trans* form (L. *cis*, on thi side; *trans*, across). The same explanation accounts for the two 1,2-dichloro ethylenes.

cis-2-Butene   *trans*-2-Butene

cis-1,2-Dichloroethylene   *trans*-1,2-Dichloroethylene

Similarly the hydroxyl groups of 1,4-dihydroxycyclohexane may be on the *Cyclic compounds* same side of the ring or on opposite sides, and the two forms cannot be inter-converted without breaking bonds.

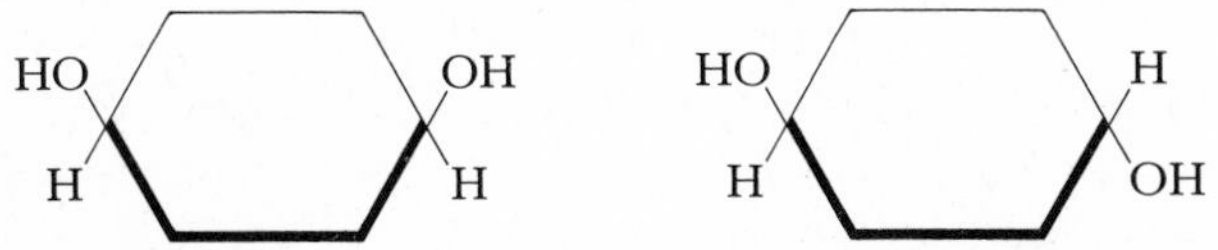

cis-1,4-Dihydroxy-   trans-1,4-Dihydroxy-
cyclohexane   cyclohexane

In these representations the rings are to be thought of as being perpendicular to the plane of the paper and the hydroxyls and hydrogens as lying in the plane of the paper.

The determination of the configuration of the two 1,2-dichloroethylenes *Determination of* was relatively easy, because the dipole moment of the carbon-halogen bond *configuration* is much larger than that of the carbon-hydrogen bond, which is very small (0.3 D). An examination of the proposed structures of the two isomers indicates that the *trans* isomer should have zero dipole moment, because the individual bond moments cancel each other. The *cis* compound on the other hand should have a resultant moment for the molecule as a whole. The arrow represents the direction of the moment, the + on the tail indi-

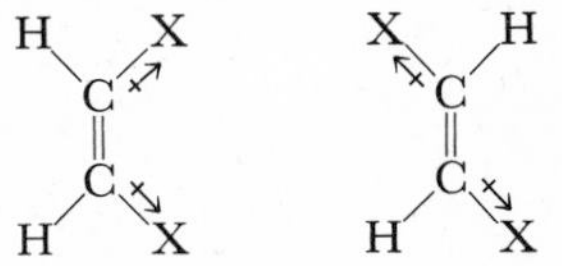

cis   trans

cating the positive end of the moment. The melting points and moments of the 1,2-dihaloethylenes are given in Table 10.

TABLE 10.   DIPOLE MOMENTS OF 1,2-DIHALOETHYLENES

	μ	M.p.	B.p.
1,2-Dichloroethylene (*trans*)	0	−50	47
(*cis*)	1.85	−80	60
1,2-Dibromoethylene (*trans*)	0	− 6	108
(*cis*)	1.35	−53	112
1,2-Diiodoethylene (*trans*)	0	+72	190
(*cis*)	0.75	−14	188

The configuration of some geometrical isomers can be determined from differences in their chemical reactions. Thus of maleic and fumaric acids, maleic acid is assigned the *cis* configuration because of the greater ease with which it forms an anhydride (p. 168).

The isomerization of the unsaturated fat acids now is understandable. *Isomerization* The naturally occurring compounds exist as one form, which in the presence of the oxides of nitrogen, which have an unpaired electron, is converted to its geometrical isomer. Thus the liquid *cis* oleic acid is transformed into an equilibrium mixture with its solid *trans* isomer, elaidic acid.

$$CH_3(CH_2)_7 \diagdown C=C \diagup (CH_2)_7COOH \qquad \underset{\substack{\text{Oxides} \\ \text{of} \\ \text{nitrogen}}}{\rightleftharpoons} \qquad CH_3(CH_2)_7 \diagdown C=C \diagup H$$

Oleic acid (33 per cent)   Elaidic acid (67 per cent)

The stability of geometrical isomers varies with their constitution. Some isomers interconvert on standing or heating, but usually light, or a free-radical catalyst such as oxides of nitrogen or metallic sodium, or an ionic catalyst such as halogen or hydrogen halide is required. In general at equilibrium under ordinary conditions the *trans* form is present in the greater amount.

Optical isomerism

Geometrical isomerism obviously cannot explain the existence of isomeric lactic or tartaric acids and another type of isomerism must be involved. Before discussing this type of isomerism it is necessary to explain the nature of **polarized light.**

The propagation of light may be considered as wave motion due to transverse vibrations like those that bring about an ocean wave. The propagation of such a wave may be represented as in Figure 19, which shows the

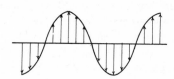

Figure 19.   Propagation of a wave by transverse vibrations.

instantaneous magnitude of the vibrations over a given distance. The behavior of the vibrators during propagation of the wave may be visualized by moving the boundary of the wave along the direction of propagation. Each vector maintains a fixed position and direction but varies continuously in magnitude from zero to $+1$ to zero to -1 to zero. Such a wave, however, lacks symmetry, whereas an ordinary light wave is symmetrical about the axis representing the direction of propagation.

Double refraction of light

In 1669 Erasmus Bartholinus discovered that a properly oriented crystal of iceland spar (calcite, a crystalline calcium carbonate) divides a single ray of ordinary light into two rays. Thus a single line viewed through the crystal appears as two lines. This phenomenon is known as *double refraction*. Eight years later Huygens found that each of the rays formed by double refraction is vibrating in a single plane and that the plane of vibration of one ray is perpendicular to the plane of vibration of the other ray (Fig. 20). Thus the symmetry of a ray of ordinary light about the direction of propagation is caused by transverse vibrations in all directions perpendicular to the direction of propagation. If two mutually perpendicular planes are passed through the ray, each vector has a component in each plane, as indi-

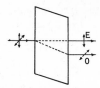

Figure 20.   Double refraction by a calcite crystal.

cated in Figure 21. The action of the calcite crystal is to separate the vectors into their components. The emergent rays, each of which is vibrating in a single plane, are said to be *plane-polarized.*   *Plane-polarized light*

Figure 21.   Vibrating vectors along direction of propagation of light ray. Dotted lines indicate how each vector may be considered to be the resultant of two components vibrating at right angles to each other.

The Nicol prism, invented in 1828, is a device for separating one plane-polarized ray from the other. The calcite crystal is a rectangular rhombohedron, the acute angles measuring 71 degrees. In the Nicol prism the two end faces are cut away until these angles are reduced to 68 degrees, and the crystal is divided in a plane perpendicular to the faces of the two ends and diagonally through the corners of the obtuse angles. The surfaces are polished and the two halves cemented together with Canada balsam, which has an index of refraction less than that of calcite for one of the polarized rays and greater than that of calcite for the other. The action of the Nicol prism is illustrated in Figure 22. A light ray, R, entering the prism parallel to the long axis is doubly refracted. The ordinary ray, O, is totally reflected from the surface of the Canada balsam. The extraordinary ray, E, is transmitted through the crystal. The reduction in the acute angles of the original calcite crystal from 71 degrees to 68 degrees is for the purpose of securing the proper angle of incidence on the balsam to produce this effect.

If a similarly oriented second Nicol prism is placed in the path of the emergent plane-polarized ray, the ray passes through the second prism without being affected. If, however, the second prism is rotated about its long axis through 90 degrees, the effect is the same as if the ray were vibrating at right angles to its original direction, and it is totally reflected from the Canada balsam layer of the second prism. Two prisms so placed that the

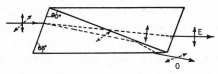

Figure 22.   Separation of ordinary light into two plane-polarized beams by a Nicol prism.

plane-polarized ray transmitted by one is not transmitted by the other are spoken of as *crossed Nicols.*

Light may be polarized by processes other than double refraction. When ordinary light passes through a crystal of the mineral tourmaline, the component vibrating in one plane is absorbed much more strongly than that vibrating perpendicular to this plane. This phenomenon is known as *dichroism.* If a dichroic crystal is of the proper thickness, the more strongly absorbed component will be practically extinguished, whereas the other is transmitted in appreciable amount as plane-polarized light. The modern Polaroid operates on the same principle, the absorbing medium being a film containing properly oriented microscopic crystals of a dichroic substance. The transmitted light is slightly colored and not completely polarized, but it is possible by this method to make polarizing plates of large area at reasonable cost.

Polarization by absorption. Polaroid

In 1811 Arago, a pupil of Malus, found that a quartz plate obtained by cutting a quartz crystal perpendicular to the crystal axis causes the rotation of the plane of polarization of plane-polarized light. This phenomenon can be observed best by placing a plate of quartz between crossed Nicols, the face of one of the Nicol prisms being illuminated from a light source. Before the quartz plate is placed between the two Nicol prisms, no light passes through the second prism. With the quartz plate between them some light passes through the second prism, which now must be rotated through a definite angle to become dark again. *The ability to rotate the plane of polarization of plane-polarized light* is called **optical activity,** and substances possessing this ability are said to be *optically active.* The number of degrees of arc through which the second crystal must be rotated to restore the original condition is called the *optical rotation* of the optically active substance and is given the symbol α.

Rotation of plane of polarization called optical activity

Häuy had discovered two kinds of quartz, the crystals differing only in the location of two facets that caused the crystals to be nonidentical mirror images. Because of the mirror image relationships, they were called *enantiomorphs* (Gr. *enantios,* opposite; *morph,* form). In 1815 Biot, another pupil of Malus, found that plates of the same thickness from the two kinds of quartz rotate plane-polarized light the same amount but in opposite directions. The form that rotates the plane of polarization to the right when facing the light source is called *dextrorotatory* and that which rotates the plane of polarization to the left is called *levorotatory.* Biot found also that other substances such as sugar solutions and turpentine are optically active, the latter even in the vapor phase.

Measurement of optical activity

The instrument used to measure the extent of rotation of plane-polarized light is called a *polarimeter* or *polariscope* (Fig. 23). It consists of a fixed Nicol prism, *A,* known as the *polarizer,* for polarizing the monochromatic light from the light source, *B.* A second Nicol prism, *C,* known as the *analyzer,* is attached to a disk, *D,* graduated in degrees and fractions of a degree, that can be rotated. The container for the sample is a tube, *E,* with clear glass ends, known as a *polarimeter tube.* The polarizer and analyzer are mounted on a suitable stand with a trough between them to hold

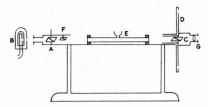

Figure 23.   Cross section of a polarimeter.

the polarimeter tube in the path of the polarized light. Because it is easier for the eye to match two adjacent areas to the same degree of brightness than to determine a point of maximum darkness or brightness, a third smaller Nicol prism, F, is placed behind the polarizer and rotated through a small angle. In this way the field is divided into two halves of unequal brightness. An eyepiece, G, focuses on this field. By rotating the analyzer the fields may be brought to equal brightness which provides a zero point. When an optically active substance is placed in the path of the light, the fields become unequally bright. Rotation of the analyzer returns the two fields to equal intensity. The number of degrees through which the analyzer is rotated measures the activity of the sample.

The amount of rotation depends on the number of molecules through which the light passes. Hence it is directly proportional to the length of the path through the active material, and this distance must be accurately known. For solutions the extent of rotation depends on the concentration or weight per unit volume of the substance in the solution. These statements are summarized in the equation

Specific and molecular rotation

$$\alpha = \frac{[\alpha]\,gl}{v} \qquad \text{or} \qquad [\alpha] = \frac{\alpha v}{gl}$$

where α = the observed rotation
   g = grams of dissolved substance
   v = volume of the solution in cubic centimeters
   l = length of tube in decimeters
   $[\alpha]$ = a constant that is characteristic of the compound and is called the *specific rotation*.

The *molecular rotation*, $[M]$, is the specific rotation multiplied by the molecular weight, M, and divided by 100 to reduce the size of the figure.

$$[M] = \frac{M\,[\alpha]}{100}$$

The extent of rotation varies with the wavelength of the light. This phenomenon is known as *rotatory dispersion*. If white light is used as a source of light, each wavelength is rotated a different amount while passing through the solution. Accordingly it is necessary to use monochromatic light when measuring optical activity. Usually the D line of sodium is used, although frequently it is preferable to use the green line of the mercury arc or the

Rotatory dispersion

red line of the cadmium arc. The rotation varies somewhat also with the temperature. For accurate work the polarimeter tube is maintained at some fixed temperature, usually $25°$. The wavelength used and the temperature of the solution are designated by subscript and superscript. For example, $[\alpha]_D{}^{25}$ indicates that the rotation was determined at $25°$ using the D line of sodium. Usually there is more or less electrical effect between solute molecules and between solvent and solute molecules, which causes the specific rotation to vary somewhat with different concentrations and with different solvents. Hence it is necessary to indicate both the concentration and the solvent used. A proper description of a specific rotation would be

$$[\alpha]_D{}^{25} = +95.01° \text{ in methyl alcohol } (c = 0.105 \text{ g./cc.})$$

Isomerism of tartaric acids

By 1848 two isomeric acids were known which had been isolated from the tartar of grapes. The common acid, called tartaric acid, is dextrorotatory, whereas its isomer, racemic acid (L. *racemes,* a bunch of berries or grapes), is optically inactive. In the spring of 1848, Pasteur (p. 64) was studying the crystal structure of sodium ammonium tartrate. He noticed that the crystals were characterized by facets that eliminated certain elements of symmetry from the crystal (cf. p. 160). Such facets are known as *hemihedral facets,* because they occur in only half the number required for complete symmetry. Pasteur proceeded to examine crystals of the inactive sodium ammonium racemate, expecting to find them holohedral. He found instead that all of the crystals obtained had hemihedral facets, but that two kinds of crystals were present. One kind was identical with the crystals of sodium ammonium tartrate; the other kind consisted of mirror images of the tartrate crystals (Fig. 24). Pasteur separated the two types of crystals under

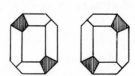

Figure 24.   Models of hypothetical enantiomorphic crystals with hemihedral facets.

the microscope and found that the type that looked like sodium ammonium tartrate was indeed dextrorotatory and identical with it, but that the mirror image crystals, when dissolved in water, rotated plane-polarized light exactly the same amount in the opposite direction. When equal weights of the two crystals were mixed, the solution was optically inactive. In other words, the reason racemic acid is inactive is that it is composed of equal quantities of two different kinds of molecules, one dextrorotatory and the other levorotatory. Isomers that have the same structural formulas but differ in their effect on plane-polarized light are called **optical isomers.** The phenomenon is known as **optical isomerism.**

Called optical isomerism

Active crystals such as sodium chlorate and magnesium sulfate are inactive in solution. Similarly, amorphous silica is optically inactive. Hence the cause of the activity in the crystal lies in the arrangement of the atoms in the crystal. Tartaric acid, on the other hand, is active in solution; moreover, pinene from oil of turpentine is active in both the liquid and gaseous states. In these compounds the activity must be due to the arrangement of the atoms in the individual molecules. Pasteur himself came to this conclusion, but because the theories of structural organic chemistry were not developed until around 1860 (p. 12), he did not recognize the principle necessary to relate optical activity to molecular structure.

By 1874 the constitutions of several active compounds were known. In September and November of that year two papers appeared, one by the Dutch physical chemist van't Hoff (1852–1891) and the other by the French chemist Le Bel (1847–1930), in which each pointed out that in every case in which optical activity existed, at least one carbon atom was present that was combined with four different groups. The following examples may be cited, the carbon atoms under discussion being marked by an asterisk. *Cause of optical isomerism*

$$CH_3CH_2\overset{*}{C}HCH_2OH$$
$$\underset{CH_3}{|}$$

Active amyl alcohol

$$CH_3\overset{*}{C}HCOOH$$
$$\underset{OH}{|}$$

Lactic acid

$$HOOCCH_2\overset{*}{C}HCOOH$$
$$\underset{OH}{|}$$

Malic acid

$$HOOCCH_2\overset{*}{C}HCOOH$$
$$\underset{NH_2}{|}$$

Aspartic acid

Wherever a pair of isomers differing in sign of rotation was known, the members of the pair had identical chemical and physical properties except for their action on plane-polarized light, and even here they differed only in the sign of rotation and not in the magnitude of rotation. Accordingly the space relationship between atoms of one isomer must be the same as that between the atoms of the other isomer. Van't Hoff and Le Bel pointed out that if the four different groups about the carbon atom are placed at the four corners of a tetrahedron, two arrangements are possible. Two

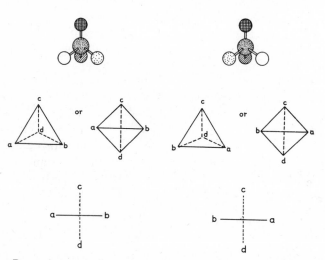

Figure 25. Representation of nonidentical mirror images by molecular models, by tetrahedra, and by projection formulas.

molecules result that are mirror images of each other, but which are not superposable and hence not identical (Fig. 25); that is, *the condition necessary for the existence of optical activity is that the arrangement of the atoms be such that a crystal or molecule and its mirror image are not superposable.* Thus optical isomers belong to another class of stereoisomers. A carbon atom joined to four different atoms or groups of atoms lacks symmetry and is known as an *asymmetric carbon atom.* Two isomers that are nonsuperposable mirror images are known as *optical antipodes, enantiomorphs,* or *enantiomers.* The term *mirror images* also frequently is used, *nonsuperposable* being implied.

Optical isomers are stereoisomers

Asymmetric carbon atom

    Actually the presence of an asymmetric carbon atom is not necessary for optical activity. Its presence is merely the most frequently encountered condition that removes the elements of symmetry that make mirror images identical. These elements of symmetry are (*1*) a plane of symmetry, (*2*) a center of symmetry, and (*3*) a fourfold alternating (or mirror) axis of symmetry. A *plane of symmetry* is a plane that divides an object into two halves that are mirror images of each other. The compound *Caabd* (Fig. 26*a*), for example, has a plane of symmetry, namely that which divides the carbon atom and the groups *b* and *d* into enantiomorphic halves, whereas the compound *Cabcd* (Fig. 26*b*) does not have a plane of symmetry. If an object

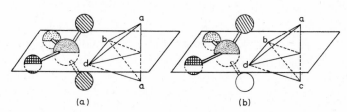

               (a)   (b)

Figure 26.   (a) Plane of symmetry in compound Caabd; (b) lack of a plane of symmetry in compound Cabcd.

possesses a plane of symmetry, the object and its mirror image are identical. The same statement holds for the other two elements of symmetry, but they need to be considered only infrequently and discussion of them is omitted.

Possible number of isomers

    Molecules containing a single asymmetric carbon atom exist in only two forms. The asymmetric atoms may be designated as $A+$ and $A-$ for the dextrorotatory and levorotatory forms respectively. If a second asymmetric carbon atom is present, the configuration of this atom may be designated as $B+$ or $B-$. Therefore a total of four isomers is possible, namely those in which the four configurations are $A + B+, A + B-, A - B+,$ and $A - B-$. Since $A+$ is the mirror image of $A-$, and $B+$ is the mirror image of $B-$, $A + B+$ is the mirror image of $A - B-$, and the two constitute an enantiomorphic pair and have identical properties except for the sign of rotation. Similarly $A + B-$ and $A - B+$ are enantiomorphic. $A + B+$, however, is not a mirror image of either $A + B-$ or $A - B+$ and has different chemical and physical properties. Similarly any active compound has only one mirror image and all others of its optical isomers differ from it in chemical and physical properties. Optical isomers that are not mirror images are called *diastereoisomers.*

Diastereoisomers

    If a third asymmetric atom is present, it also may exist in two configu-

rations, $C+$ and $C-$, and similarly for a fourth atom, $D+$ and $D-$.
Hence two active forms exist if a single asymmetric carbon atom is present,
and the number of active forms is doubled each time a new asymmetric
atom is added. The total number of active forms, therefore, is 2^n, where n
is the number of asymmetric carbon atoms.

To represent space models on plane paper, perspective drawings of
tetrahedra may be used. It is more convenient, however, to use **projection**   *Projection formulas*
formulas. The convention has been adopted that the two groups at the top
and bottom of the projection formulas always are directly over each other
and behind the plane of the paper in the corresponding perspective formulas (Fig. 25). In any comparison of projection formulas with each other,
neither the formula as a whole, nor any portion of the formula may be
rotated out of the plane of the paper. Otherwise the top and bottom groups
would not bear the same relation to the other formulas as was assumed when
the formulas were projected. Any rotation within the plane of the paper
must be through 180°. If a projection formula has been rotated through
90°, it must be rotated clockwise or counterclockwise through 90° before
an interpretation of the configuration can be made. General examples of
several methods for representing active forms are shown in Figure 27.

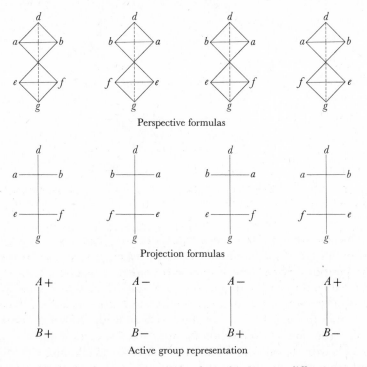

Perspective formulas

Projection formulas

Active group representation

Figure 27.   Methods of representing active forms having two different asymmetric
carbon atoms.

In the formulation of the 2^n rule the assumption was made that all of
the asymmetric carbon atoms were different, that is, that no two of them
were attached to the same four kinds of groups. If any of the asymmetric   *Reduction in*
carbon atoms are alike, the number of possible isomers is decreased. Thus   *number of isomers*

if a compound contains two like asymmetric carbon atoms, the possible configurations are $A + A+$, $A + A-$, $A - A+$, and $A - A-$. However, $A + A-$ is identical with $A - A+$, and only three optical isomers exist. The tartaric acids are examples of this situation. They have the constitution HOOCCHOHCHOHCOOH. Each of the two asymmetric carbon atoms bears the groups H, OH, COOH, and CHOHCOOH, and hence they are alike. The four possible combinations of active groups are shown by both perspective and projection formulas in Figure 28.

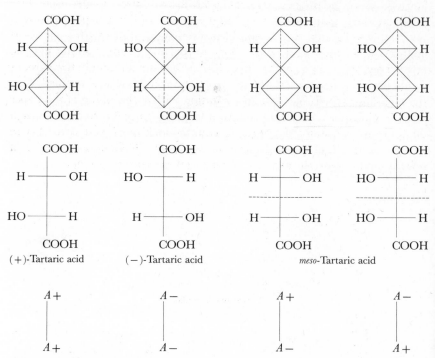

Figure 28.   Methods of representing the optical isomers of a compound having two like asymmetric carbon atoms.

The first two forms are nonsuperposable. The second two arrangements, however, have a plane of symmetry. These structures are not superposable in the positions shown, but if one or the other is inverted, they become superposable. Similarly in the projection formulas the dotted line indicates a plane of symmetry, and rotation of one or the other formula in the plane of the paper through 180° causes the two to coincide. Although it may appear that rotation of a projection formula about a vertical axis also makes it coincide with the other formula, such is not the case, because the carboxyl groups are not in the plane of the paper.

Not only is the number of optical isomers reduced from four to three when two like asymmetric carbon atoms are present, but the third form, having a plane of symmetry, is optically inactive. It is known as a *meso-form* (Gr. *mesos*, middle). Therefore a compound having two like asymmetric carbon atoms has three optical isomers. Two are active enantiomorphs with identical chemical and physical properties except for their opposite effect

Meso forms

on plane-polarized light. The third is an inactive *meso* form that is a diastereoisomer of the other two and hence differs from them in chemical and physical properties. In addition a fourth form, known as the *racemic form* (after racemic acid), consists of a mixture of equal amounts of the two active forms and hence is optically inactive. It differs from the *meso* form, however, in that it can be separated into active forms, whereas the *meso* form cannot. The solid racemic form usually differs in physical properties from the other forms, but in solution it dissociates into the two active forms, and its properties in solution are identical with the properties of the active forms, except that the solution is not optically active.

Many naturally occurring organic compounds that contain an asymmetric carbon atom are optically active. For example lactic acid, $CH_3CHOHCOOH$, isolated from muscle is the $(+)$ isomer. Lactic acid produced by fermentation may be $(+)$, or $(-)$, or racemic, depending on the fermenting organism. On the other hand, lactic acid produced by synthesis always is racemic. The reason is that when the asymmetric carbon atom is formed by synthesis, there always is an equal chance of producing the $(+)$ or the $(-)$ form, and, as the number of molecules involved is very large, equal quantities of both forms are produced. Suppose, for example, that lactic acid is being synthesized by brominating propionic acid to α-bromopropionic acid and hydrolyzing to the hydroxy acid. In the bromination step either of the two α hydrogen atoms may be replaced. Replacement of one gives rise to the $(+)$ form and of the other to the $(-)$ form.

Synthetic compounds inactive

Because the introduction of asymmetric carbon atoms by synthesis always leads to racemic products, the separation of racemic mixtures into their active components is of considerable importance. This process is known as *resolution,* and the racemate is said to be *resolved* into its active components. By far the most practical procedure for the separation of racemic mixtures was developed by Pasteur. It involves the conversion of the enantiomorphs into compounds that are diastereoisomers. Since diastereoisomers are not mirror images, they do not have the same physical properties and may be separated by ordinary physical methods such as fractional crystallization. After the separation of the diastereoisomers, they are converted into the original reactants. If $(A+)$ and $(A-)$ represent the two active forms present in the racemic mixture and $(B+)$ represents a single active form of another compound that will combine with the racemic mixture, the process of separation may be illustrated schematically as follows:

Resolution of racemic mixtures

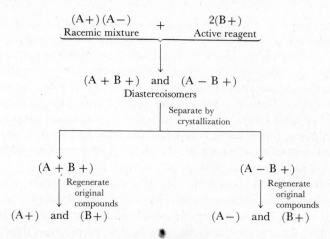

In practice the type of compound formation that takes place most readily and from which the original reactants can be regenerated most easily is salt formation. Thus a racemic acid can be resolved by an active base, or a racemic base by an active acid.

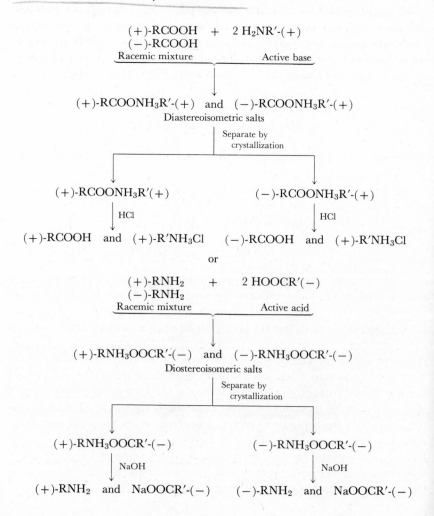

The naturally occurring alkaloids (p. 221) are active bases that give readily crystallizable salts. Those most commonly used for effecting resolution of racemic acids are (−)-brucine, (−)-strychnine, (−)-quinine, (+)-cinchonine, (+)-quinidine, and (−)-morphine. The easily available naturally occurring acids suitable for the resolution of racemic bases are (+)-tartaric acid and (−)-malic acid. Once a synthetic racemic mixture has been resolved, the active components can be used to resolve other racemic mixtures. Indirect methods and reactions other than salt formation have been used for the resolution of compounds that do not contain acidic or basic groups.   *Reagents for resolution*

Although it has been indicated that enantiomorphs have identical chemical properties, this statement holds only if the reagent itself is not optically active; that is, if the reagent is dissymmetric, the rates at which two like bonds are broken are no longer equal. Pasteur found, for example, that many organisms destroy one form of a pair of enantiomorphs and not the other. Thus the enzymes of the mold *Penicillium glaucum*, when allowed to act on ammonium racemate, destroy ammonium (+)-tartrate and leave the (−) form unchanged. In fact enantiomorphs differ in any property that involves the intervention of an optically active material. For example only one form of an amino acid commonly is present in proteins and is utilizable by the organism in the synthesis of proteins; (+)-glucose is the form synthesized by plants and the only form fermentable by yeast or utilizable by living matter; (+)-leucine is sweet whereas (−)-leucine is faintly bitter; (−)-tartaric acid is more toxic than (+)-tartaric acid; (−)-epinephrine has twenty times the activity of (+)-epinephrine in raising blood pressure. These differences merely emphasize the fact that enantiomorphs have identical properties only if they are reacting with nonactive reagents. Even the degrees of adsorption of two enantiomorphs on a solid surface differ if the adsorbent is optically active.   *Enantiomorphs differ in properties if reagent is optically active*

Two methods for producing racemic mixtures have been discussed, one by mixing equal amounts of the (+) and (−) forms (p. 158) and the other by producing an asymmetric carbon atom by a synthesis in which none of the reagents is optically active (p. 163). A third method consists in converting either a (+) or (−) form into a mixture of equal amounts of both forms. This process is known as *racemization*.   *Racemization*

Since conversion of a (+) form to a (−) form or of a (−) form to a (+) form involves the change in position of at least two groups on the asymmetric atom, bonds must be broken during the racemization, and the molecule must pass through a nondissymmetric intermediate. In the subsequent reformation of the compound, equal amounts of the two forms are produced. The most easily racemized compounds, and those for which the racemization is most readily explainable, are those in which a carbonyl group is α to an asymmetric atom that carries a hydrogen atom. The racemization undoubtedly involves enolization. The enol form does not contain an asymmetric atom, and when ketonization takes place, the double bond may be attacked from either side with equal ease, and equal quantities of both (+) and (−) forms are produced. Eventually racemization becomes complete. Thus the racemization of active lactic acid may be represented by the following equilibria.   *by enolization*

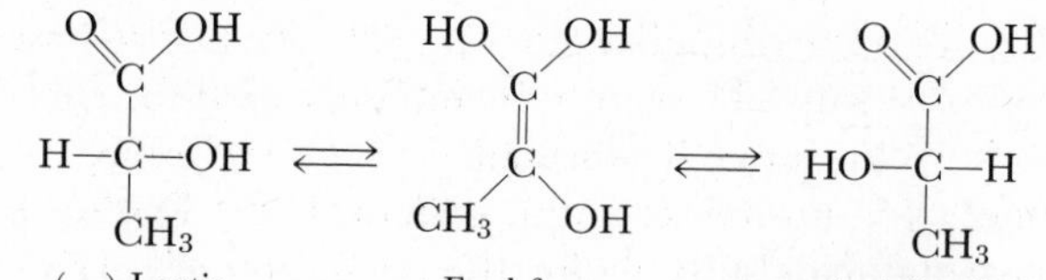

enolization

$$\underset{\substack{(-)\text{-Lactic}\\ \text{acid}}}{\underset{\overset{|}{CH_3}}{H-\overset{|}{C}-OH}}\overset{\overset{O}{\diagdown}\overset{OH}{\diagup}}{C} \rightleftharpoons \underset{\substack{\text{Enol form}}}{\underset{CH_3\quad OH}{\overset{HO}{\diagdown}\overset{OH}{\diagup}}C} \rightleftharpoons \underset{\substack{(+)\text{-Lactic}\\ \text{acid}}}{\underset{\overset{|}{CH_3}}{HO-\overset{|}{C}-H}}\overset{\overset{O}{\diagdown}\overset{OH}{\diagup}}{C}$$

Absolute and relative configuration

    Absolute configuration is the actual configuration of the molecule in space; that is, it is the answer to the question, "Which of two enantiomorphic models represents the dextrorotatory form of a compound and which the levorotatory form?" Prior to 1951, no procedure was known by which this question could be answered. If, however, the configuration of some reference compound is assumed, it is possible to relate the configuration of other active compounds to this substance and to each other. *The configuration of a compound with reference to the arbitrarily assigned configuration of the reference substance is known as its* **relative configuration.**

    The substance used for reference is **glyceraldehyde,** the ($+$) form of which is assigned the configuration represented by the perspective formula I. In this formula the asymmetric carbon atom is in the plane of the paper, the aldehyde and the hydroxymethyl groups behind the plane of the paper, and the hydrogen atom and the hydroxyl group in front of the plane of the paper. Formula II is a projection of this space formula in the plane of the paper. Frequently the projection formula is written as in III. The solid lines indicate that the H and OH groups lie in front of the plane of the paper and the dotted lines that the CHO and CH_2OH groups lie behind the plane of the paper.

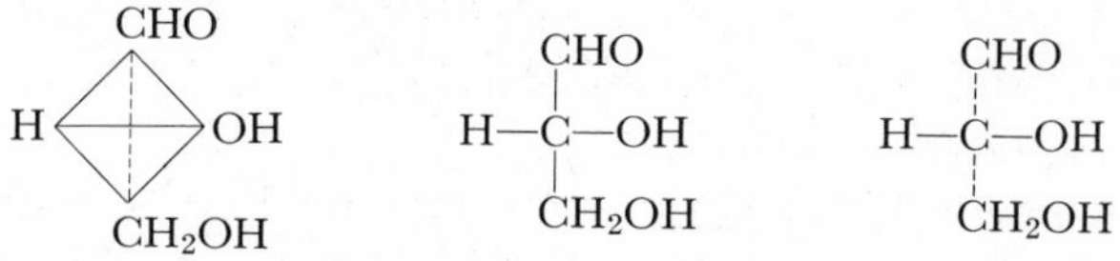

I   II   III

($+$)-Glyceraldehyde

    If ($+$)-glyceraldehyde is oxidized carefully, the product is ($-$)-glyceric acid.

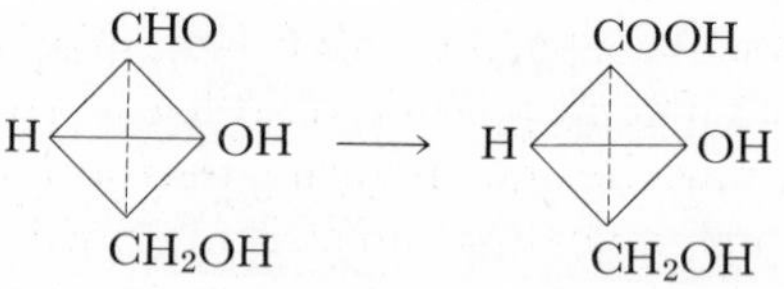

($+$)-Glyceraldehyde   ($-$)-Glyceric acid

Obviously if the configuration of ($+$)-glyceraldehyde is known, this reaction determines the configuration of ($-$)-glyceric acid. In any event, it determines the configuration of ($-$)-glyceric acid relative to that of ($+$)-glyceraldehyde.

D and L families

    There is no readily apparent relationship between the configuration and the sign of rotation. Since it is the configuration and not the sign of rotation that is important, active compounds have been divided into two families. Those that are related to ($+$)-glyceraldehyde are said to belong to the D family, and those that are related to $(-)$-glyceraldehyde are said to belong to the L family. The small capital D and capital L are pronounced *dee* and *ell* respectively and not dextro and levo. They refer to configuration and not to optical rotation. The names D($+$)-glyceraldehyde and D($-$)-glyceric acid reveal both the configuration and the rotation.

A point that frequently is misunderstood is that it is not sufficient to say that a compound is related to $(+)$-glyceraldehyde configurationally without specifying the correspondence of its functional groups to those of *Correspondence of* $(+)$-glyceraldehyde. Thus the configuration of $(-)$-glyceric acid is the same *groups important* as that of $(+)$-glyceraldehyde only if it is understood that the carboxyl group and the hydroxymethyl group of glyceric acid correspond to the aldehyde group and the hydroxymethyl group of glyceraldehyde. If the correlation had been carried out by converting the hydroxymethyl group of $(+)$-glyceraldehyde to a carboxyl group and the aldehyde group to a hydroxymethyl group, then $(+)$-glyceraldehyde would have yielded $(+)$-glyceric acid.

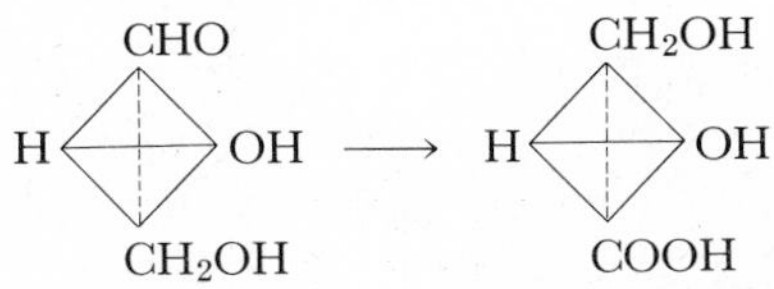

(+)-Glyceraldehyde   (+)-Glyceric acid

Regardless of which interconversion is carried out, the configurations of the glyceric acids relative to $(+)$-glyceraldehyde are established.

It has been shown also, by converting the aldehyde group of $(+)$-glyceraldehyde to the CHOHCOOH group, that relative to the arbitrarily assigned configuration of $(+)$-glyceraldehyde, $(-)$-tartaric acid has configuration IV, whence $(+)$-tartaric acid is V.

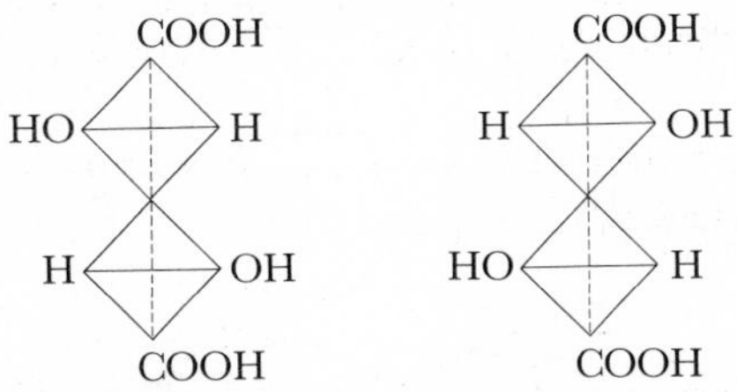

(−)-Tartaric acid   (+)-Tartaric acid
IV   V

In 1951 a special type of x-ray analysis of the sodium rubidium salt of   *X-ray determination of* $(+)$-tartaric acid demonstrated unequivocally that $(+)$-tartaric acid has   *absolute configuration* configuration V. Hence the configuration I, arbitrarily assigned to $(+)$-glyceraldehyde, is in fact the absolute configuration.

Where more than one asymmetric carbon atom is involved, confusion may arise as to whether to assign a given configuration of the molecule to the L family or to the D family. A new system has been developed in which the configuration of each asymmetric carbon atom can be unequivocally specified by the symbol R or S. However, it undoubtedly will be some time before this system is universally adopted.

UNSATURATED ACIDS

Skip from here on

Natural and synthetic unsaturated acids

Numerous unsaturated acids may be obtained by the hydrolysis of fats and oils (p. 119). Of the synthetic unsaturated monocarboxylic acids, **acrylic acid,** CH_2=CHCOOH, and **α-methylacrylic acid** (*methacrylic acid*), CH_2=C(CH$_3$)COOH, and their derivatives are the most important. The methyl and higher alkyl esters are polymerized to the acrylic resins (p. 235). **Acrylonitrile,** CH_2=CHCN, is the chief chemical for the production of the acrylic fibers (p. 235), and it is copolymerized with butadiene and with vinyl chloride to yield important synthetic rubbers and plastics (p. 237).

Configuration of maleic and fumaric acids

A few unsaturated dicarboxylic acids are of special interest. **Maleic** and **fumaric acids** (*cis-* and *trans*-ethylenedicarboxylic acids) are the classic examples of geometrical isomerism (p. 152). Maleic acid readily yields an anhydride when heated, indicating that the carboxyl groups are on the same side of the double bond. Fumaric acid on the other hand does not yield an anhydride easily. When heated to a sufficiently high temperature (250°– 300°), isomerization takes place and maleic anhydride is formed.

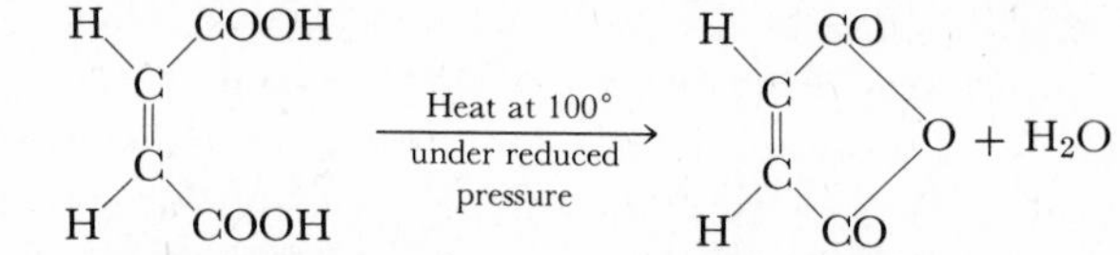

Maleic acid → (Heat at 100° under reduced pressure) → Maleic anhydride + H₂O

Fumaric acid → (Heat at 200°) → Sublimes unchanged

Fumaric acid can be made by the isomerization of maleic acid or by a fermentation process from starch or other carbohydrates using molds of the genus *Rhizopus.*

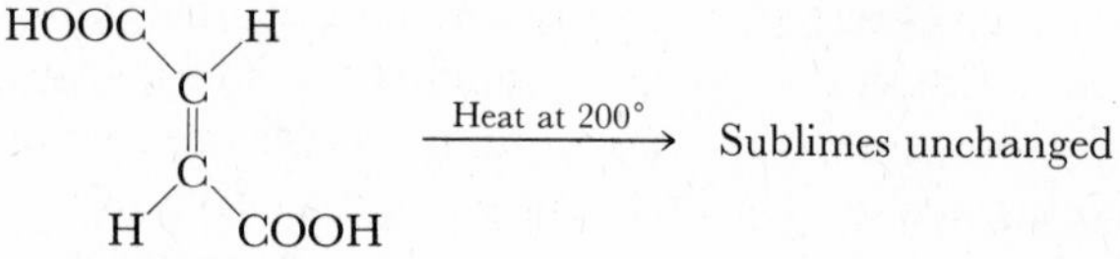

Maleic anhydride from benzene

Maleic acid is obtained in the form of its anhydride by the catalytic air oxidation of benzene.

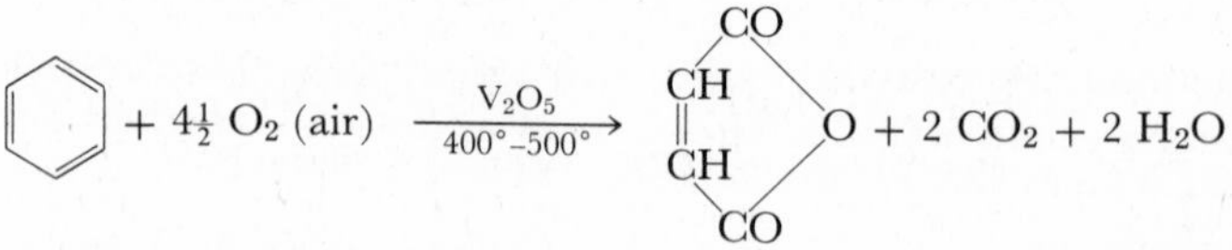

benzene + 4½ O₂ (air) → (V₂O₅, 400°–500°) → maleic anhydride + 2 CO₂ + 2 H₂O

It is used chiefly in the formulation of alkyd and other polyester resins (p. 239). **Maleic acid hydrazide** (*MH 30*) is made from maleic anhydride and hydrazine.

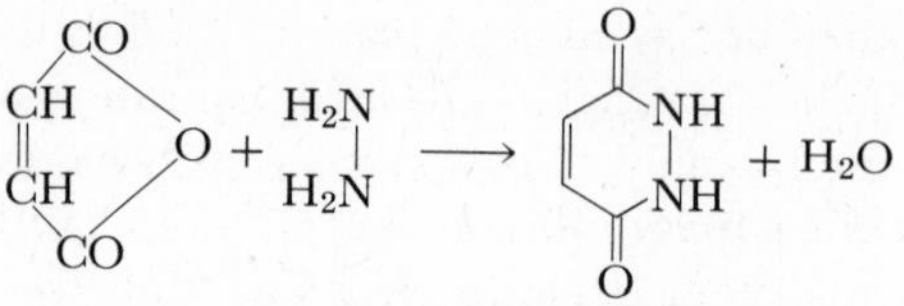

Maleic acid hydrazide + H₂O

It is used to retard the growth of plants and to prevent the sprouting of potatoes in storage.

HYDROXY ACIDS

Hydroxyacetic acid, $HOCH_2COOH$, is called **glycolic acid** and can be made by the hydrolysis of chloroacetic acid or by the oxidation of ethylene glycol with dilute nitric acid. The commercial product, used by tanners and dyers, is made by the reaction of formaldehyde with carbon monoxide.

$$HCHO + CO + H_2O \xrightarrow{[H^+]} HOCH_2COOH$$
$$\text{Glycolic acid}$$

Thioglycolic acid is made from sodium chloroacetate and sodium hydrosulfide.

Thioglycolate for waving hair

$$HSNa + ClCH_2COONa \longrightarrow HSCH_2COONa$$

The ammonium salt is the active agent in the preparations used for the cold permanent-waving of hair (p. 201).

Lactic acid is α-hydroxypropionic acid, $CH_3CHOHCOOH$, the acid formed when milk turns sour because of the action of *Lactobacillus* on lactose. It was isolated from sour milk in 1780 by Scheele, a Swedish apothecary (1742–1786). It is manufactured by the fermentation of lactose from whey, of molasses, or of starch hydrolysates, in the presence of an excess of calcium carbonate. Esters of lactic acid are valuable high-boiling solvents for the formulation of lacquers. Lactic acid contains an asymmetric carbon atom, and the lactic acid formed on muscular contraction is dextrorotatory. It is known as **sarcolactic acid** (Gr. *sarx*, flesh). Fermentation lactic acid may be dextro- or levorotatory or inactive, depending on the organisms involved.

Lactic acid in sour milk

α-Hydroxy acids undergo bimolecular esterification with the formation of a six-membered ring. Such cyclic esters are known as *lactides*.

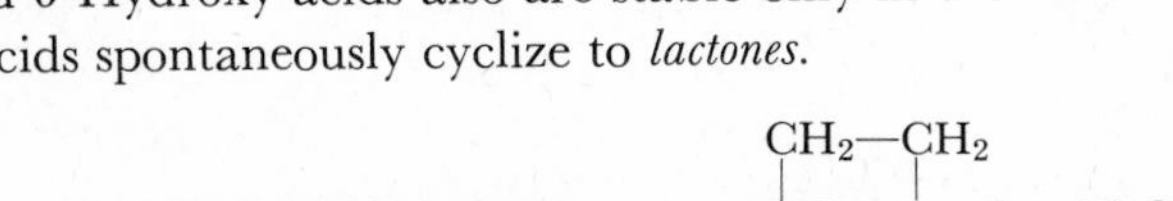

α-Hydroxy acids form lactides

Lactic acid   Lactide

This reaction takes place so readily that it is not possible to keep α-hydroxy acids in their monomolecular state except in the form of their sodium salts.

γ- and δ-Hydroxy acids also are stable only in the form of their salts. The free acids spontaneously cyclize to *lactones*.

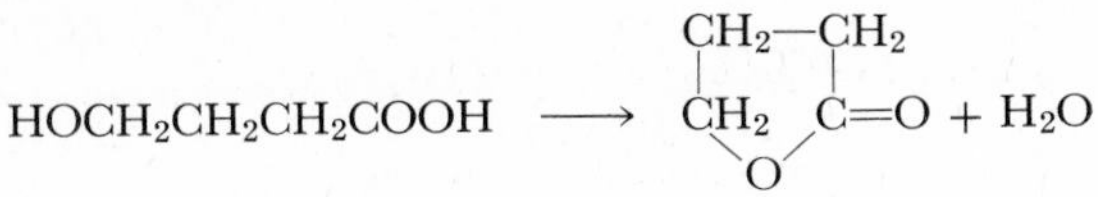

γ- and δ-Hydroxy acids form lactones

γ-Hydroxybutyric acid γ-Butyrolactone

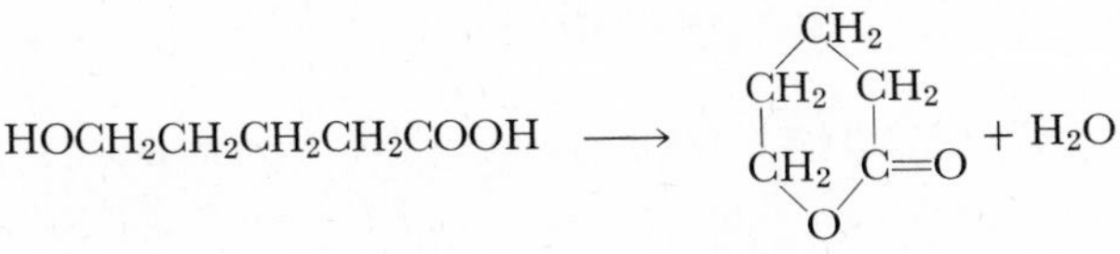

δ-Hydroxyvaleric acid δ-Valerolactone

Malic acid in fruit juices

Malic acid is hydroxysuccinic acid, $HOOCCH_2CHOHCOOH$. It is present in many fruit juices and was isolated by Scheele in 1785 from unripe apples (L. *malum*, apple). Calcium acid $(-)$-malate separates during the concentration of maple sap and is known as *sugar sand*. Malic acid has the property of attracting plant spermatozoa; that is, they migrate toward the point of highest concentration. Surprisingly $(+)$- or $(-)$-malic acid is equally effective. Racemic malic acid is manufactured by the hydration of maleic or fumaric acid.

Thiomalic acid is made by the addition of hydrogen sulfide to malic acid.

$$HOOCCH{=}CHCOOH + H_2S \longrightarrow HOOCCH_2CH(SH)COOH$$

Sodium thiomalate is reported to be an effective antidote for heavy metal poisoning. Addition of *0,0*-diethyldithiophosphate to ethyl maleate gives the mixed dithiophosphate known as **malathion.** It is an important insecticide because of its high toxicity to a variety of insects and its low toxicity to mammals.

$$4\ C_2H_5OH + P_2S_5 \longrightarrow 2\ (C_2H_5O)_2PSSH + H_2S$$

$$(C_2H_5O)_2PSSH + \begin{matrix} CHCOOC_2H_5 \\ \| \\ CHCOOC_2H_5 \end{matrix} \longrightarrow (C_2H_5O)_2PSSCHCOOC_2H_5 \\ \hspace{4cm} | \\ \hspace{4cm} CH_2COOC_2H_5$$

Malathion

Tartaric acid from tartar of grapes

The **tartaric acids** are dihydroxysuccinic acids, $HOOCCHOHCHOHCOOH$. The $(+)$ form is one of the most widely distributed plant acids. Its potassium acid salt is present in grape juice and is the chief component of the lees of wine (p. 158). The crude product is called *argol,* and the purified material is called *cream of tartar.* It is used as the acid component in some baking powders. Neutralization of cream of tartar with sodium hydroxide yields sodium potassium tartrate, which is known as *Rochelle salts* (after Rochelle, France) and is used as a purgative. Tartar was known to the ancients, but tartaric acid was isolated first by Scheele in 1769.

Fehling solution

Fehling solution (p. 96) is prepared from copper sulfate, sodium hydroxide, and Rochelle salts. The tartrate ion forms a chelate complex (p. 133) which decreases the cupric ion concentration below that necessary for the precipitation of cupric hydroxide. The complex salt is formed by a series of steps analogous to those for the formation of the cupric complex of biuret (p. 140).

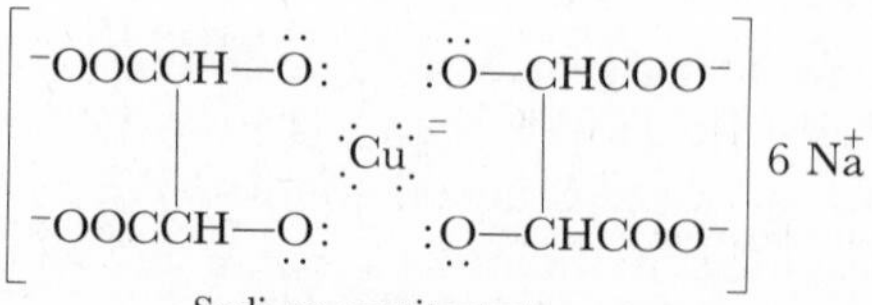

$$\left[\begin{matrix} {}^{-}OOCCH{-}\ddot{O}{:} & {:}\ddot{O}{-}CHCOO^{-} \\ | & | \\ & \overset{=}{:}\overset{.}{Cu}{:} \\ | & | \\ {}^{-}OOCCH{-}O{:} & {:}O{-}CHCOO^{-} \end{matrix}\right]\ 6\ \overset{+}{Na}$$

Sodium cupritartrate

Citric acid in lemons

Citric acid, $HOOCCH_2COHCH_2COOH$, is 2-hydroxy-1,2,3,-propane-
$$| \\ COOH$$

tricarboxylic acid. It is the chief acid component of citrus fruits, amounting to 6 to 7 per cent of lemon juice. It is present also in currants, gooseberries, and many other fruits, as well as in the roots and leaves of many plants. It was obtained in a crystalline form from unripe lemons by Scheele in 1784. Commercial manufacture is from cull lemons, or by the fermentation of molasses or starch with *Aspergillus niger* at pH 3.5.

Benedict solution

Benedict solution (p. 96) is prepared from copper sulfate, sodium carbonate, and sodium citrate. The structure of the complex is similar to that of the tartrate complex, except that a carboxyl group has entered into complex formation instead of a hydroxyl group.

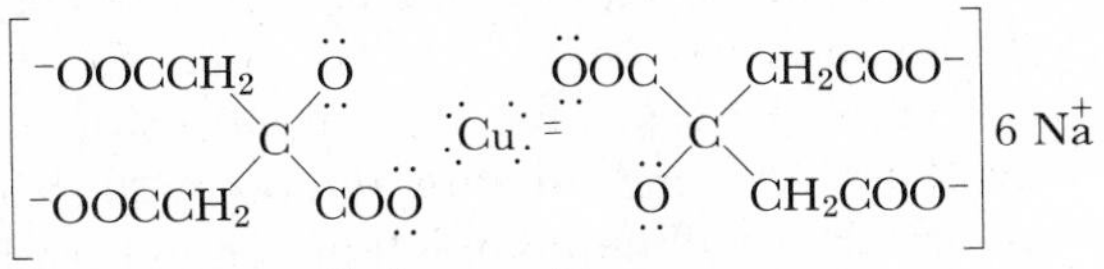

Sodium cupricitrate

Salicylates are febrifuges and analgesics

Of the aromatic hydroxy acids, *o*-hydroxybenzoic acid, known as **salicylic acid,** is by far the most important. It is prepared by the action of carbon dioxide on sodium phenoxide at 150° (*Kolbe synthesis*).

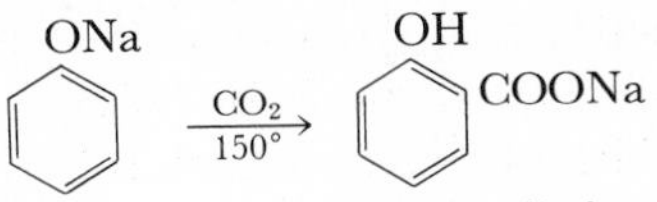

Sodium salicylate

Salicylic acid was prepared first by Piria in 1838 from salicylaldehyde, which derived its name from the fact that it could be obtained by the oxidation of saligenin from the glucoside salicin.

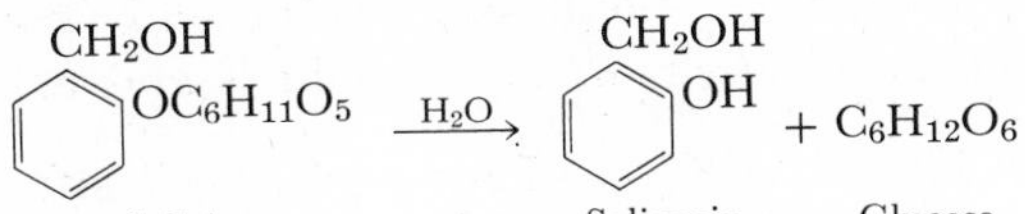

Salicin   Saligenin   Glucose

Salicylic acid also was known as *spirsaeure* in the older German literature because salicylaldehyde is present in the volatile oil from the blossoms and leaves of various species of *Spiraea*.

The importance of salicylic acid and its derivatives lies in their antipyretic and analgesic action. **Sodium salicylate** was used first for this purpose in 1875. In the following year it was used for the treatment of rheumatic fever. The irritating action of sodium salicylate on the lining of the stomach led to the investigation of the action of various derivatives.

Salol (*phenyl salicylate*) was introduced in 1886. It passes unchanged through the stomach and is hydrolyzed to phenol and salicylic acid in the alkaline juices of the intestines. However, the weight of phenol liberated is almost equal to that of salicylic acid, and there is considerable danger of phenol poisoning. Salol now is used only as an enteric coating for medicinals that otherwise would be destroyed by the secretions of the stomach. When the pill reaches the alkaline intestines, the salol is hydrolyzed and dissolved, and the medicinal is liberated. Salicylic acid now is administered

Aspirin widely used

almost exclusively as the acetyl derivative, which is known as **aspirin** (from the German *acetylspirsaeure*). Like salol it passes through the stomach unchanged and is hydrolyzed to salicylic acid in the intestines.

     Salol   Aspirin   Methyl salicylate

    Salicylates lower body temperature rapidly and effectively in subjects having fever (antipyretic action) but have little effect if the temperature is normal. They are mild analgesics, relieving certain types of pain such as headaches, neuralgia, and rheumatism. The threshold for cutaneous pain by heat is raised about 35 per cent when 2 grams of aspirin is taken orally. The extensive use of aspirin is indicated by the production in the United States in 1960 of over 23.5 million pounds, enough for one hundred and eighty five-grain pills for every member of the entire population. Although the toxic dose is large, promiscuous use of salicylates is not without danger, especially to children. Single doses of 5 to 10 grams have caused death, and 12 grams taken over a period of twenty-four hours causes symptoms of poisoning. Moreover, in some persons salicylates cause skin rashes.

    The chief component of oil of wintergreen (*Gaultheria procumbens*) was identified as **methyl salicylate** in 1843. It is used to a considerable extent as a flavoring agent and in rubbing liniments. It has a mild irritating action on the skin and acts as a counterirritant for sore muscles.

Tanning agents and inks from oak galls

    Gallic acid (3,4,5-trihydroxybenzoic acid) is found free in sumach, tea, and many other plants. It is prepared by the hydrolysis of the **tannin** (*tannic acid*) present in oak galls (gall nuts or nutgall), which are the excrescences on young twigs of oaks caused by parasitic insects. This particular tannin, called *gallotannin,* is a mixture of digallic acid esters of glucose (p. 184). The digallic acid is itself an ester, **m-galloylgallic acid.**

    Gallic acid   *m*-Galloylgallic acid

Compounds of this type are known as **depsides** (Gr. *depsein,* to tan) because many of them have tanning properties. Tannins in general are substances that have the property of rendering the gelatin of hides insoluble, thereby converting the hide to leather.

    Gallic acid and tannic acid are used in the manufacture of permanent writing inks. They form colorless water-soluble ferrous salts, which oxidize in air to give black insoluble ferric salts. The latter are more permanent to light than the dye used to make the ink initially visible. Gallic acid is decarboxylated to produce pyrogallol (p. 80).

    Mandelic acid (*α-hydroxyphenylacetic acid*) is prepared by the hydrolysis of benzaldehyde cyanohydrin (*mandelonitrile*).

$$C_6H_5CHO \xrightarrow{HCN} C_6H_5CHOHCN \xrightarrow[{[H^+]}]{H_2O} C_6H_5CHOHCOOH$$

                           Mandelonitrile   Mandelic acid

Its name arises from the fact that it first was obtained by heating an extract of bitter almonds (Ger. *mandel,* almond) with hydrochloric acid (p. 98). Mandelic acid administered orally is excreted unchanged in the urine. Since it is bactericidal in acidic medium, it is used in the treatment of urinary infections.

o-Hydroxycinnamic acid yields perfume

Cinnamic acid is β-phenylacrylic acid. *o*-Hydroxycinnamic acid cannot be isolated in the free state because it cyclizes spontaneously to the lactone, which is known as **coumarin.**

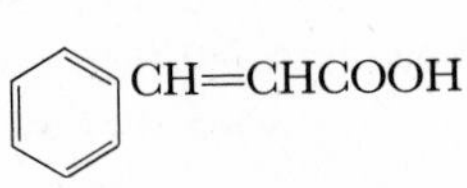

Cinnamic acid

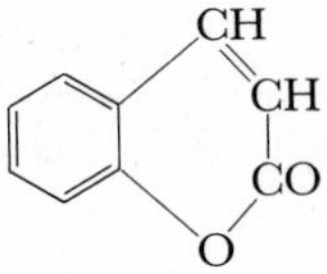

Coumarin

Coumarin is present in the tonka bean, the seed of a tropical South American tree (*Dipteryx odorata*) known to the natives as *cumaru,* and has been isolated also from numerous other plants. It has the odor of newly mown hay and was the first natural perfume to be synthesized from a coal tar chemical. Its use as a flavoring agent has been discontinued because of its toxicity.

Rat poison related to coumarin

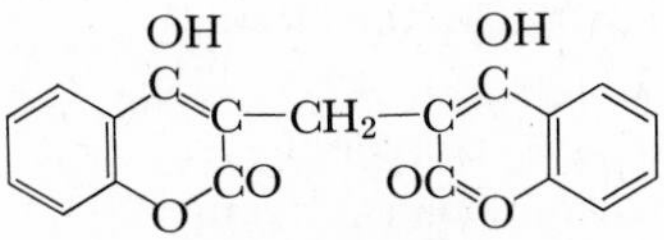

Dicumarol (*dicoumarin*) prevents the coagulation of blood and is the agent responsible for the hemorrhagic disease that results when cattle eat spoiled sweet clover. Dicumarol and certain related compounds are used medicinally to reduce the possibility of blood clot formation, for example, after surgery or in the treatment of coronary thrombosis. Another coumarin derivative, called *Warfarin,* is an effective rat poison.

Dicumarol (dicoumarin)

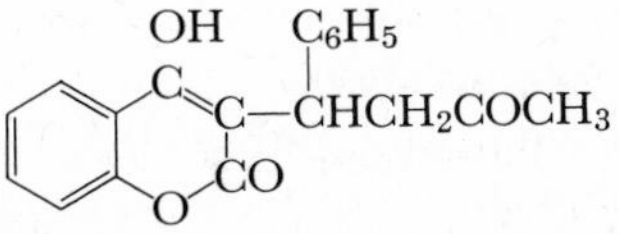

Warfarin

KETO ACIDS

α-, β-, and γ-keto acids

Pyruvic acid (*α-oxopropionic acid*), the first true α-keto acid, is made by the pyrolysis of tartaric acid and hence frequently is called *pyrotartaric acid.*

$$\underset{\text{Tartartic acid}}{\begin{array}{l}\text{HOCHCOOH}\\ \quad|\\ \text{HOCHCOOH}\end{array}} \xrightarrow{\text{Heat}} H_2O + \left[\begin{array}{l}\text{CHCOOH}\\ \quad\|\\ \text{HOCCOOH}\end{array} \rightleftharpoons \begin{array}{l}\text{CH}_2\text{COOH}\\ \quad|\\ \text{COCOOH}\end{array}\right] \longrightarrow \underset{\text{Pyruvic acid}}{\begin{array}{l}\text{CH}_3\\ \quad|\\ \text{COCOOH}\end{array}} + CO_2$$

It plays an important part in the fermentation and metabolism of carbohydrates.

Acetoacetic acid and diabetes

Of the β-keto acids, **acetoacetic acid** (*β-oxobutyric acid, diacetic acid*) is the most important. In the combustion of fat acids by the animal organism, two carbon atoms are removed at a time, the intermediates being the

β-hydroxy and β-keto acids. In the next to the last stage acetoacetic acid is converted to acetic acid. This step requires the simultaneous combustion of carbohydrates, which in turn requires the hormone insulin. The diabetic, lacking insulin, excretes carbohydrates as glucose, and acetoacetic acid accumulates in the blood stream. Decarboxylation of the acetoacetic acid gives rise to acetone.

$$CH_3COCH_2COOH \longrightarrow CH_3COCH_3 + CO_2$$
Acetoacetic acid

Both acetoacetic acid and acetone can be detected in the blood and in the urine of uncontrolled diabetics. The toxic effects of the acetoacetic acid (sometimes called *diacetic acid*) and acetone lead to coma and death. Easy decarboxylation is characteristic of β-keto acids. The esters of β-keto acids are very useful in the synthesis of other organic compounds. The only γ-keto acid readily available is **levulinic acid** (*γ-oxovaleric acid*), which is formed by the hydrolysis of hexoses (p. 185) with strong acids.

$$C_6H_{12}O_6 \xrightarrow{\text{Conc. HCl}} HCOOH + CH_3COCH_2CH_2COOH + H_2O$$
Levulinic acid

SUMMARY

1. Structural isomerism results from the different order in which atoms are bonded to each other. Stereoisomerism results from the possibility of different spatial arrangements of the same groups within molecules having the same structure. The structure of a compound is referred to as its constitution, whereas the spatial arrangement is called its configuration.

2. Stereoisomers are divided into two groups. Members of a group of stereoisomers, no one of which shows optical activity, are called geometrical isomers. If any member of a group of stereoisomers is optically active, all members of the group are optical isomers.

3. The existence of geometrical isomers is dependent on the fact that a double bond or a ring prevents rotation of the attached groups about an axis joining the atoms to which the groups are attached. Groups on the same side of a double bond or ring are said to be *cis* to each other, whereas those on opposite sides are said to be *trans* to each other. *Cis-trans*, i.e., geometrical, isomers differ from each other in both chemical and physical properties.

4. Plane-polarized light is light vibrating in a single plane. The ability to rotate the plane of plane-polarized light is called optical activity. Compounds that rotate the plane of polarization to the right are said to be dextrorotatory and are designated by the symbol ($+$), whereas those that rotate to the left are said to be levorotatory and are designated by the symbol ($-$).

5. The number of degrees through which the plane of polarization is rotated is called the optical rotation. The specific rotation of a compound is that which would be produced when plane-polarized light is passed through 1 dcm. of a solution having a concentration of 1 gram per cubic centimeter.

6. A compound is optically active if its mirror image is nonsuperposable. Mirror images are nonsuperposable if the object lacks a plane of symmetry, a center of

symmetry, or a four-fold alternating axis of symmetry. A carbon atom united to four different groups lacks these elements of symmetry and is called an asymmetric carbon atom.

7. Nonsuperposable mirror images are called enantiomorphs. Members of a set of optical isomers that are not optically active are called *meso* compounds. Members of a set of optical isomers that are not enantiomorphs are called diastereoisomers.

8. Enantiomorphs have identical chemical and physical properties except that they rotate plane-polarized light in opposite directions. Diastereoisomers differ from each other in both chemical and physical properties.

9. Because enantiomorphs rotate plane-polarized light in equal amounts in opposite directions, a mixture of equal amounts of enantiomorphs is optically inactive. Such a mixture is said to be racemic. Racemic mixtures are most easily separated (resolved) by converting them into diastereoisomers, usually by salt formation, separating the diastereoisomers, and regenerating the original compounds.

10. If all of the asymmetric carbon atoms in a molecule are different, the number of possible optical isomers is 2^n, where n is the number of asymmetric carbon atoms. If identical asymmetric carbon atoms are present, the total number of isomers possible is less, and some of them are *meso* forms.

11. Relative configuration is the configuration of a compound with respect to that of another compound. Absolute configuration is the actual configuration. The absolute configuration of (+)-tartaric acid has been determined. Because the configuration of (+)-glyceraldehyde relative to that of (+)-tartaric acid has been established, the absolute configuration of (+)-glyceraldehyde also is known.

12. Some of the more important unsaturated acids are the unsaturated fat acids, the acrylic acids, and maleic and fumaric acids.

13. Many hydroxy acids are found in plant products. Lactic, malic, tartaric, and citric acids are among the more important ones.

14. α-Hydroxy acids are characterized by the ease with which they form lactides, and γ- and δ-hydroxy acids by the ready formation of γ- and δ-lactones. Tartaric and citric acids form stable chelate complexes with heavy metal ions.

15. Of the hydroxy aromatic acids, salicylic acid is the most important. Others of interest are gallic and mandelic acids and the lactone of *o*-hydroxycinnamic acid.

16. The α-, β-, and γ-keto acids of most importance are pyruvic, acetoacetic, and levulinic acids. When heated above their melting point, β-keto acids lose carbon dioxide with the formation of ketones.

EXERCISES

1. Predict the number and kind of stereoisomers (active, *meso*, or geometrical) theoretically possible for each of the following compounds: (a) $(CH_3)_2CHCH(NH_2)COOH$; (b) $C_2H_5CH(CH_3)CH_2OH$; (c) $CH_3CHBrCH_2CHBrCH_3$; (d) $CH_2OH(CHOH)_4CHO$; (e) $CH_2(NH_2)CH_2COOH$; (f) $CH_2ClCHClCH_2COOH$; (g) $CH_3CH_2CHBrCHBrCH_3$; (h) $CH_3(CH=CH)_3CH_3$; (i) $CH_2=CHCH_2COOH$; (j) $CH_3CHOHCH=CHCH_3$; (k) $CH_3CBr=CHC_2H_5$; (l) linoleic acid;

2. Give structures for the simplest aliphatic alcohol, the simplest aromatic alcohol, and the simplest hydrocarbon that can exist in optically active forms.

3. (a) A sample of pure active amyl alcohol having a density of 0.8 g. per cc. at 20° in a 20-cm. tube gave a rotation of 9.44 degrees. Calculate the specific rotation of the alcohol.

(b) A fraction of fusel oil boiling between 125° and 135° and having a density of 0.8 g. per cc. at 20° gave a rotation of 3.56 degrees in a 4-dcm. tube. What per cent of active amyl alcohol was present?

4. (a) When 5.678 g. of cane sugar was dissolved in water and brought to a total volume of 20 cc. at 20°, the rotation of the solution in a 10-cm. tube was 18.88 degrees. What is the specific rotation of cane sugar?

(b) The observed rotation of an aqueous solution of cane sugar in a 2-dcm. tube was 10.75 degrees. What was the concentration of the sugar solution?

5. Write the equation for (a) the hydrolysis of salol; (b) the hydrolysis of aspirin.

6. When ferric chloride solution is added to the urine several hours after one has taken aspirin, a burgundy red color is formed. Why?

7. Why does coumarin have an odor whereas cinnamic acid is odorless?

CHAPTER 15

CARBOHYDRATES

Carbohydrates are polyhydroxy aldehydes or polyhydroxy ketones or substances which yield such compounds on hydrolysis. They are distributed universally in plants and animals, and constitute one of the three important classes of animal foods. The combustion of carbohydrates to carbon dioxide and water yields about 4 kcal. of energy per gram. The term *carbohydrate* came into use for these compounds because ordinarily the ratio of hydrogen to oxygen is 2 to 1; for example $C_6H_{10}O_5$, $C_6H_{12}O_6$, $C_{12}H_{22}O_{11}$. For some carbohydrates, however, this ratio does not hold; thus, rhamnose has the molecular formula $C_6H_{12}O_5$.

Definition

The simpler carbohydrates commonly are called *sugars* or *saccharides* (L. *saccharon*, sugar). The ending for sugars is *ose*, for example arabinose, glucose, maltose. Frequently the generic term *glycose* is used from which is derived the prefix *glyco*. The generic terms are used when it is not desired to designate a particular sugar or derivative. The number of carbon atoms may be indicated by a prefix; for example, a sugar having five carbon atoms is called a *pentose* and one with six carbon atoms is called a *hexose*. Similarly the prefix may indicate whether the sugar contains an aldehyde group or a ketone group, giving rise to the terms *aldose* and *ketose*. Both the number of carbon atoms and the type of carbonyl group may be indicated by terms such as *aldopentose* and *ketohexose*.

Nomenclature and classification

MONOSACCHARIDES

Monosaccharides are carbohydrates that cannot be hydrolyzed. Most of the naturally occurring monosaccharides are aldopentoses, having the structural formula $HOCH_2(CHOH)_3CHO$, and aldohexoses, having the formula $HOCH_2(CHOH)_4CHO$. They have three and four asymmetric carbon atoms respectively, giving rise to eight and sixteen stereoisomers.

Aldopentoses and aldohexoses most abundant

Of the sixteen aldohexoses, the most important is (+)-glucose or *dextrose*. It occurs free, along with fructose and sucrose, in the juices of fruits and in honey, and to the extent of about 0.1 per cent in the blood of normal mammals, but is obtained most readily by the hydrolysis of starch or cellulose (pp.191, 192).

Glucose the most important

Two other aldohexoses are important, namely, (+)-mannose and (+)-galactose. (+)-**Mannose** is one of the products of hydrolysis of a number of polysaccharides. It is obtained most readily by the hydrolysis of the vegetable ivory nut, which is the hard endosperm of the seed of the Tagua palm, *Phyletephas macrocarpa*. (+)-**Galactose** is formed along with (+)-glucose by the hydrolysis of the disaccharide lactose or milk sugar (p. 188), and is one of the products of hydrolysis of several polysaccharides. The following configurations are assigned to these three sugars.

Configurations of aldoses

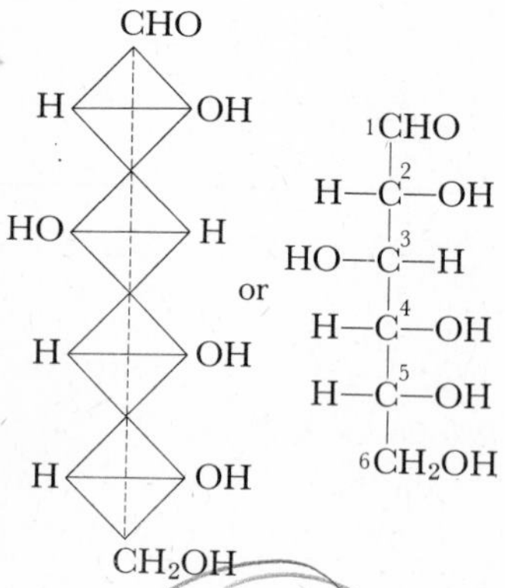

(+)-Glucose 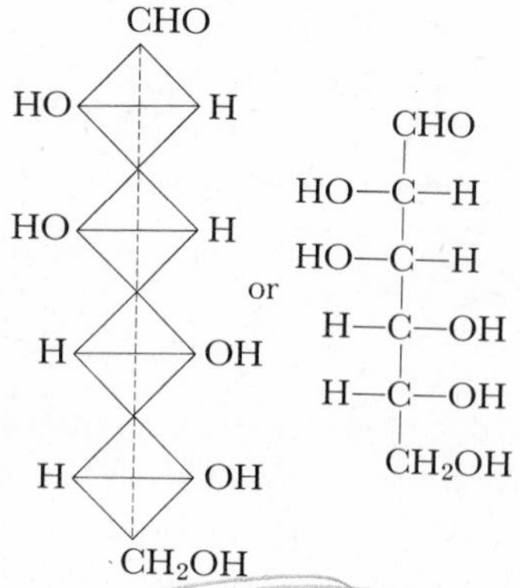   (+)-Mannose 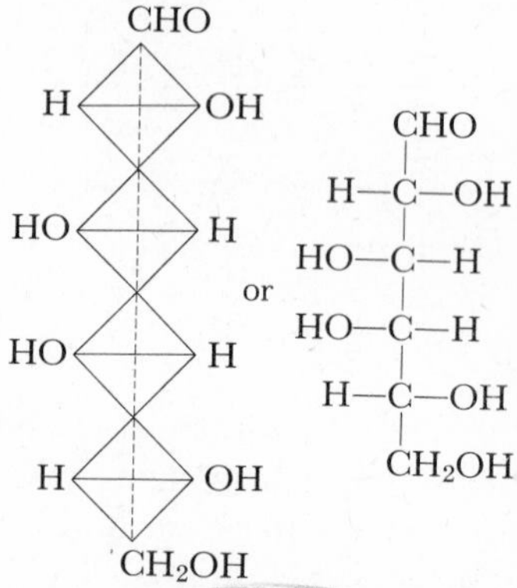   (+)-Galactose

Eight aldopentoses are possible and all are known. (+)-**Arabinose** and (+)-**xylose** may be obtained by the hydrolysis of a wide variety of plant polysaccharides. Thus corn cobs, straw, oat hulls, and cottonseed hulls yield 8 to 12 per cent of (+)-xylose. (+)-Arabinose is obtained by the hydrolysis of many plant gums. (−)-**Ribose** is important because it is one of the products of hydrolysis of the nucleic acids (p. 227).

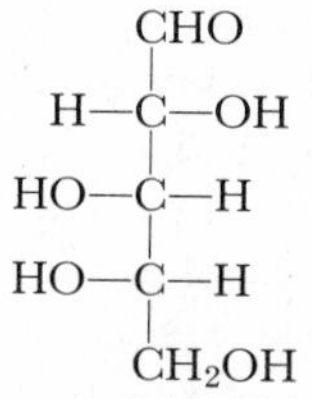

(+)-Arabinose 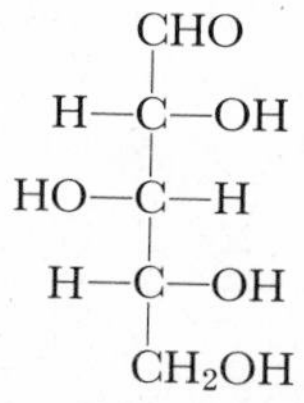   (+)-Xylose 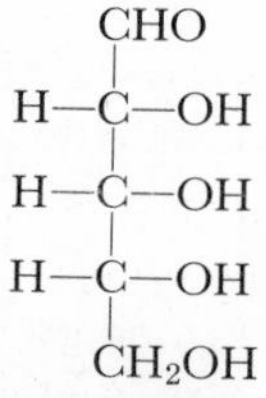   (−)-Ribose

Family of sugars

Figure 29 indicates that half of the aldoses may be considered as having D(+)-glyceraldehyde (p. 167) as a parent compound. Similarly their enantiomorphs may be considered as having L(−)-glyceraldehyde as a parent compound. Sugars for which the highest-numbered asymmetric carbon atom has the same configuration as D(+)-glyceraldehyde (hydroxyl group on the right in the projection formula) are said to belong to the D (*dee*) family; those having the enantiomorphic configuration belong to the L (*ell*) family (cf. p. 166).

Some naturally occurring sugars have a hydrogen atom in place of one or more of the hydroxyl groups. In naming these compounds the prefix *deoxy* is used with the name of the oxygen analog to indicate the lack of oxygen, and the class as a whole is known as the **deoxy sugars**. L(+)-**Rhamnose** (*6-deoxy-L-mannose*) is a hydrolytic product of many glycosides and the most common naturally occurring deoxy sugar. L(−)-**Fucose** (*6-deoxy-L-galactose*) is one of the products of the hydrolysis of the cell walls of marine algae and of gum tragacanth.

Deoxy sugars deficient in hydroxyl groups

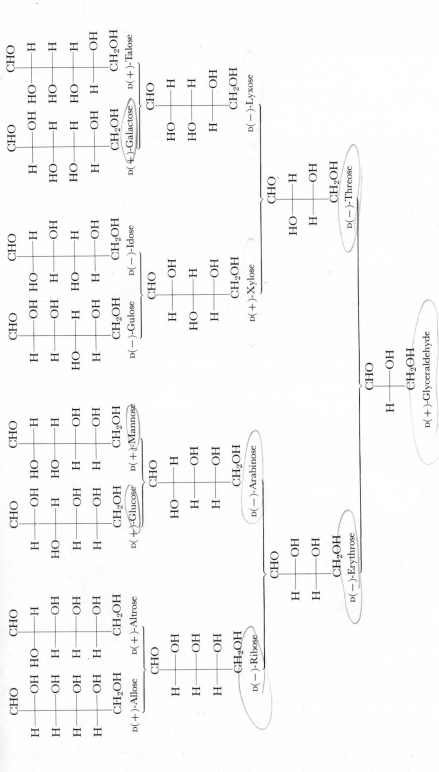

Figure 29.   Configurations of the D family of aldoses.

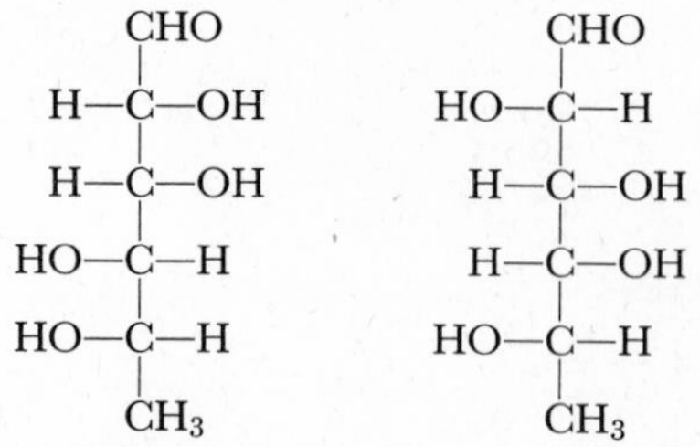

```
        CHO                    CHO
   H—C—OH              HO—C—H
   H—C—OH               H—C—OH
  HO—C—H                H—C—OH
  HO—C—H               HO—C—H
       CH₃                    CH₃
   L(+)-Rhamnose         L(−)-Fucose
```

$$\text{L}(+)\text{-Rhamnose} \qquad \text{L}(-)\text{-Fucose}$$

Rhamnose and fucose sometimes are called *methylpentoses*, but this term may cause ambiguity when dealing with the methylated sugars.

Alkali causes isomerization and degradation

Aqueous alkali can produce two types of reactions with sugars, isomerization and degradation. *Isomerization* can be brought about by very dilute alkali at room temperature. Thus if glucose is allowed to stand for several days with dilute calcium hydroxide, a mixture is formed containing 63.5 per cent glucose, 2.5 per cent mannose, and 31 per cent of the 2-ketohexose, fructose (p. 186), along with 3 per cent of other substances. Other aldoses behave similarly. The reaction has been called the *Lobry de Bruyn* and *Alberda van Ekenstein transformation* after its discoverers, and has been used for the preparation of ketoses. The reaction is reversible, but true equilibrium is not reached. The composition of the reaction product depends on the initial sugar and on the concentration and nature of the basic catalyst. An enediol form, postulated by Nef, an American chemist (1862–1915), is considered to be an intermediate.

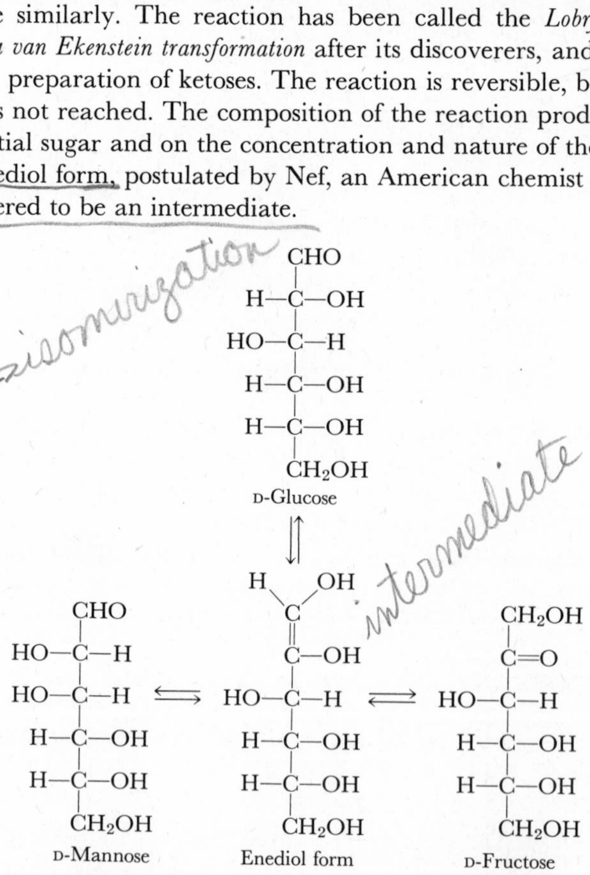

```
                       CHO
                   H—C—OH
                  HO—C—H
                   H—C—OH
                   H—C—OH
                      CH₂OH
                    D-Glucose
                       ⇊
             H    OH
               \ /
        CHO      C                   CH₂OH
   HO—C—H       C—OH                  C=O
   HO—C—H  ⇌  HO—C—H  ⇌  HO—C—H
    H—C—OH      H—C—OH               H—C—OH
    H—C—OH      H—C—OH               H—C—OH
      CH₂OH       CH₂OH                 CH₂OH
   D-Mannose   Enediol form          D-Fructose
```

The second important type of action of alkali on monosaccharides is cleavage into smaller molecules, or *degradation*. The natural ketoses and those formed by isomerization of aldoses give rise in the presence of alkali to formaldehyde and hydroxyaldehydes and polyhydroxy ketones of lower molecular weight.

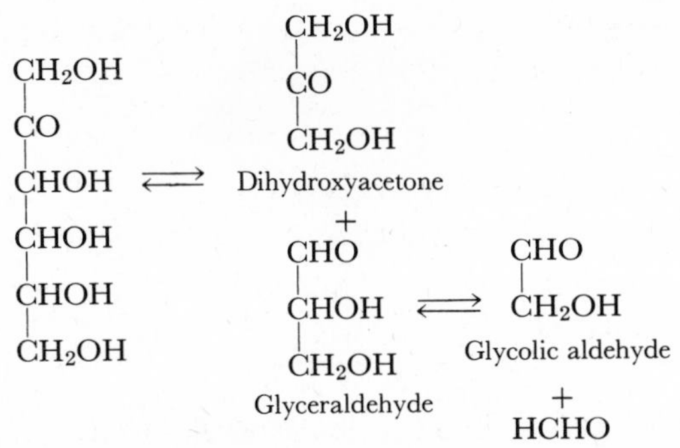

$$
\begin{array}{ccc}
\text{CH}_2\text{OH} & & \text{CH}_2\text{OH} \\
| & & | \\
\text{CO} & & \text{CO} \\
| & & | \\
\text{CHOH} & \rightleftarrows & \text{CH}_2\text{OH} \\
| & & \text{Dihydroxyacetone} \\
\text{CHOH} & & + \\
| & & \\
\text{CHOH} & & \text{CHO} \qquad\qquad \text{CHO} \\
| & & | \qquad\qquad\quad | \\
\text{CH}_2\text{OH} & & \text{CHOH} \rightleftarrows \text{CH}_2\text{OH} \\
& & | \qquad\quad \text{Glycolic aldehyde} \\
& & \text{CH}_2\text{OH} \\
& & \text{Glyceraldehyde} \qquad + \\
& & \qquad\qquad\quad \text{HCHO}
\end{array}
$$

The salts of many heavy metals such as copper, silver, mercury, and bismuth are reduced by alkaline sugar solutions. Reagents containing copper usually are used for analytical purposes. Cupric hydroxide oxidizes carbohydrates, but its slight solubility in dilute alkali permits only a slow reaction. The rate of oxidation is increased greatly if the copper is kept in solution by the formation of a complex salt with tartrate ion (Fehling solution) or citrate ion (Benedict solution) (p. 171). Benedict solution is the more stable and is not affected by substances such as uric acid (p. 227). Hence it is preferred for detecting and estimating glucose in urine.

Sugars oxidized by alkaline solutions of cupric salts

Evidence for reduction is the formation of red cuprous oxide, which precipitates because the cuprous ion does not form complexes with tartrates or citrates. If protective colloids are present, as in urine samples, the color of the precipitate may vary from yellow to red depending on the state of subdivision of the particles. In the presence of an excess of carbohydrate, some of the cuprous oxide may be reduced to metallic copper.

every sugar is reducing but sucrose

The equation for the oxidation of an aldehyde group to a carboxyl group requires a ratio of two moles of cupric salt per mole of aldehyde.

$$
\text{RCHO} + 2\,\text{Cu(OH)}_2 \longrightarrow \text{RCOOH} + \text{Cu}_2\text{O} + 2\,\text{H}_2\text{O}
$$

Actually one mole of glucose reduces between five and six moles of cupric salt, depending on the conditions of the reaction. Moreover ketoses reduce just as well as aldoses, although simple ketones do not reduce Fehling solution. The explanation lies in the above reactions of the sugars with alkali, which not only interconvert aldoses and ketoses but give degradation products that have reducing properties. Furthermore, some of the excess reduction may be caused by the CHOH groups adjacent to the carbonyl group, because even simple compounds containing this grouping are oxidized by alkaline cupric solutions to give dicarbonyl compounds.

$$
\underset{\substack{| \\ \text{O} \quad \text{OH}}}{\text{R}-\text{C}-\text{CH}-\text{R}} + 2\,\text{Cu(OH)}_2 \longrightarrow \underset{\substack{|| \quad || \\ \text{O} \quad \text{O}}}{\text{R}-\text{C}-\text{C}-\text{R}} + \text{Cu}_2\text{O} + 3\,\text{H}_2\text{O}
$$

Despite the complexity of the reaction, oxidation can be used successfully for the quantitative estimation of sugars by standardizing conditions rigidly and by using empirically determined tables relating the amount of sugar to the amount of cupric ion reduced.

The reaction of phenylhydrazine with reducing sugars introduces two phenylhydrazine residues instead of one (p. 95). A yellow crystalline product known as a **phenylosazone** separates from the hot aqueous solution.

Phenylhydrazine gives osazones

The other products of the reaction are aniline and ammonia. This reaction is characteristic of the grouping RCOCHOHR.

$$
\begin{array}{l}
CHO \\
CHOH \\
(CHOH)_3 \\
CH_2OH
\end{array}
+ 3\ C_6H_5NHNH_2 \longrightarrow
\begin{array}{l}
CH{=}N{-}NHC_6H_5 \\
C{=}N{-}NHC_6H_5 \\
(CHOH)_3 \\
CH_2OH
\end{array}
+ C_6H_5NH_2 + NH_3 + 2\ H_2O
$$

A phenylosazone   Aniline

Other substituted hydrazines of the general formulas $RNHNH_2$ and R_2NNH_2 may be used also to form osazones. Since the osazones from different hydrazines and different sugars differ in melting point, crystal form, and rate of formation, osazone formation is a valuable reaction for the identification of sugars.

Glucose and mannose give same osazone

When osazones are formed, the asymmetry of carbon atom 2 is destroyed. Therefore sugars that differ only in the configuration of this carbon atom, such as glucose and mannose, yield the same osazone.

$$
\begin{array}{c}
CHO \\
H{-}C{-}OH \\
HO{-}C{-}H \\
H{-}C{-}OH \\
H{-}C{-}OH \\
CH_2OH
\end{array}
\xrightarrow{C_6H_5NHNH_2}
\begin{array}{c}
CH{=}NNHC_6H_5 \\
C{=}NNHC_6H_5 \\
HO{-}C{-}H \\
H{-}C{-}OH \\
H{-}C{-}OH \\
CH_2OH
\end{array}
\xleftarrow{C_6H_5NHNH_2}
\begin{array}{c}
CHO \\
HO{-}C{-}H \\
HO{-}C{-}H \\
H{-}C{-}OH \\
H{-}C{-}OH \\
CH_2OH
\end{array}
$$

D-Glucose   D-Glucose phenylosazone   D-Mannose
(yellow precipitate)

Aldehydes form hemiacetals and acetals

Aldehydes add alcohols in the presence of acid catalysts to form hemiacetals. Further reaction of the hemiacetals with alcohol forms acetals with the elimination of water.

$$
RCHO + HOR' \underset{[H^+]}{\overset{[H^+]}{\rightleftarrows}} RCH\begin{array}{c} OH \\ OR' \end{array} \underset{}{\overset{R'OH,[H^+]}{\rightleftarrows}} RCH\begin{array}{c} OR' \\ OR' \end{array} + H_2O
$$

Hemiacetal   Acetal

When E. Fischer (a famous German chemist, 1852–1919) attempted to prepare an acetal from glucose, methyl alcohol, and hydrogen chloride, definite crystalline products were obtained, but analysis showed that although a molecule of water had been eliminated, only one methyl group had been introduced. Furthermore two isomeric products were obtained. These compounds no longer reduced Fehling solution nor formed osazones. Moreover they behaved like acetals in that they were hydrolyzed readily in acid solutions but were stable in alkali. This behavior is explainable if it is assumed that the aldehyde group of the sugar first reacts with the alcohol group on the fifth carbon atom to form an internal cyclic hemiacetal having a six-membered ring. The hemiacetal then reacts with methyl alcohol to form the acetal. Because a new asymmetric carbon atom is produced in this process, two diastereoisomers are formed.

These acetals are called *glycosides,* and the two forms are designated and β. Isomers of this type are known as *anomers* and the carbon atom responsible for the existence of anomers is known as the *anomeric* (Gr. *ano,* above) carbon atom. Hereafter the anomeric carbon atom is indicated by bold-faced type. It can be distinguished readily from the other carbon atoms by the fact that it is united to two oxygen atoms. For glycosides the anomeric carbon atom also is known as the *glycosidic* carbon atom. The designation α is given to the form in which the hydroxyl or substituted hydroxyl group is on the right in the projection formulas for members of the D family and on the left for members of the L family. Hence when indicating the configuration of the anomeric carbon atom, it is necessary to indicate the family of the sugar as well.

Acetals of sugars called glycosides

$$
\begin{array}{ccc}
\text{H—C—OCH}_3 & \text{H—C—OH} & \text{CHO} \\
\text{CHOH} & \text{CHOH} & \text{CHOH} \\
\text{CHOH} & \text{CHOH} & \text{CHOH} \\
\text{CHOH} & \text{CHOH} & \text{CHOH} \\
\text{H—C} & \text{H—C} & \text{H—C—OH} \\
\text{CH}_2\text{OH} & \text{CH}_2\text{OH} & \text{CH}_2\text{OH} \\
\end{array}
$$

Methyl α-D-glycoside ⟵ CH₃OH [H⁺] hemiacetal ⇌ glucose ⇌

(handwritten: glycoside acetal)

$$
\begin{array}{cc}
\text{HO—C—H} & \text{CH}_3\text{O—C—H} \\
\text{CHOH} & \text{CHOH} \\
\text{CHOH} & \text{CHOH} \\
\text{CHOH} & \text{CHOH} \\
\text{H—C} & \text{H—C} \\
\text{CH}_2\text{OH} & \text{CH}_2\text{OH} \\
\end{array}
$$

CH₃OH [H⁺] ⟶

Methyl β-D-glycoside *(handwritten: up of glucose)*

Numerous plant products are glycosides, such as amygdalin (p. 98) and salicin (p. 171), the bitter principle of fruit pit seeds and of willow bark.

Many optically active compounds give solutions, the rotation of which changes with time. This phenomenon, which is called *mutarotation* (L. *mutare,* to change), must result from some structural change in the molecule. The mutarotation of glucose solutions was reported first in 1846. By 1895 readily interconvertible isomeric modifications of glucose had been isolated. Three such forms are obtainable. The form designated α crystallizes as the hydrate from 70 per cent alcohol below 30°. Its freshly prepared aqueous solutions have a specific rotation of +112°. The β form crystallizes from aqueous solutions evaporated at temperatures above 98°. It has a specific rotation of +18.7°. The third form is obtained by adding alcohol to a concentrated aqueous solution and has a rotation of +52.7°. However, only α- and β-glucose mutarotate, and each finally attains the value +52.7°. The third form therefore is nothing more than an equilibrium mixture of the α and β forms.

The existence of the two forms of glucose and their mutarotation is

Change in optical rotation of sugars

Sugars are cyclic hemiacetals

explainable if it is assumed that they have cyclic hemiacetal structure analogous to the acetal structures postulated for the methyl α- and β-gly cosides. It usually is assumed that their interconversion takes place by wa of the open chain form.

$$
\begin{array}{ccc}
\text{H—C—OH} & \text{CHO} & \text{HO—C—H} \\
\text{CHOH} & \text{CHOH} & \text{CHOH} \\
\text{CHOH} \quad \text{O} & \text{CHOH} & \text{CHOH} \quad \text{O} \\
\text{CHOH} & \text{CHOH} & \text{CHOH} \\
\text{H—C} & \text{H—C—OH} & \text{H—C} \\
\text{CH}_2\text{OH} & \text{CH}_2\text{OH} & \text{CH}_2\text{OH} \\
\text{α-\textsc{d}-Glycose} & & \text{β-\textsc{d}-Glycose}
\end{array}
$$

That the equilibrium rotation of glucose is not the average of the rotation of α- and β-glucose is not surprising, since they are diastereoisomers and not enantiomorphs, and the equilibrium composition need not be a 50–5 mixture. The anomeric carbon atom of the hemiacetal structure frequently is called the *reducing carbon atom,* because it is involved in the reduction c Fehling solution. The anomeric hydroxyl group frequently is called th *hemiacetal hydroxyl group.*

<u>*Esters of sugars*</u>

    <u>The hydroxyl groups of sugars can be converted readily to ester groups</u> The aldoses acetylate with acetic anhydride in the presence of acidic o basic catalysts. The hexoses yield pentaacetates and the pentoses tetraace tates, thus indicating the presence of five and four hydroxyl groups. The acetates, however, do not reduce Fehling solution and therefore do not con tain a free aldehyde group. Moreover two isomeric α and β forms of eacl acetate are obtained. Hence it is the cyclic form of the sugar that i acetylated. The acid catalysts commonly used are sulfuric acid or zinc chlo ride, and the basic catalysts are pyridine (p. 131) or sodium acetate (acetate ion). Zinc chloride is an acid catalyst because the zinc atom lacks electron in its valence shell and like the proton can combine with an unshared pai of electrons. Acetate ion in acetic acid solution is a base analogous to the hydroxide ion in water solution.

Strong acids yield furfural from pentoses

    Although dilute acids at room temperature have little effect on aldose other than catalyzing α,β interconversion, hot strong acids produce com plex changes that involve dehydration. Thus all pentoses when distilled with 12 per cent hydrochloric acid give approximately theoretical yield of furfural (p. 99). The reaction is used both as a qualitative test for pen toses or substances yielding pentoses on hydrolysis and for their quantitative etimation, by detecting or estimating the furfural that distills (p. 80).

$$
\begin{array}{ccc}
\text{CHO} & \text{CHO} & \\
\text{CHOH} & \text{C} & \text{HC——CH} \\
\text{CHOH} \xrightarrow[\text{acid}]{\text{Hot}} & \text{CH} \quad \text{O} \quad \text{or} & \text{HC} \quad \text{C—CHO} \quad + 3\,\text{H}_2\text{O} \\
\text{CHOH} & \text{CH} & \text{O} \\
\text{CH}_2\text{OH} & \text{CH} & \\
& & \text{Furfural}
\end{array}
$$

Hexoses yield 5-(hydroxymethyl)furfural, but this compound is more soluble in water than furfural and is not volatile with steam. Hence it is acted upon further by the hot acid, giving levulinic acid and considerable amounts of dark insoluble condensation products known as *humins*.

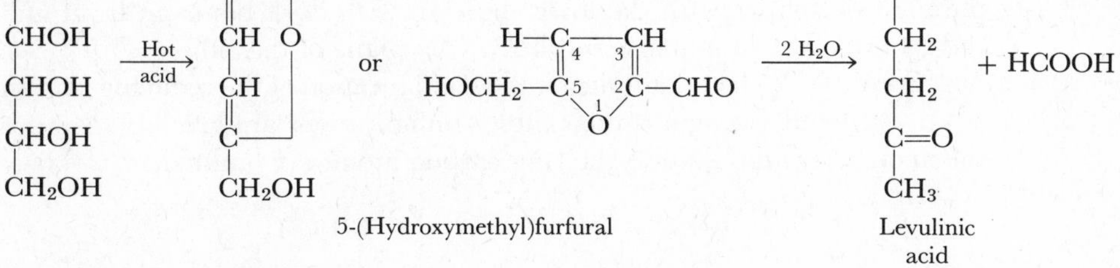

Levulinic acid from hexoses

5-(Hydroxymethyl)furfural

Levulinic acid

The different furfurals give characteristic color reactions with polyhydric phenols such as resorcinol (p. 79), and phloroglucinol (p. 80), which may be used to distinguish between pentoses and hexoses.

Nitric acid oxidizes sugars to dibasic acids. The reaction may be used to distinguish between certain sugars, because some give optically inactive dibasic acids whereas others give optically active acids, depending on whether the product has a plane of symmetry.

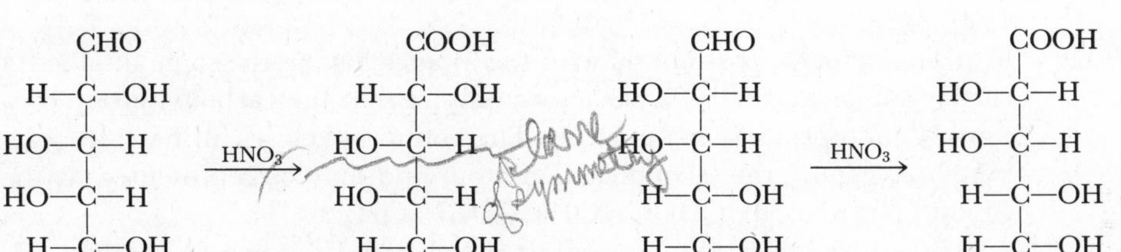

Oxidation to dibasic acids

(+)-Galactose

Galactaric acid (mucic acid) Inactive

(+)-Mannose

Mannaric acid Active

The formulas used thus far to represent the structure of the sugars do not indicate adequately the space relationships within the molecules, particularly those of the groups on the last two carbon atoms. With a molecular model the open-chain formula for glucose (I) can be represented in a coiled manner (II) to portray better the 109.5 degree angle between carbon atoms.

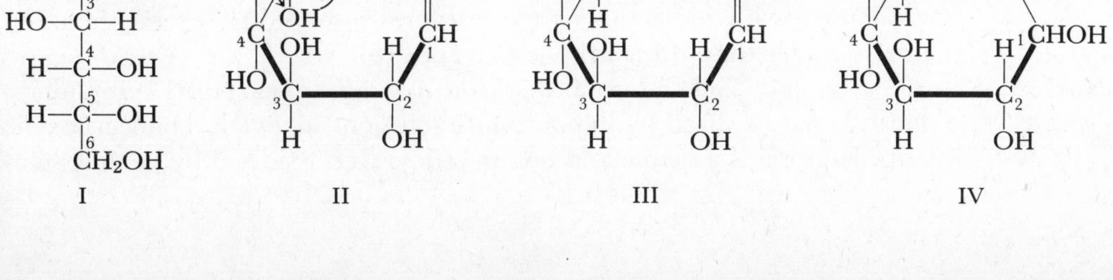

Perspective formulas for sugars

I

II

III

IV

However, for the oxygen atom of the 5-hydroxyl group to become a member of the ring in the cyclic hemiacetal form (IV), rotation must take place about the bond between the fourth and fifth carbon atoms (III), with the result that the hydrogen atoms on the fourth and fifth carbon atoms are on opposite sides of the ring instead of on the same side as in the projection representation (I). Formula IV is not a projection formula but is a perspective formula. The ring may be considered as perpendicular to the plane of the paper with the lower portion with dark bonds in front and the groups extending above and below the plane of the ring.

Formula IV does not indicate the configuration of the reducing carbon atom. In the following formulas these configurations are given. Except for the anomeric carbon atoms the ring carbon atoms are omitted.

α-D-Glucose   β-D-Glucose

The perspective formulas, frequently called Haworth formulas, are useful also in representing the structures of oligo- and polysaccharides (pp. 188, 192).

The **ketoses** are isomeric with the aldoses having the same number of carbon atoms and differ in structure only in that the carbonyl group contains a nonterminal carbon atom. The common ketoses all have the carbonyl oxygen on the second carbon atom and may be represented by the general formula, $HOCH_2(CHOH)_nCOCH_2OH$.

Fructose is a ketohexose

D(−)-**Fructose** is the most abundant ketose. It occurs free, along with glucose and sucrose, in fruit juices and honey, and combined with other sugars in oligosaccharides. It is the chief product of the hydrolysis of the polysaccharide inulin (p. 192). Naturally occurring fructose has a high negative rotation which gave rise to the common name *levulose*. It is the sweetest of the sugars.

Relative sweetness of sugars

Individuals vary greatly in their sensory perceptions, and it is possible to state only average opinions regarding taste. The results of early workers based on threshold methods, that is, the highest dilution that can be tasted, are valueless. When comparing concentrations of equal sweetness, the relative sweetness varies with the concentration. Moreover since α-glucose is sweeter than β-glucose, solutions that have reached equilibrium must be used. When compared with a 10 per cent glucose solution, the relative sweetness of some of the common sugars is lactose 0.55, galactose 0.95, glucose 1.00, sucrose 1.45, and fructose 1.65. Many synthetic compounds are known whose sweetness is from several hundred to several thousand times greater than that of the sugars (p. 116).

Fructose reduces Fehling solution

Fructose gives the usual addition reactions of carbonyl compounds, but it is not oxidized by hypobromite solutions to give a monocarboxylic acid. Hence it is a ketose and not an aldose. It is oxidized by Fehling solution and has a reducing power comparable to that of glucose. As a ketone it would not be expected to reduce Fehling solution. However, in the presence of alkali it is converted to glucose and mannose (p. 180) and is degraded to compounds of lower molecular weight (p. 181), all of which are oxidized readily. Moreover CHOH groups adjacent to a carbonyl group also are oxidized by Fehling solution (p. 170).

When fructose reacts with phenylhydrazine, a phenylosazone is formed which is identical with that obtained from (+)-glucose. Hence the carbonyl group must contain C-2, the configuration of the rest of the molecule must be identical with that of (+)-glucose, and (−)-fructose must belong to the D family.

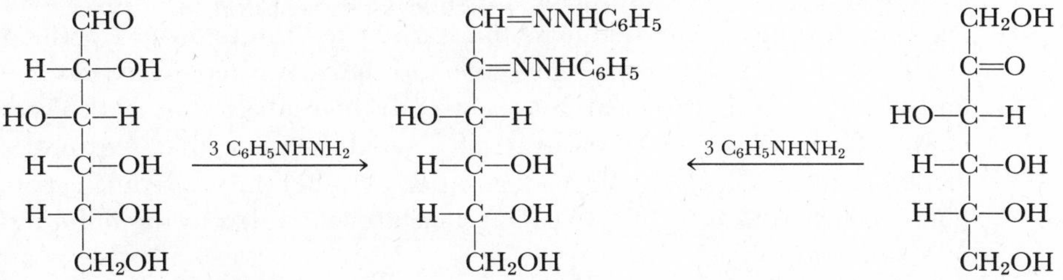

gives same osazone as glucose

CHO	CH=NNHC$_6$H$_5$	CH$_2$OH
H—C—OH	C=NNHC$_6$H$_5$	C=O
HO—C—H	HO—C—H	HO—C—H
H—C—OH $\xrightarrow{3\ C_6H_5NHNH_2}$	H—C—OH $\xleftarrow{3\ C_6H_5NHNH_2}$	H—C—OH
H—C—OH	H—C—OH	H—C—OH
CH$_2$OH	CH$_2$OH	CH$_2$OH
D(+)-Glucose	D-Glucose phenyl-osazone	D(−)-Fructose

L(−)-Sorbose is the only other ketohexose of importance. It does not occur naturally but is produced by the action of sorbose bacteria (*Acetobacter xylinum* or better *Acetobacter suboxydans*) on sorbitol.

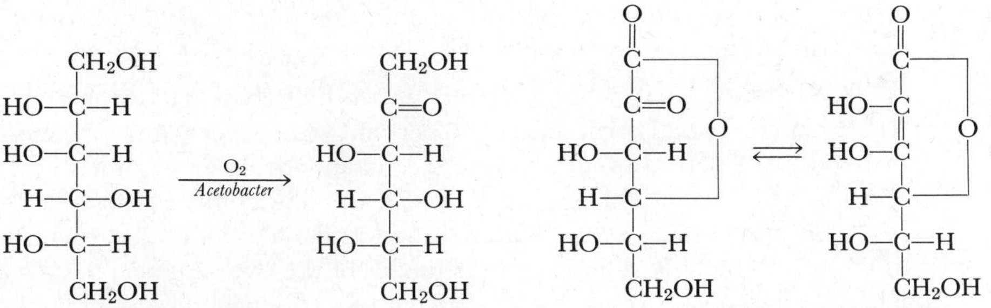

CH$_2$OH	CH$_2$OH	C=O	C
HO—C—H	C=O	C=O	HO—C
HO—C—H	HO—C—H	HO—C—H	HO—C
H—C—OH $\xrightarrow[Acetobacter]{O_2}$	H—C—OH	H—C	H—C
HO—C—H	HO—C—H	HO—C—H	HO—C—H
CH$_2$OH	CH$_2$OH	CH$_2$OH	CH$_2$OH
Sorbitol	L(−)-Sorbose	Vitamin C (ascorbic acid)	

L-Sorbose is important as an intermediate for the commercial synthesis of **vitamin C,** otherwise known as *ascorbic acid,* which is a necessary dietary factor for the prevention of scurvy.

Vitamin C from sorbose

DISACCHARIDES

Disaccharides are carbohydrates that can be hydrolyzed to two molecules of monosaccharide. Reducing disaccharides reduce Fehling solution and nonreducing disaccharides do not. **Maltose,** C$_{12}$H$_{22}$O$_{11}$, is formed by the enzyme-catalyzed hydrolysis of starch.

Reducing disaccharide from starch

$$(\text{C}_6\text{H}_{10}\text{O}_5)_x + \frac{x}{2}\,\text{H}_2\text{O} \xrightarrow{\text{Diastase}} \frac{x}{2}\,\text{C}_{12}\text{H}_{22}\text{O}_{11}$$
Starch   Maltose

Acid- or enzyme-catalyzed hydrolysis of maltose yields two molecules of glucose.

$$C_{12}H_{22}O_{11} + H_2O \xrightarrow[\substack{\text{Maltase} \\ \text{(α-glucosidase)}}]{\text{[H}^+\text{] or}} 2\ C_6H_{12}O_6$$

Maltose   Glucose

Maltose reduces Fehling solution, forms an osazone and undergoes muta-rotation. Hence it contains a potential aldehyde group and a hemiacetal ring structure. The formation of an octaacetate and octamethyl derivative indicates the presence of eight hydroxyl groups.

Hydrolysis to two molecules of glucose points to a linkage through oxygen rather than directly between two carbon atoms, and the ease of hydrolysis by enzymes and acids indicates an acetal linkage rather than an ether linkage. The two glucose units are linked through the 1 position of the nonreducing half of the molecule and the 4 position of the reducing half. Maltose is hydrolyzed by *maltase,* a glucosidase that hydrolyzes methyl α-glucoside, and not by *emulsin,* a glucosidase that hydrolyzes methyl β-glucoside. Hence the configuration of C-1 of the nonreducing portion is believed to be α. These conclusions are embodied in the following perspective formula.

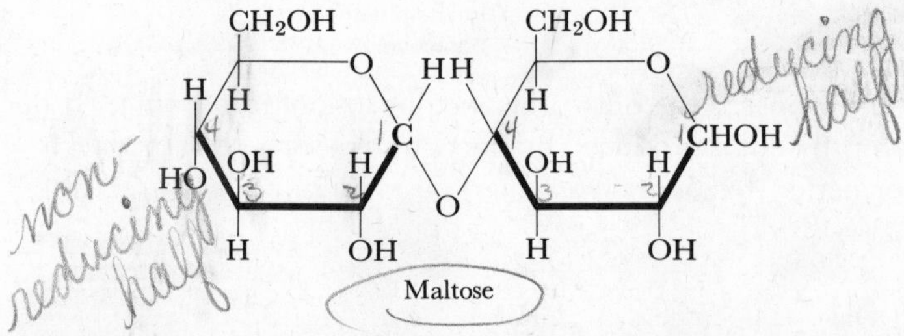

Maltose

from cellulose

Cellobiose is a disaccharide formed by the hydrolysis of its octaacetate. The latter compound is obtained in 40 per cent yield when cellulose (cotton or paper) is dissolved in a mixture of acetic anhydride and sulfuric acid, and allowed to stand for one week at 35°. Cellobiose like maltose yields two molecules of glucose on hydrolysis and undergoes all of the reactions of maltose. The only difference in behavior of the two sugars is that cellobiose is hydrolyzed in the presence of emulsin (β-glucosidase) and not in the presence of maltase (α-glucosidase). Hence cellobiose differs from maltose only in that the linkage between the two glucose units has the β configuration instead of the α configuration.

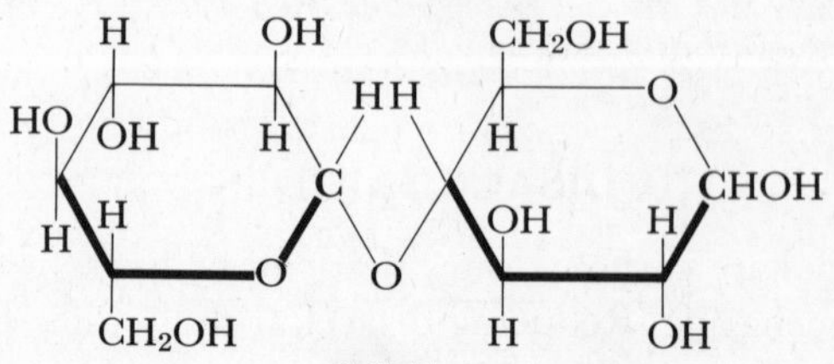

Cellobiose

from milk

Lactose (*milk sugar*) is present in about 5 per cent concentration in the milk of all mammals. It is prepared commercially from whey, the aqueous solution left after the coagulation of the proteins of milk in the manufacture of cheese. Lactose is a reducing disaccharide, and on acid or enzyme hydrolysis it yields one molecule of galactose and one molecule of glucose. If it first is oxidized to lactonic acid and then hydrolyzed, the products are galactose and gluconic acid. Hence the glucose unit contains the reducing portion of the molecule. Because lactose is hydrolyzed by β-galactosidase, the linkage between the galactose and glucose molecule is believed to be β.

Lactose

Although both monosaccharides and reducing disaccharides produce osazones, the reaction can be used to distinguish between them because the osazones of monosaccharides are less soluble than those of disaccharides and crystallize from the hot solution, whereas the osazones of disaccharides crystallize only on cooling.

Sucrose (*cane sugar, beet sugar*) is the most important disaccharide. It occurs universally in plants and in all portions of the plant. It also is present in honey along with glucose and fructose. The principal sources are sugar cane, sugar beets, and the sugar maple tree. The great ease with which sucrose crystallizes probably accounts for its isolation in a pure state as early as 300 A.D. Sugar cane (*Saccharum officinarum*) belongs to the grass family and probably originated in northeastern India (Skr. *sakara,* gravel or sugar). From there it was introduced into China about 400 A.D. and into Egypt by the Arabians in 640 A.D. It is believed that it was introduced into Santo Domingo by Columbus on his second voyage to America in 1494. Although sucrose was discovered in beet juice in 1747, it was not produced from this source until the Napoleonic Wars (1796–1814) made the price of cane sugar prohibitive in Europe. *(Nonreducing disaccharide)*

Sucrose is obtained from cane by grinding the stalk and expressing the juice with rollers. The juice, which contains about 15 per cent sucrose, is made slightly alkaline with lime to prevent hydrolysis. Heating causes most of the impurities to separate as a heavy scum and as a precipitate, and these are removed. This process is known as *defecation*. The clear juice is concentrated under reduced pressure and allowed to crystallize. The raw sugar is removed by centrifuging and is washed in the centrifuge. The centrifugate is reconcentrated and the operation repeated until no more crystals can be obtained economically. The final mother liquor is a dark viscous liquid that contains about 50 per cent fermentable sugars. It is known as *blackstrap* and is used for preparing cattle feeds and for the production of alcohol (p. 65). *(from cane)*

The raw sugar is shipped to refineries where the brown color is removed by dissolving the sugar in water and passing the solution through decolorizing carbon. Concentration and crystallization yield the pure sugar of commerce. *Brown sugars* are prepared by adding various amounts of molasses to the white product. If the white crystalline sugar is ground with 3 per cent of starch to prevent caking, the product is known as *powdered sugar.*

from sugar beet

The white sugar beet, a cultivated variety of *Beta maritima,* has been bred to contain up to 18 per cent sucrose. The beet root, free of leaves, is washed and sliced into V-shaped pieces about 1 cm. thick. These pieces are extracted countercurrently by hot water to yield a dark solution containing about 12 per cent sucrose. By diffusing the sugar from the plant cells, the amount of protein and high molecular weight impurities extracted is much less than if the beet were crushed and pressed. The warm extract is agitated with 2 to 3 per cent of lime and the mixture then saturated with carbon dioxide. The precipitate carries down most of the impurities and the yellow filtrate is decolorized with sulfur dioxide. After concentrating, crystallizing, and washing, the product is ready for market.

from maple sap

Isolation of sucrose from the sugar maple (*Acer saccharinum*) is relatively unimportant. Small amounts are prepared also from other sources such as sorghum and palm sap, but sucrose from these sources does not enter the world market.

Sucrose is produced in larger amounts than any other pure organic chemical. World production in 1959 (excluding U.S.S.R.) was 54 million tons, of which about one-third was from beets and two-thirds from cane. Production in the United States (mainland) was 2.8 million tons of which only one-fourth was from cane. Consumption was 8.4 million tons or 95 pounds per capita.

Hydrolysis gives invert sugar

Hydrolysis of sucrose in the presence of acids or of the enzyme *sucrase* (*invertase*) yields one molecule of fructose and one molecule of glucose. Sucrose has a positive rotation, $[\alpha]_D^{20} = +66.53$, but during hydrolysis the sign of rotation changes because the high negative rotation of fructose, $[\alpha]_D^{20} = -92.4$ for the equilibrium mixture, more than balances the positive rotation of glucose, $[\alpha]_D^{20} = +52.7$ for the equilibrium mixture. Because of the change in sign of rotation during hydrolysis the process is known as *inversion,* and the mixture of fructose and glucose is known as **invert sugar.** It has about the same sweetening power as sucrose (p. 186) but has much less tendency to crystallize and hence is used in the manufacture of candies and syrups. It is of interest that **sucrose octaacetate** is extremely bitter.

Structure of sucrose

Sucrose does not reduce Fehling solution, form an osazone, undergo mutarotation, or form methyl glycosides. Accordingly the fructose and glucose portions are linked through the two anomeric carbon atoms. The glucose portion has a six-membered (pyranose) ring, and the fructose portion has a five-membered (furanose) ring. Sucrose is hydrolyzed by yeast α-glucosidase and not by the β-glucosidase of emulsin. It is hydrolyzed also by sucrase, an enzyme that hydrolyzes β- but not α-fructofuranosides. Accordingly the anomeric carbon of the glucose portion is assigned the α configuration, and that of the fructose portion the β configuration.

Sucrose

POLYSACCHARIDES *Don't know*

As the name implies, polysaccharides are substances of high molecular weight (average 30,000 to 10,000,000) that yield many molecules of monosaccharide on hydrolysis. They are insoluble in liquids and are altered readily by the acids and alkalies required to catalyze their conversion into soluble derivatives. Hence their purification is extremely difficult. Moreover even the purified products are not molecularly homogeneous; the same substance may consist of polymers of various molecular weights. Polysaccharides such as starch, glycogen, or inulin are reserve foodstuffs for the plant or animal; others, such as the cellulose of plants and chitin of crustacea, have a structural function; for still others, such as gums and mucilages, the function is unknown.

During the growth of a plant, carbohydrate is stored in various parts, such as the seeds, bulbs, and tubers, in the form of microscopic granules of starch. Seeds may contain up to 70 per cent starch, and roots and tubers up to 30 per cent. Corn, potatoes, wheat, rice, tapioca, sago, and sweet potatoes constitute the chief commercial sources.

Starch from corn

In the United States most starch is derived from corn (maize). The corn grains are soaked in warm water containing sulfur dioxide until soft and then are shredded to free the germ. When the ground mass is mixed with water, the germ floats because of the high oil content and is collected, dried, and pressed to produce corn oil (p. 120). The remainder of the grain sinks and is ground as finely as possible without rupturing the starch granules. The mixture is washed through screens to remove most of the hull. The starch suspension is passed through continuous centrifuges to remove the starch granules, which then are washed free of any remaining gluten. The gluten, which contains the protein components of the grain (p. 204), is recovered from the steep water and from the water that leaves the centrifuges. Corn steep water now finds an important outlet as a nutrient for the mold used in the production of penicillin (p. 228). The separation of starch *from potatoes* from potatoes is somewhat simpler in that steeping and germ removal are not required. Annual production of cornstarch in the United States is about 4 billion pounds, and of potato starch about 100 million pounds.

Starch a mixture

When starch is heated with water, the granules swell greatly and a colloidal suspension is produced. This dispersion has been separated into two components. When it is saturated with a slightly soluble alcohol such as butanol, a microcrystalline precipitate forms which is known as *A-fraction* or *amylose*. Addition to the mother liquors of a water-miscible alcohol such as methanol gives an amorphous material known as *B-fraction* or *amylopectin*. Most starches contain amylose and amylopectin in the ratio of from 1:4 to 1:6. However, some genetically pure mutant varieties of grains, known as waxy corn, sorghum, millet, rice, and barley, contain only amylopectin, whereas another recessive mutant strain of wrinkled pea has been reported to contain from 70 to 98 per cent of amylose.

Amylose is a linear polymer

Both amylose and amylopectin give only glucose on hydrolysis. **Amyloses** from different sources have average molecular weights of 78,000 to 1,100,000 (270–3800 C_6 units). The glucose units are joined by α linkages through the 1,4 positions to give an essentially linear molecule coiled into a spiral. The typical blue color reaction of starch with iodine is due to the amylose fraction, which absorbs 18 to 20 per cent of its weight of iodine. The blue product is an inclusion compound (p. 139) in which iodine molecules fit into the open spaces of the helix.

Amylopectin and glycogen are highly branched

Amylopectins have average molecular weights between 250,000 and 10,000,000 (850–35,000 C_6 units). The molecules are randomly branched. The branches consist of 20 to 25 glucose units joined by 1,4-α linkages and are joined to each other by 1,6-α linkages.

Glycogen is the reserve carbohydrate of animals. It does not occur as granules but is distributed throughout the protoplasm. Glycogens have average molecular weights around 2,000,000. The structure is similar to that of amylopectin except that it is even more highly branched, the branches having shorter chain lengths of 10 to 12 C_6 units.

Inulin is a fructoside

Inulin is a starchlike substance that occurs in many plants, particularly members of the *Compositae*, for example inula, Jerusalem artichoke, dahlia tubers, and chicory. Hydrolysis yields chiefly fructose and a small amount of glucose. Molecular weights correspond to a chain length of about 30 C_6 units. It has been postulated that the chain consists of β-fructofuranose units joined at the 1 and 2 positions and terminated with a sucrose type linkage to glucose.

Cellulose has 1,4-β linkages

The cell membranes of higher plants are composed of **cellulose.** It makes up about 10 per cent of dry leaves, 40 per cent of the woody structure of plants, and 98 per cent of cotton fiber. Average molecular weights are above 1,000,000 (2500 C_6 units). The glucose units are joined entirely by β linkages through the 1,4 positions.

Cellulose

The chief source of cellulose for chemical conversions is **wood pulp.** It is prepared from wood by extracting the lignin, which binds the fibers together, with hot solutions of sodium hydroxide (*soda pulp*), of calcium, magnesium, or ammonium bisulfites (*sulfite pulp*), or of a mixture of sodium hydroxide and sodium sulfide (*sulfate or kraft pulp*).

Rayon from cellulose

The first important **synthetic fibers** were made from cellulose. The manufacture of **viscose rayon** is based on the reaction of the hydroxyl groups of cellulose with carbon disulfide in the presence of sodium hydroxide to give *xanthates*, which are soluble in water. The reaction can be reversed by acidification.

$$ROH + CS_2 + NaOH \longrightarrow \left[ROC{\overset{\displaystyle S}{\underset{\displaystyle \|}{}}}-S^-\right]Na^+ + H_2O$$

Sodium alkyl
xanthate

$$\left[ROC{\overset{\displaystyle S}{\underset{\displaystyle \|}{}}}-S^-\right]Na^+ + NaHSO_4 \longrightarrow ROH + CS_2 + Na_2SO_4$$

The solution of the cellulose xanthate is forced through the fine holes of a die called a *spinneret,* and the filaments are passed through a solution of sodium bisulfate, which reprecipitates the cellulose. If the solution is extruded through a slot, sheets of **cellophane** are formed.

Acetylation of cellulose with acetic anhydride gives **cellulose triacetate,** which is thermoplastic and can be molded into useful articles. It is soluble in methylene chloride containing a little alcohol. If the solution is forced through a spinneret and the solvent evaporated, **cellulose acetate fiber** is produced. Cellulose acetate sheet, used for **photographic film base,** is formed by spreading the solution continuously on a large rotating drum, evaporating the solvent, and stripping the sheet from the drum.

Cellulose acetates and nitrates are useful esters

Cellulose trinitrate is the chief ingredient of **smokeless powder.** The dinitrate is soluble in organic solvents and is used as the vehicle in the formulation of **lacquers.**

Pectins from fruits, **alginic acid** and **agar** from sea weeds, and various plant **gums** and **mucilages** are complex polysaccharides. **Chitin,** the structural substance of insects and the shells of crustacea, contains acetylamino groups, $CH_3CONH—$, instead of hydroxyl groups in the 2 positions of cellulose. Polysaccharides present in peanut shells, corn cobs, straw, and grain hulls that yield chiefly pentoses on hydrolysis are known as **pentosans.**

Many other natural products are polysaccharides

SUMMARY

1. Carbohydrates are important because they form one of the three chief sources of energy for biological organisms.
2. The pentoses are tetrahydroxy aldehydes or ketones and the hexoses are pentahydroxy aldehydes or ketones. Because of the three and four asymmetric carbon atoms present, there are eight aldopentoses and sixteen aldohexoses.
3. The simple sugars normally exist in cyclic forms in which the hydroxyl group on the fifth carbon atom has added to the carbonyl group to give hemiacetals, which exist in α and β forms. When one form of a sugar is dissolved in water, the optical rotation changes as the two forms come into equilibrium with each other. This phenomenon is called *mutarotation.*
4. Reducing sugars reduce Fehling solution, form osazones, and undergo isomerization and degradation in the presence of strong alkali. Reaction with methanol in the presence of a strong acid gives a cyclic acetal, called a methyl glycoside.
5. Disaccharides and polysaccharides consist of sugar molecules joined by glycosidic linkages. If the glycosidic hydroxyl and an alcoholic hydroxyl are involved in bond formation, the disaccharide still reduces Fehling solution and is called a reducing disaccharide. If two glycosidic hydroxyls are involved, the product is a nonreducing disaccharide.
6. Starch and cellulose are the most important polysaccharides. Both yield only glucose molecules on hydrolysis. They differ in that the glucose molecules are joined through an α-linkage in starch and through a β-linkage in cellulose. In addition, starch has two components, amylose and amylopectin. Amylose has linearly linked glucose molecules which may coil into a spiral, whereas amylopectin has a branched structure.

7. Cellulose can be converted into esters that yield many important useful products such as guncotton, lacquers, photographic film base, viscose rayon, acetate fibers, and plastics.

8. Many gums, mucilages, and thickening agents are complex polysaccharides.

EXERCISES

D family

1. To what family does (+)-arabinose belong?
2. Give the projection formula for α-L(−)-glucose.
3. What other sugars would give the same phenylosazone as (−)-sorbose?
4. How could one distinguish by chemical reactions between: (a) glucose and galactose; (b) glucose and maltose; (c) maltose and sucrose; (d) xylose and arabinose; (e) xylose and glucose?
5. Assuming that all hydroxyl groups react, write an equation for the reaction of a cellulose C_6 unit: (a) with acetic anhydride; (b) with nitric acid.
6. How could one distinguish: (a) cellulose nitrate from cellulose acetate; (b) viscose rayon from cellulose acetate fiber; (c) starch from finely powdered cellulose?

2. α-L(−) glucose

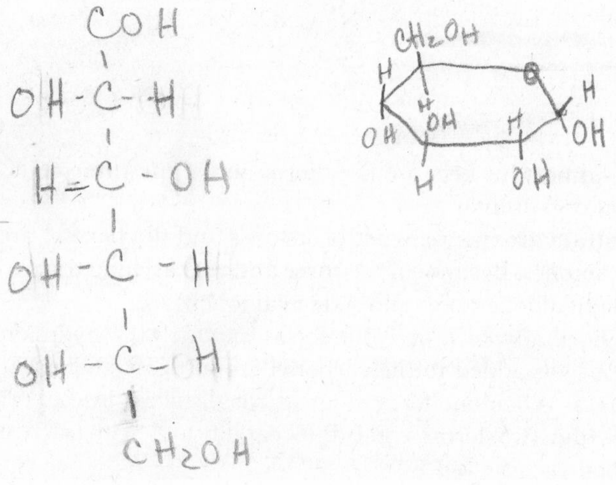

CHAPTER 16

PROTEINS AND
AMINO ACIDS

Proteins (Gr. *proteios,* of first importance) are complex compounds of high molecular weight that yield **α-amino acids,** $RCH(NH_2)COOH$, on hydrolysis. Proteins are present in all living tissue, but certain tissues, such as seeds and flesh, contain larger amounts than others, such as fatty and structural tissues. Plants and bacteria are the ultimate source of all proteins, because the animal organism is unable to synthesize certain essential amino acids (p. 203) from inorganic nitrogen compounds.

Hydrolysis of proteins yields α-amino acids

In the synthesis of amino acids, plants are aided by soil microorganisms. The nitrite bacteria change ammonia to nitrites, and nitrate bacteria change nitrites to nitrates. The nitrates and ammonia are converted by the plant first into α-amino acids and then into proteins. Other soil bacteria are able to change organic nitrogen into ammonia, thus completing the cycle. In addition certain soil bacteria in conjunction with the plants on whose roots they grow, namely the legumes, are capable of converting atmospheric nitrogen into amino acids.

Origin of amino acids and proteins

Because of the high molecular weight of the proteins and their similarity in being composed of amino acids, it is not possible to determine the empirical formulas of proteins from the elementary analysis. The elementary composition of all proteins is approximately 50 per cent carbon, 7 per cent hydrogen, 16 per cent nitrogen, 25 per cent oxygen, and 0–2 per cent sulfur. Phosphorus, iron, copper, and other elements also may be present. Proteins, when mixed with non-nitrogenous substances as in foodstuffs, usually are estimated by determining the total per cent nitrogen and dividing by 0.16.

Composition of proteins

The proteins are classified into **simple proteins,** yielding only α-amino acids on hydrolysis, and **conjugated proteins,** which yield α-amino acids and one or more groups of a nonprotein nature. The latter are known as **prosthetic groups** (Gr. *prosthesis,* an addition). Because the exact structures of most individual proteins are unknown, the further classification of proteins is arbitrary and is based largely on their solubility characteristics. This classification was devised when there was little knowledge of the structure of proteins and is useful only as a means of dividing proteins into smaller groups. As knowledge of a pure protein increases, it frequently is found to have properties characteristic of more than one group.

Simple proteins yield
only α-amino acids

Albumins are soluble in water, coagulated by heat and precipitated from solution on saturation with ammonium sulfate. Examples are *serum albumin* from blood serum, *ovalbumin* from egg white, and *lactalbumin* from milk.

Globulins are insoluble in water but soluble in dilute salt solutions, for example 5 per cent sodium chloride solution, and are precipitated by half-saturation with ammonium sulfate. They are soluble also in dilute solutions of strong acids and alkalies. They occur in serum and tissue and make up largely the proteins of seeds and nuts. Antibodies that prevent several diseases have been found in the γ-globulin fraction of human serum.

Prolamines are insoluble in water and absolute alcohol but soluble in 70–80 per cent ethyl alcohol. They are obtained principally from cereal seeds. Zein from corn is prepared industrially.

Glutelins are insoluble in water and dilute salt solutions but are soluble in dilute solutions of strong acids and alkalies. They occur in cereal seeds and are the proteins that remain after the removal of albumins, globulins, and prolamines.

Scleroproteins (albuminoids) are soluble only in concentrated solutions of strong acids and alkalies. They are the fibrous proteins having a supporting or protective function in the animal organism. Submembers are the *collagen* of the skin, tendons, and bones, the *elastins* of elastic tissues such as tendons and arteries, and the *keratins* from hair, nail, and horn.

Histones are soluble in water but are precipitated by dilute ammonia solution. They are basic compounds and occur combined as salts with acidic substances such as nucleic acids (p. 227) or heme (p. 226) in animal tissues.

Protamines are soluble in water, not coagulated by heat, and precipitated from aqueous solutions by the addition of alcohol. They are more basic than histones and simpler in structure, and are combined as salts with nucleic acids in ripe fish sperm.

Conjugated proteins
yield α-amino acids
and prosthetic group

Nucleoproteins are proteins combined with nucleic acids (p. 227), either as salts or by covalent bonds. They occur in the nucleus of every cell and sometimes in the cytoplasm as well.

Glycoproteins are proteins combined with a carbohydrate but do not contain phosphoric acid, purines, or pyrimidines. They are the *mucins* and *mucoids* (mucus-like substances) of bone, tendons, fish eggs, snails, and other tissue and glandular secretions.

Phosphoproteins have only phosphoric acid as a prosthetic group. Examples are the *casein* of milk and *vitellin* of egg yolk.

Chromoproteins are colored proteins. They contain a metallic element in the molecule, for example iron, magnesium, copper, manganese, vanadium, or cobalt, and may contain a prosthetic group, especially a metalloporphyrin (p. 225). *Hemoglobins* from red blood cells and *hemocyanins* from the blood of mollusks and arthropods are examples.

Purification of
proteins difficult

Because of the complexity of the proteins, their high molecular weights, the large number, the complex mixtures that occur naturally, and the similarity in their chemical and physical properties, it is difficult to be certain that a protein is pure; that is to say, a single molecular species. Several proteins have been obtained in a crystalline state, but even crystallinity does not guarantee that a protein is homomolecular. Proteins that once were thought to be pure have been separated into a number of fractions by taking advantage of the different rates of migration under an applied electromotive force (*electrophoresis*). Criteria of purity which must be applied, in addition to chemical analysis and crystalline homogeneity, are constancy of solubility at a given temperature regardless of the amount of excess protein present, constancy of diffusion rate, of rate of transfer under an electrical potential (electrophoretic mobility), of rate of sedimentation in the ultracentrifuge, and of dielectric constant.

The molecular weights of proteins are so high that methods such as those dependent on the lowering of the freezing point or elevation of the boiling point cannot be used. If the protein contains a characteristic group or atom, the equivalent weight can be found by determining the weight of the group or atom in a given weight of protein and calculating the weight of protein associated with one gram molecular weight of the group, or one atomic weight of the atom. For example, an equivalent weight can be calculated for hemoglobin from the amount of iron present. Molecular weights have been determined by the measurement of osmotic pressure, rates of diffusion, sedimentation in the ultracentrifuge, and the scattering of light. These values are particle sizes and do not preclude the possibility of subdivision into smaller units without breaking covalent bonds. For example, a particle size as high as 48,000 has been reported for the insulin molecule as determined by sedimentation, but osmotic pressure measurements indicate a value of 12,000 under conditions of maximum dissociation. Still other work supports a minimum molecular weight of about 6000. Table 11 gives the molecular weights for a number of proteins as determined by several methods. There is fair agreement among the values obtained by the different procedures. The fact that the molecular weights are not integral multiples of the equivalent weights must be ascribed to inexact methods of analysis.

Some proteins have been shown by sedimentation in the ultracentrifuge to be definitely polymolecular; that is, they are composed of mixtures of molecules having different molecular weights. For example, the molecu-

Molecular weights very high

TABLE 11.   PARTICLE SIZES OR MOLECULAR WEIGHTS OF PURIFIED PROTEINS

PROTEIN \ PROCEDURE	OSMOTIC PRESSURE	SEDIMENTATION-DIFFUSION	LIGHT SCATTERING	EQUIV. WT. BY CHEM. ANAL.
Insulin (beef)	12,000	6, 12,24, 36, and 48 thousand		5734 (complete amino acid analysis)
Lysozyme	17,500	14,000–17,000	15,000	
Pepsin	36,000	35,000		
β-Lactoglobulin	35,000	41,000	36,000	
Ovalbumin	45,000	44,000	46,000	35,000 (tryptophan)
Hemoglobin	67,000	63,000		16,700 (iron)
Serum albumin (horse)	73,000	70,000	76,000	8000 (cystine)
Hemocyanin (lobster)		760,000	625,000	
Hemocyanin (snail)		8,900,000	6,300,000	25,500 (copper)
Tobacco mosaic virus		59,000,000	40,000,000	
Influenza virus			322,000,000	

Number of kinds
of amino acids small

lar weights of the molecules of lactalbumin vary from 12,000 to 25,000, of gelatin from 10,000 to 100,000, and of casein from 75,000 to 375,000.

The amino acids derived from proteins are given in Table 12. The monoamide of aspartic acid (asparagine, $H_2NCOCH_2CH(NH_2)COOH$) and of glutamic acid (glutamine, $H_2NCOCH_2CH_2CH(NH_2)COOH$) also take part in protein structure. Numerous other α-amino acids such as citrulline, $H_2NCONH(CH_2)_3CH(NH_2)COOH$, and ornithine, $H_2N-(CH_2)_3CH(NH_2)COOH$, have been isolated from natural sources but have not been established as building units of proteins.

TABLE 12.   AMINO ACIDS ACCEPTED AS BEING DIRECT PRODUCTS OF HYDROLYSIS OF PROTEINS

Neutral Amino Acids (equal number of amino and carboxyl groups)

1. Glycine or aminoacetic acid, $CH_2(NH_2)COOH$
2. Alanine or α-aminopropionic acid, $CH_3CH(NH_2)COOH$
3. Valine or α-aminoisovaleric acid, $(CH_3)_2CHCH(NH_2)COOH$
4. Leucine or α-aminoisocaproic acid, $(CH_3)_2CHCH_2CH(NH_2)COOH$
5. Isoleucine or α-amino-β-methylvaleric acid, $CH_3CH_2CH(CH_3)CH(NH_2)COOH$
6. Serine or α-amino-β-hydroxypropionic acid, $HOCH_2CH(NH_2)COOH$
7. Threonine or α-amino-β-hydroxybutyric acid, $CH_3CH(OH)CH(NH_2)COOH$
8. Cysteine or α-amino-β-mercaptopropionic acid, $HSCH_2CH(NH_2)COOH$
9. Cystine or 2-amino-2-carboxyethyl disulfide,
$$HOOCCH(NH_2)CH_2SSCH_2CH(NH_2)COOH$$
10. Methionine or α-amino-γ-(methylthio)butyric acid, $CH_3SCH_2CH_2CH(NH_2)COOH$
11. Phenylalanine or α-amino-β-phenylpropionic acid,

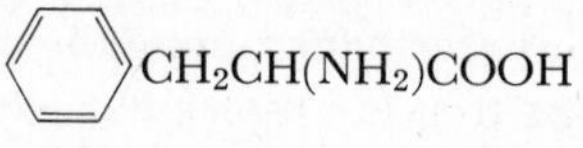

$CH_2CH(NH_2)COOH$

12. Tyrosine or α-amino-β-(4-hydroxyphenyl)propionic acid,

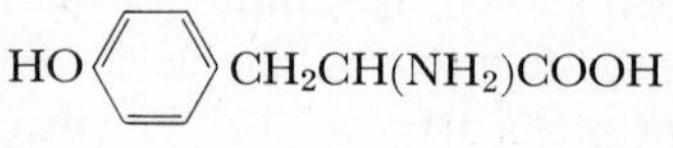

HO $CH_2CH(NH_2)COOH$

13. Halogenated tyrosines
    (*a*) 3-Bromotyrosine
    (*b*) 3-Iodotyrosine
    (*c*) 3,5-Dibromotyrosine
    (*d*) 3,5-Diiodotyrosine (*iodogorgoric acid*)
14. Halogenated thyronines

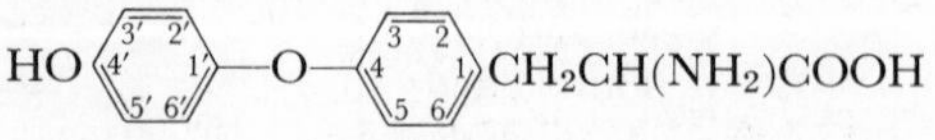

HO $—O—$ $CH_2CH(NH_2)COOH$

Thyronine

    (*a*) 3,5,3'-Triiodothyronine
    (*b*) 3,5,3',5'-Tetraiodothyronine (*thyroxine*)

$$H_2C\!-\!-\!-\!CH_2$$

15. Proline or 2-pyrrolidinecarboxylic acid, $H_2C \quad CHCOOH$

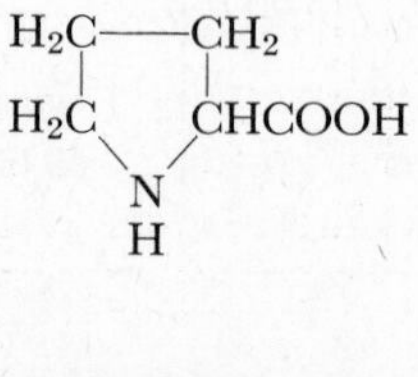

16. Hydroxyproline or 4-hydroxy-2-pyrrolidinecarboxylic acid,
$$HOCH-CH_2$$
$$H_2C \qquad CHCOOH$$
$$\diagdown N \diagup$$
$$H$$

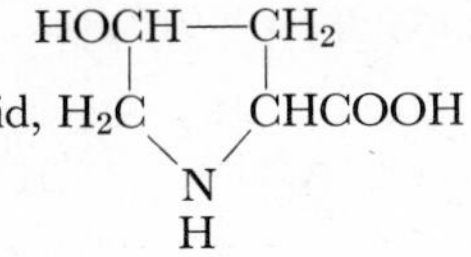

17. Tryptophan or α-amino-β-(3-indolyl)propionic acid,

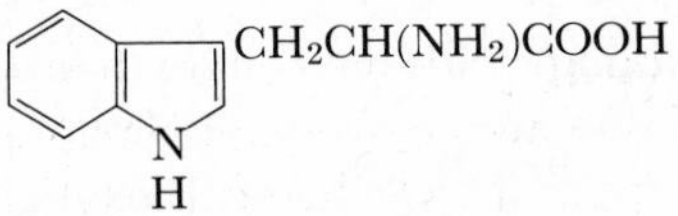

$$CH_2CH(NH_2)COOH$$
$$N$$
$$H$$

Basic Amino Acids (more basic groups than carboxyl groups)

18. Lysine or α,ϵ-diaminocaproic acid, $H_2NCH_2CH_2CH_2CH_2CH(NH_2)COOH$

19. Hydroxylysine or α,ϵ-diamino-δ-hydroxycaproic acid,
$$H_2NCH_2CH(OH)CH_2CH_2CH(NH_2)COOH$$

20. Arginine or α-amino-δ-guanidinovaleric acid,

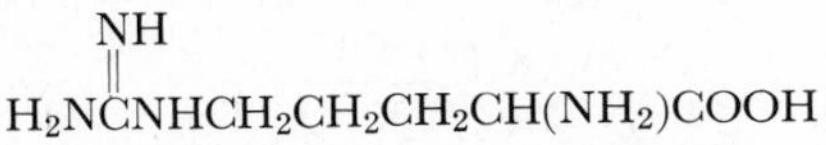

$$NH$$
$$\|$$
$$H_2NCNHCH_2CH_2CH_2CH(NH_2)COOH$$

21. Histidine or α-amino-β-(5-imidazolyl)propionic acid,

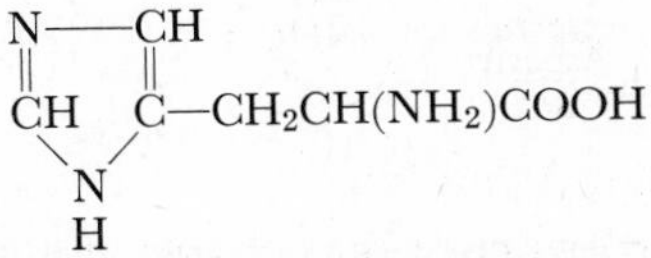

$$N-CH$$
$$\| \qquad \|$$
$$CH \quad C-CH_2CH(NH_2)COOH$$
$$\diagdown N \diagup$$
$$H$$

Acidic Amino Acids (more carboxyl groups than amino groups)

22. Aspartic acid or aminosuccinic acid, $HOOCCH_2CH(NH_2)COOH$

23. Glutamic acid or α-aminoglutaric acid, $HOOCCH_2CH_2CH(NH_2)COOH$

With the exception of glycine, all of the amino acids derived from proteins have at least one asymmetric carbon atom and are optically active. It is of further interest that all have been shown to have the same configuration at the α carbon atom. Indirect evidence indicated that this configuration is that indicated by the following tetrahedral or projection formulas. *Configuration of amino acids from proteins*

$$COOH \qquad\qquad COOH$$
$$H_2N \diamond H \quad or \quad H_2N-C-H$$
$$R \qquad\qquad R$$

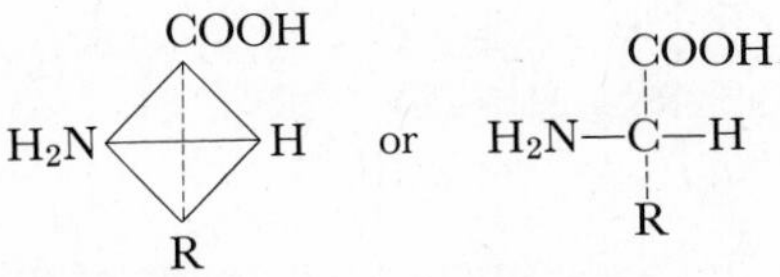

If the carboxyl, hydrogen, amino, and R groups correspond respectively to the aldehyde, hydrogen, hydroxy, and hydroxymethyl groups of glyceral-dehyde, this configuration is the same as that of ($-$)-glyceraldehyde, and all amino acids derived from proteins are said to belong to the L family. This configuration was confirmed in 1954 when the absolute configuration of isoleucine hydrobromide was established by x-ray diffraction.

Often the only functional groups present in amino acids are the amino group and the carboxyl group. Hence an amide linkage is the only logical mode of joining the amino acids. If the α-amino acids are represented by *Structure of proteins that of polyamide* the structure, $RCH(NH_2)COOH$, the protein may be represented by the partial structure I.

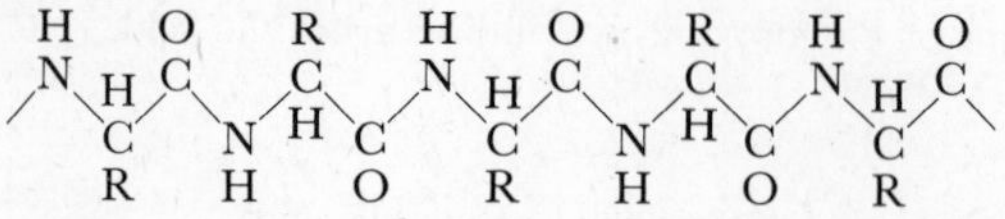

$$\begin{array}{ccccccccc}
H & O & R & H & O & R & H & O \\
N\,H\,C & C & N\,H\,C & C & N\,H\,C \\
C & N\,H\,C & C & N\,H\,C & C \\
R & H & O & R & H & O & R
\end{array}$$

I

However, a few of the amino acids have more than one carboxyl group and a few have more than one amino group. Therefore in a molecule such as I some free amino groups and some free carboxyl groups may be expected to be present. Because ammonia also is a product of protein hydrolysis, some of the carboxyl groups must be combined with ammonia as simple amide groups, $CONH_2$. Hence a section of a protein molecule containing lysine, aspartic acid, and glutamic acid conceivably could have the structure II.

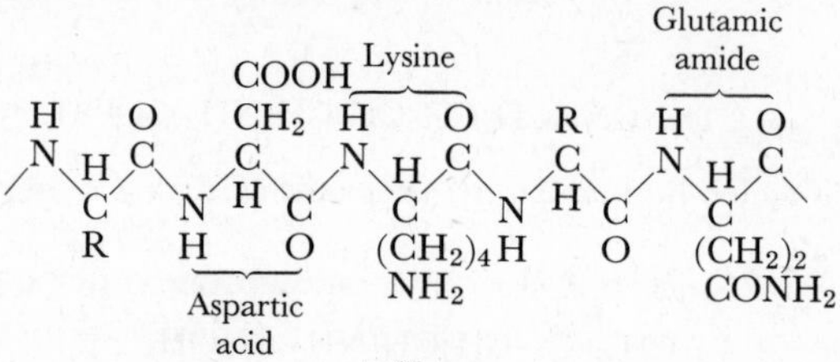

Lysine · Glutamic amide

$$\begin{array}{ccccccccc}
 & & COOH & & & & & Glutamic \\
 & & CH_2 & & & & & amide \\
H & O & CH_2\ H & O & R & H & O \\
N\,H\,C & C & N\,H\,C & C & N\,H\,C \\
C & N\,H\,C & C & N\,H\,C & C \\
R & H & O & (CH_2)_4\,H & O & (CH_2)_2 \\
 & & & NH_2 & & CONH_2
\end{array}$$

Aspartic acid

II

May have disulfide cross links

Moreover there is some evidence that chains of amino acids may be cross linked by means of the disulfide linkage in the cystine portions of the molecule as represented in structure III.

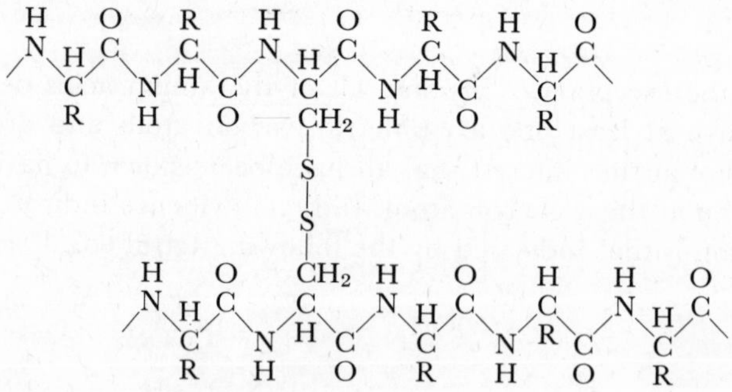

$$\begin{array}{ccccccccc}
H & O & R & H & O & R & H & O \\
N\,H\,C & C & N\,H\,C & C & N\,H\,C \\
C & N\,H\,C & C & N\,H\,C & C \\
R & H & O & CH_2\ H & O & R
\end{array}$$

$$\begin{array}{c}
| \\
S \\
| \\
S \\
|
\end{array}$$

$$\begin{array}{ccccccccc}
H & O & CH_2\ H & O & H & H & O \\
N\,H\,C & C & N\,H\,C & C & N\,R\,C & C \\
C & N\,H\,C & C & N\,R\,C & C \\
R & H & O & R & H & O & R
\end{array}$$

III

Other types of cross linkages, such as the amide or imide linkage, are conceivable, but there is no evidence as yet for their existence. Chains of amino acid residues linked through the carboxyl and amino groups by amide linkages frequently are called **peptides,** and this particular type of amide linkage is called a **peptide linkage.**

Some proteins fibrous, others globular

The fibrous proteins, such as silk, wool, hair, and connective tissues, are notably lacking in the dibasic amino acids, aspartic and glutamic, and probably are best represented by structure I. In fibroin of silk, the molecules are stretched out, but keratin of hair has a folded structure that can be stretched to a linear molecule. Globular proteins also may have their chains folded in an unknown fashion. The forces keeping the molecules in a folded structure probably are proton bonds between NH groups and C=O groups. It is possible to convert nonfibrous proteins such as zein, casein, albumin, or soybean protein into a fibrous form by dissolving in aqueous sodium hydroxide, forcing the solution through fine holes, and coagulating the filament by passing it into an acidified formaldehyde bath. The molecules become uncoiled on solution, and are stretched out and oriented parallel to each other during the spinning process. The product is known as **synthetic wool.** In another process the disulfide bonds in the keratin of chicken feathers are reduced to sulfhydryl groups. The keratin then dissolves in aqueous urea and can be extruded into fibers to give artificial bristles. The permanent waving of hair is based on the reduction of the disulfide linkages with ammonium thioglycolate (p. 169) to permit shaping of the hair.

$$RSSR + 2\ HSCH_2COONH_4 \longrightarrow 2\ RSH + (NH_4OOCCH_2S)_2$$

Subsequent reformation of the disulfide linkage by oxidation with potassium bromate sets the wave.

$$6\ RSH + KBrO_3 \longrightarrow 3\ RSSR + KBr + 3\ H_2O$$

The postulated structural formulas explain one other important physical property of the proteins. The proteins contain potentially free amino groups and carboxyl groups; that is, amino groups and carboxyl groups that are not joined to other carboxyl or amino groups by amide linkages. Many of these groups undoubtedly are present in salt form, the protons of the carboxyl groups having been transferred to the basic amino groups. In the presence of strong acids, however, undissociated carboxyl groups exist, and in the presence of strong bases the amino groups are free. Hence the proteins are amphoteric electrolytes. A simple amino acid molecule also contains a free amino group and a free carboxyl group and can be used to illustrate the equilibria involved.

Amino acids and proteins are amphoteric

$$\left[\begin{array}{c} R \\ | \\ H_2N-CH-COO^- \end{array} \right] \xrightleftharpoons[H_2O]{[OH^-]} \left[\begin{array}{c} R \\ | \\ \overset{+}{H_3N}-CH-COO^- \end{array} \right] \xrightleftharpoons{[H^+]} \left[\begin{array}{c} R \\ | \\ \overset{+}{H_3N}-CH-COOH \end{array} \right]$$

Basic salt form, as in the sodium salt of the amino acid

Normal salt form, as in the free amino acid

Acidic salt form, as in the amino acid hydrochloride

When the amino acid is in its normal salt form, it is a **dipolar ion** (*zwitter ion*) in which the negative charge on the carboxyl group balances the positive charge on the amino group. If an aqueous solution of the amino acid in this condition is subjected to a potential difference, no migration of the ion takes place. If the solution is made more strongly acid, some of the acidic salt is formed, and the positively charged amino acid migrates to the negative electrode. If the solution is made more strongly basic, some of the basic salt is produced, and the negatively charged amino acid migrates to the positive electrode. The acid concentration expressed as pH ($\log 1/[H^+]$) at which no migration takes place is known as the **isoelectric point.** This point is not necessarily the neutral point (pH 7), because the basicity of

Isoelectric point is important

the amino group and the acidity of the carboxyl group vary with the structure of the amino acid and need not be the same. Proteins also contain free amino groups and free carboxyl groups, and the same considerations apply to them as apply to the amino acids. Differences in isoelectric point are important particularly in the isolation and purification of amino acids and proteins, because minimum solubility occurs at the isoelectric point, and because direction and rate of migration in an electric field can be controlled by regulating the acidity of the solution.

Order of attachment of amino acids

Marked progress has been made since about 1937 in the development of methods for the separation and estimation of amino acids, and the relative amounts of the different amino acids is known for numerous proteins. Less is known about the arrangement of the amino acids in the protein molecules. That the molecules of amino acids are not randomly distributed, in which case the differences in proteins might be ascribed to differences in the number and kind of amino acids present, is known from the remarkable specificity of proteins. Thus proteins are not only specific for different tissues but also for different species of animals and even for individual members within a species. For example, whole blood of humans must be typed before blood transfusions may be made, because not all of the blood proteins of two individuals are necessarily identical and foreign proteins in the blood stream are toxic to the animal organism.

The number of possible structures for proteins is staggering. Tryptophan has the highest molecular weight (204) of the common amino acids. Therefore a protein such as ovalbumin, with a molecular weight of 45,000, must contain a minimum of 200 molecules of amino acids. It has been calculated that if only fifty molecules of nineteen different kinds, apportioned ten of one kind, four of four kinds, two of ten kinds, and one of four kinds, were present in a protein molecule, the number of possible arrangements is 10^{48}. As a comparison the diameter of the Milky Way (300,000 light years) expressed in Ångstrom units (10,000,000 per millimeter) is only 10^{32}. Nevertheless, remarkable progress is being made in determining the exact structure of proteins, and in 1954 the complete elucidation of the structure

Structure of insulin

of the subunit of the **insulin** molecule of molecular weight ca. 6000 was reported.

$$H_2NCO \qquad\qquad\overline{\qquad\quad S-S\qquad\quad}\qquad\qquad CONH_2 \qquad CONH_2 \qquad CONH_2$$

H₂N–Gly–Ileu–Val–Glu–Glu–Cy–Cy–Ala–Ser–Val–Cy–Ser–Leu–Tyr–Glu–Leu–Glu–Asp–Tyr–Cy–Asp–COOH

H₂NCO CONH₂   S

H₂N–Phe–Val–Asp–Glu–His–Leu–Cy–Gly–Ser–His–Leu–Val–Glu–Ala–Leu–Tyr–Leu–Val–Cy–Gly–Glu–Arg–

Gly–Phe–Phe–Tyr–Thr–Pro–Lys–Ala–COOH

Insulin from beef pancreas

Digestion of proteins

The animal organism normally obtains its supply of nitrogen predominantly by ingesting proteins from plants and other animals. These proteins are hydrolyzed progressively to peptides (p. 200) and amino acids. The hydrolyses are catalyzed by the enzyme *pepsin* under acid conditions (pH 1–2) in the stomach and by *trypsin*, *chymotrypsins*, and *peptidases* under slightly acid to slightly alkaline conditions (pH 6–8) in the intestines. The amino acids pass through the walls of the intestine into the portal blood stream, which carries them to the liver and other tissues of the body. Under the influence of specific cellular enzymes, the amino acids are reconverted into proteins characteristic of the particular tissue. The liver converts the amino acids also into plasma proteins, which are carried to peripheral tissues where they can be used as a source of amino acids for the synthesis of tissue proteins. That an organism can synthesize a specific protein for each particular purpose by picking out the desired amino acids from the blood stream and putting them together in the proper order is a striking example of the exactness with which life processes are regulated.

The organism also is able to convert some amino acids into others and *Some amino acids must* to synthesize them from ammonium salts and α-keto acids derived from *be supplied by diet* carbohydrates. Amino acids that can be so formed need not be ingested. On the other hand it is known that the rat cannot produce valine, leucine, isoleucine, phenylalanine, threonine, tryptophan, methionine, lysine, arginine, or histidine, and hence they have been termed *indispensable* or *essential amino acids*. The term "indispensable" should not be taken to mean that these amino acids are more important than the "dispensable" amino acids, because all natural amino acids undoubtedly are necessary for the development and maintenance of the organism. Ind'spensable merely means that these amino acids must be supplied in the proteins of the diet and cannot be synthesized from other amino acids or from ammonia nitrogen. Approximately 6 per cent of the protein intake must consist of these amino acids. Studies made so far indicate that the requirements of other species appear to be similar to those of the rat. Arginine, however, is dispensable in dogs and histidine is dispensable in man. For growing chicks glycine is an indispensable amino acid, although it is dispensable in rats. One of the more interesting facts discovered in recent years through the aid of isotopes is that the proteins in the body are being actively built up and torn down continuously, and that there is a fairly rapid turnover of amino acids. It has been calculated that the average "half-life" of proteins, that is, the time required for half of the original amino acids in the body protein to be replaced by other amino acids, is about 17 days for the rat and 80 days for the adult human.

Because amino acids are important to the biochemist and physician, *Synthetic amino acids* numerous ingenious syntheses have been devised. With the exception of glycine, naturally-occurring amino acids are optically active, consisting of a single form of the compound (cf. Chapter 14), whereas the synthetic amino acids are optically inactive, being composed of equal amounts of the naturally occurring L form and of the unnatural D form that cannot be utilized by the animal organism. Of the essential amino acids, the animal organism can convert the D form of tryptophan, phenylalanine, methionine, and histidine to the L form. Hence the DL mixture is as useful as the pure L form. For the other essential amino acids only half of the synthetic mixture can be utilized, and twice the amount must be fed for a given effect. Methods are available for separating the synthetic compounds into their active components, but it usually is a difficult process. DL-**Tryptophan** is synthesized commercially, because most of that occurring in proteins is

as food supplements

destroyed during acid hydrolysis and, as an indispensable amino acid, it must be added to the protein hydrolysates used to treat cases of serious malnutrition. Synthetic L-lysine is used as a food supplement. DL-Methionine is synthesized for the fortification of protein hydrolysates and for enriching foodstuffs. Small amounts fed to animals greatly increase their rate of growth. It appears also to have high therapeutic value in the treatment of metabolic deficiencies.

as a condiment

Monosodium glutamate is used widely as a condiment and for bringing out the flavor of foods. It is prepared commercially by the hydrolysis of wheat gluten or of residues from the production of beet sugar, or by a bacterial synthesis from carbohydrate and ammonium salts. Over 21 million pounds valued at 22.5 million dollars was produced in the United States in 1960.

Tests for amino acids and proteins

Several general tests for amino acids and proteins are available. In the **ninhydrin reaction,** α-amino acids, and proteins or their degradation products that contain an amino group α to a free carboxyl group, give a blue color when treated in dilute solution with *triketohydrindene hydrate (ninhydrin)*. The initial product decomposes and hydrolyzes to give 2-amino-1,3-diketohydrindene, an aldehyde, and carbon dioxide. Reaction of the amino diketone with hydrindene gives a deep blue product.

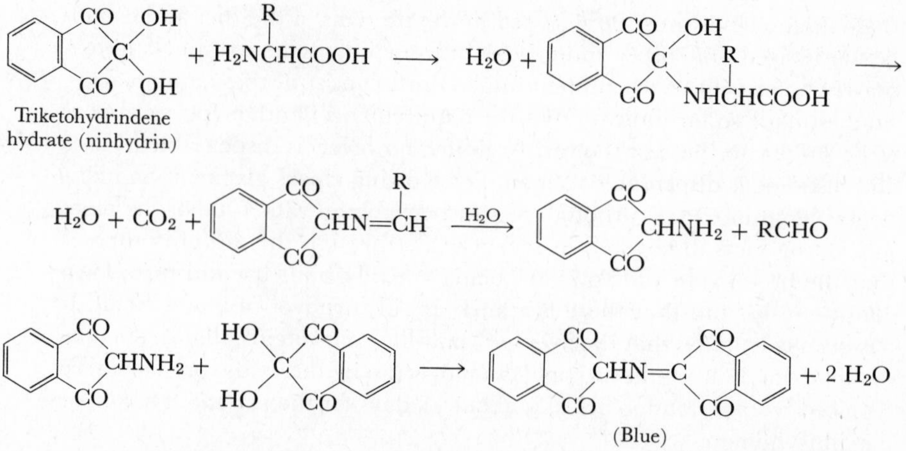

Ammonium salts, dilute ammonia solutions, and some amines also give a blue color under certain conditions, apparently because of an intermolecular oxidation and reduction of the ninhydrin in the presence of ammonia.

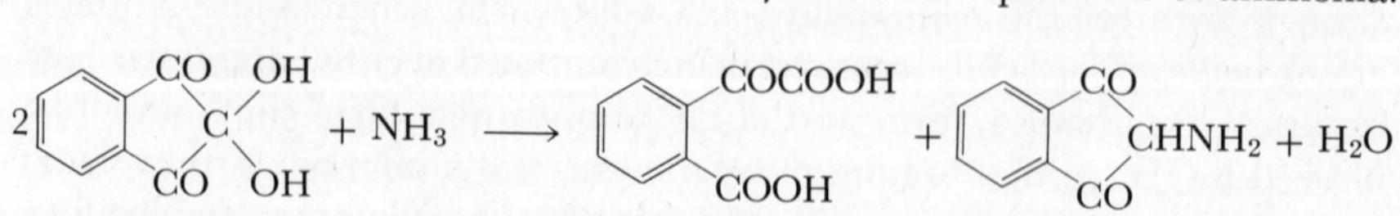

When a dilute solution of copper sulfate is added to an alkaline solution of a peptide or polypeptide, a pink to violet color is produced. This behavior is known as the **biuret reaction** because it is shown also by biuret (p. 140). The structure of the product of reaction with a section of a polypeptide chain may be represented by the formula

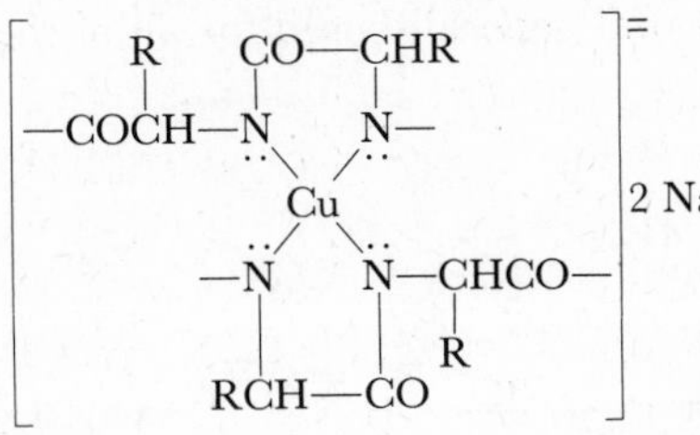

$$\left[\begin{array}{c} \text{R} \qquad \text{CO—CHR} \\ \text{—COCH—N} \qquad \text{N—} \\ \text{Cu} \\ \text{—N} \qquad \text{N—CHCO—} \\ \text{R} \\ \text{RCH—CO} \end{array}\right]^{=} 2\,\text{Na}^+$$

The yellow color produced when concentrated nitric acid comes in contact with skin or other proteins (**xanthoproteic reaction**) presumably is caused by the nitration of aromatic nuclei to give yellow nitro compounds (p. 145).

Free amino groups in either amino acids or proteins may be estimated quantitatively by measuring the volume of nitrogen liberated on reaction with nitrous acid (*Van Slyke method*).

$$\text{RCH}_2\text{CHNH}_2\text{COOH} + \text{HONO} \longrightarrow \text{RCH=CHCOOH} + \text{N}_2 + 2\,\text{H}_2\text{O}$$

Although the reaction as usually written indicates the replacement of the amino group by a hydroxyl group, unsaturated and rearranged compounds usually are formed. The important fact is that one mole of nitrogen is eliminated for each free amino group in the molecule.

Aromatic amino acids

Amino acids having the amino and carboxyl group attached to a benzene ring are not found in the products of hydrolysis of proteins. However, several representatives of this group and their derivatives are of considerable importance.

p-Aminobenzoic acid necessary for growth of bacteria

Of the three aminobenzoic acids, **p-aminobenzoic acid** (*PABA*) is of most general interest. It is present in the mixture of substances known as the vitamin B complex, but its necessity in the human diet has not been established. Bacteria, however, must be supplied with it, presumably for the synthesis of the folic acid group of vitamins, which are necessary for their growth. Because *m*-nitrobenzoic acid is the chief product of the nitration of benzoic acid, *p*-aminobenzoic acid is made by the oxidation of *p*-nitrotoluene followed by reduction.

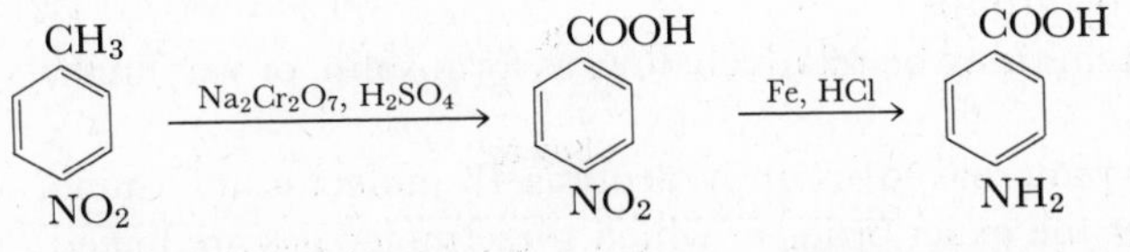

Esters are local anesthetics

Certain *p*-aminobenzoic esters have a local anesthetic action. The ethyl ester is known as **Anesthesin** (*benzocaine*) and the butyl ester as **Butesin.** They are used for relieving the pain of burns and open wounds. The most important derivatives are the aminoalkyl *p*-aminobenzoates, which on injection at the proper site anesthetize nerve fibers or endings or block the transmission of pain by the nerve trunks. Their development resulted from attempts to find agents less toxic than cocaine, the first local anesthetic (p. 222). **Novocain** (*procaine*, β-diethylaminoethyl *p*-aminobenzoate hydrochloride) was synthesized by Einhorn in 1905. It still is the most frequently used local and spinal anesthetic, although literally thousands of related compounds have been synthesized and many placed on the market. Its method of synthesis is that generally used for all of the compounds of this type.

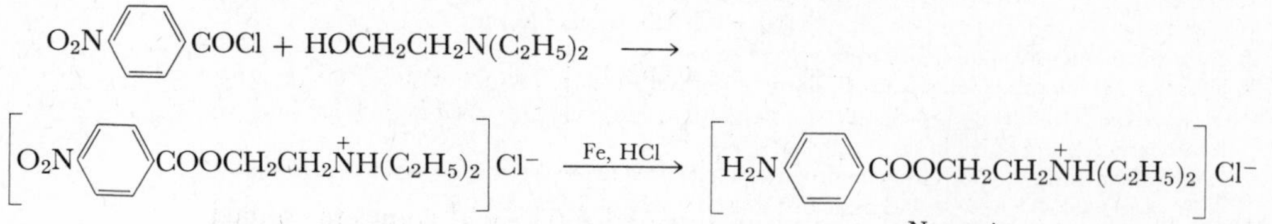

$$O_2N-\langle\ \rangle-COCl + HOCH_2CH_2N(C_2H_5)_2 \longrightarrow$$

$$\left[O_2N-\langle\ \rangle-COOCH_2CH_2\overset{+}{N}H(C_2H_5)_2\right]Cl^- \xrightarrow{\text{Fe, HCl}} \left[H_2N-\langle\ \rangle-COOCH_2CH_2\overset{+}{N}H(C_2H_5)_2\right]Cl^-$$

Novocain
(procaine)

Butyn (*butacaine*) is more active but also is more toxic than Novocain. **Pontocaine** (*tetracaine*) is used for surface anesthesia of the eye and for spinal anesthesia.

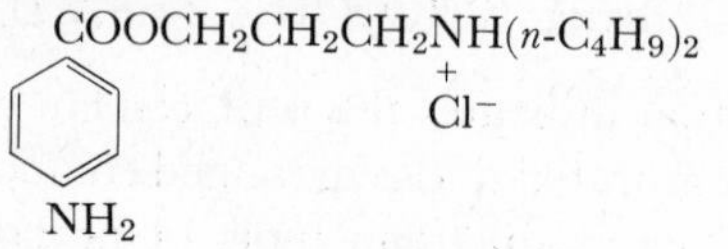

COOCH$_2$CH$_2$CH$_2$NH(n-C$_4$H$_9$)$_2$
$\overset{+}{}$
Cl$^-$

NH$_2$

Butyn (butacaine)

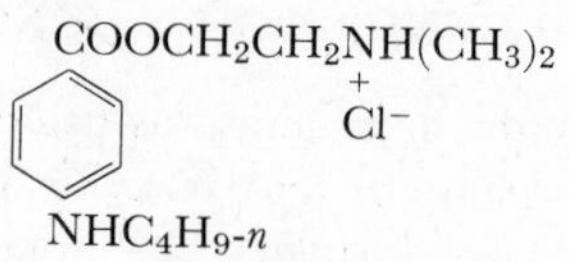

COOCH$_2$CH$_2$NH(CH$_3$)$_2$
$\overset{+}{}$
Cl$^-$

NHC$_4$H$_9$-n

Pontocaine (tetracaine)

Methyl anthranilate responsible for grape odor and flavor

o-Aminobenzoic acid is known as **anthranilic acid.** It is used chiefly as an intermediate for the synthesis of dyes. The methyl ester is present in several odorous oils and contributes to the odor and flavor of Concord grapes. The synthetic product is used in artificial grape flavors.

SUMMARY

1. Proteins are polyamides that yield α-amino acids on hydrolysis. Upwards of twenty amino acids have been obtained from proteins. The conjugated proteins yield in addition one or more prosthetic groups.

2. The molecular weights of proteins may be relatively low, as for insulin, or very high, as for the influenza virus.

3. The insulin molecule of beef pancreas gives on hydrolysis 48 molecules of amino acids of 16 different kinds. Yet the exact order in which these molecules are joined has been determined.

4. The configuration of the α-carbon atom is the same in all amino acids isolated from proteins. The absolute configuration has been established, and they usually are designated as belonging to the L-family.

5. Man gets all of his nitrogen requirements by the ingestion of proteins. They are hydrolyzed in the intestines, and the amino acids are transported by the blood stream to the various sites in the body where they are resynthesized into body proteins.

6. The amide and amino nitrogen atoms in proteins are so spaced that they can give colored complexes with cupric ion in alkaline solution (biuret reaction).

7. Local anesthetics such as procaine are alkylaminoalkyl esters of *p*-aminobenzoic acid.

EXERCISES

1. Write structural formulas for all the possible ways in which one molecule each of glycine, alanine, and serine can be bonded together using only amide linkages.
2. How could one distinguish silk from viscose rayon?
3. What is the characteristic feature in the structure of each of the following amino acids: (a) cysteine; (b) the thyronines; (c) cystine; (d) tryptophan; (e) arginine; (f) proline and hydroxyproline; (g) histidine?
4. If a protein contains more free amino groups than free carboxyl groups, would the isoelectric point be expected to lie on the basic or the acidic side of neutrality?
5. What aldehyde would be formed in the reaction of ninhydrin with alanine?
6. Which amino acids in Table 12 may be responsible for the yellow color produced when nitric acid reacts with proteins?
7. Give the structural formula for: (a) anesthesin; (b) methyl anthranilate.

CHAPTER 17

DYES AND DYEING

Color always has played an important role in the life of man, even though its significance is almost wholly esthetic. Throughout man's history dyes and pigments, both natural and synthetic, have been an important article of commerce.

Color in organic compounds is associated with an extended system of conjugated double bonds. However, only those colored substances that can be attached to a material and that are fast to light and washing are classed as dyes. Dyes may be grouped according to their chemical structure or according to the method by which they are applied. Many different types of compounds have dyeing properties, but only about a dozen types are represented in commercial products. Of these, three classes make up 80 per cent of the weight and 73 per cent of the value of all dyes produced in the United States. They are the azo dyes, the anthraquinone dyes, and the sulfur dyes.

Chemical classification   The **azo dyes** contain the azo group, —N=N—. They are made by treating a strongly acidic solution of an aromatic amine at 0° with nitrous acid to form a diazonium salt. This reaction is called **diazotization.**

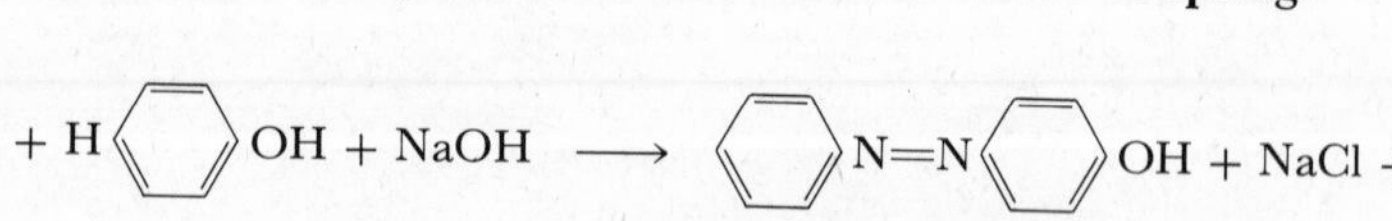

$$\left\langle\bigcirc\right\rangle NH_2 + HONO + HCl \longrightarrow \left[\left\langle\bigcirc\right\rangle \overset{+}{N}\equiv N\right]\left[Cl^-\right] + 2\ H_2O$$

Benzenediazonium
chloride

Diazonium salts react with phenols or with aromatic amines in a buffered solution to give azo compounds. This reaction is called **coupling.**

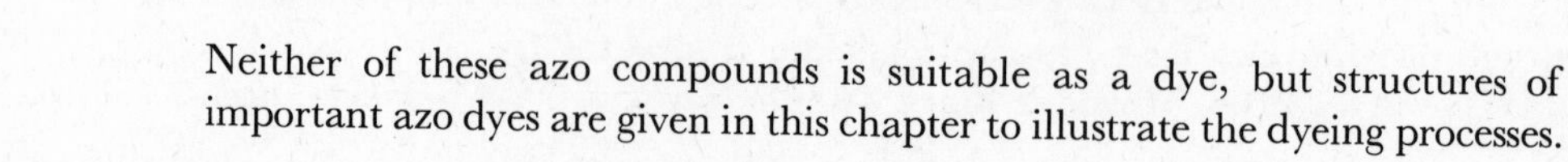

$$\left[\left\langle\bigcirc\right\rangle \overset{+}{N}\equiv N\right]\left[Cl^-\right] + H\left\langle\bigcirc\right\rangle OH + NaOH \longrightarrow \left\langle\bigcirc\right\rangle N=N\left\langle\bigcirc\right\rangle OH + NaCl + H_2O$$

p-Hydroxyazobenzene

$$+ H\left\langle\bigcirc\right\rangle N(CH_3)_2 + NaOAc \longrightarrow \left\langle\bigcirc\right\rangle N=N\left\langle\bigcirc\right\rangle N(CH_3)_2 + NaCl + HOAc$$

p-Dimethylaminoazobenzene

Neither of these azo compounds is suitable as a dye, but structures of important azo dyes are given in this chapter to illustrate the dyeing processes.

The **anthraquinone dyes** have the anthraquinone nucleus (p. 210). The structures of commercial anthraquinone dyes are given in the discussion of certain types of dyeing.

The structure of most **sulfur dyes** is not known. They are mixtures of complex compounds made by heating organic materials with sulfur and sodium sulfide, a process known as *thionation*.

The various materials most commonly dyed, namely animal fibers, cellulosic fibers, and synthetic fibers, have different chemical constitutions. They not only require different types of dyes as regards structure, but different processes must be used to apply the dyes. The **direct dyes** are those that are applicable by immersing the fiber or cloth in a hot solution of the dye in water. Those dyes suitable for dyeing *animal fibers*, which contain basic and acidic groups in the protein molecules, are divided into **acid dyes** and **basic dyes**. **Acid dyes** are sodium salts of sulfonic acids and are dyed from a bath acidified with sulfuric or acetic acid. **Basic dyes** are the hydrochlorides or zinc chloride complexes of dyes having basic groups. They are dyed from a neutral bath, usually on a fiber that has been treated with tannic acid. Basic dyes frequently also contain sodium sulfonate groups to make them more soluble in water. **Acid Orange 7** and **Basic Orange 2** are typical examples.

Methods of application

Direct dyes

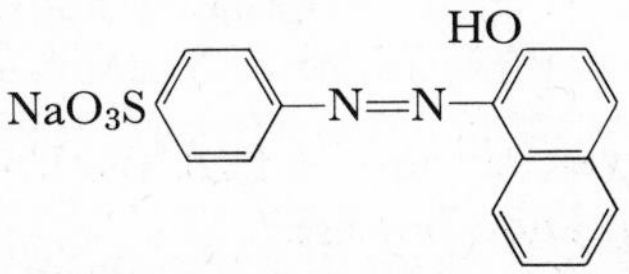

Acid Orange 7
(Orange II, β-Naphthol Orange)

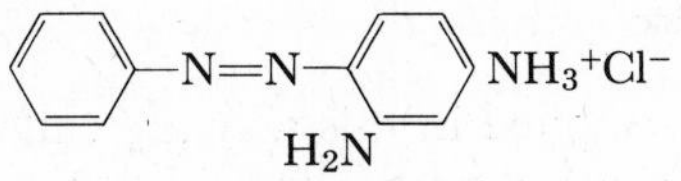

Basic Orange 2
(Chrysoidine Y)

In cellulose there are no strongly acidic or basic groups, and the colored compounds of lower molecular weight that dye protein fibers are not fixed by cotton or viscose rayon. However, dyes that have a molecular weight sufficiently high to give colloidal solutions are adsorbed more strongly and are **direct dyes for cotton and viscose rayon.** These dyes also are called **salt colors** because adsorption on the fiber usually is assisted by the addition of a salt such as sodium sulfate. An example is **Direct Red 2.**

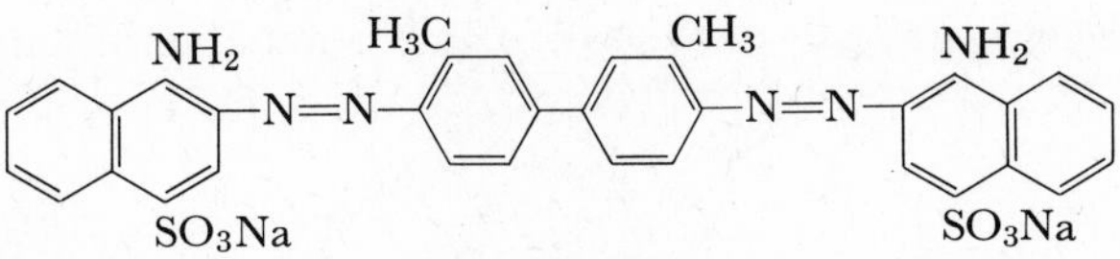

Direct Red 2
(Benzopurpurin 4B)

Another process for fixing dyes to cotton is by **mordanting.** A mordant is any substance that can be fixed to the fiber (L. *mordere*, to bite) and that later can be dyed. Usually mordants are hydroxides of iron, aluminum, or chromium that have been precipitated within the fibers. The dyes have structures that can form insoluble chelate complexes (p. 133) with the metallic hydroxides. **Mordant Black 11** (*Chrome Black T*) is a widely used

Mordant dyes

monoazo mordant dye. The fiber may be treated with chroming solution before, after, or during the dyeing. Each atom of chromium can form three chelate rings giving a complex polymeric molecule within the fibers.

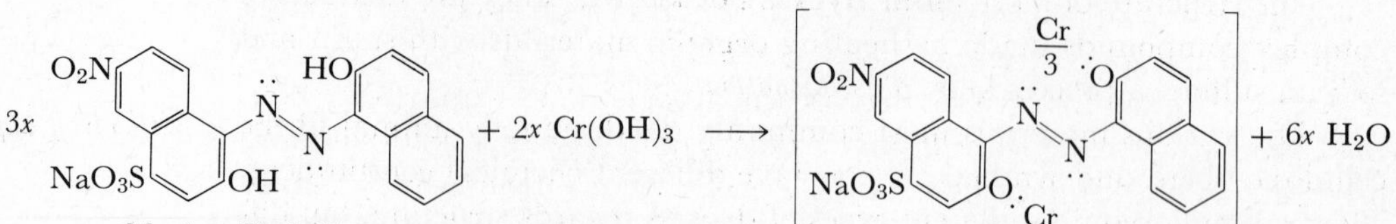

Mordant Black 11
(Chrome Black T)

Vat dyes

Anthraquinones are insoluble in water or aqueous alkali, but can be rendered soluble in alkali by reduction, which converts the carbonyl groups into acidic phenolic groups. These phenols are oxidized readily back to the insoluble anthraquinones by air or other oxidizing agents.

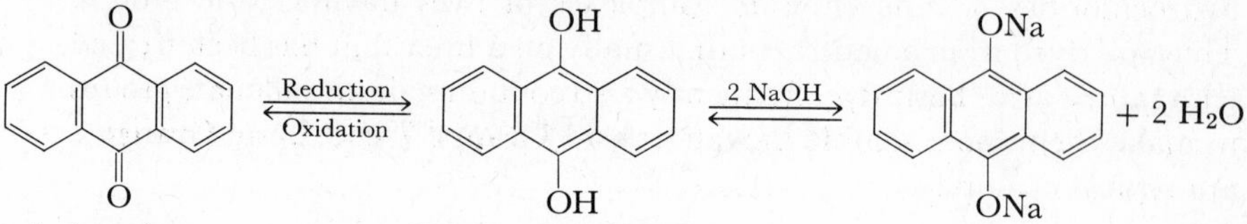

Anthraquinone
Insoluble

Dihydroanthraquinone

Soluble

Dyes applied in this way are called **vat dyes,** because indigo, the first vat dye, was reduced in large vats by a fermentation process.

Anthraquinone is not highly colored or fixed to fibers, but the more complex compounds are. **Vat Blue 4,** the first anthraquinone vat dye, is one of the most stable organic compounds known. It can be heated in air at 470°, with strong hydrochloric acid at 400°, and with potassium hydroxide at 300° without decomposition. When applied to cloth, it is extremely fast to washing and light, a property shared by most anthraquinone vat colors.

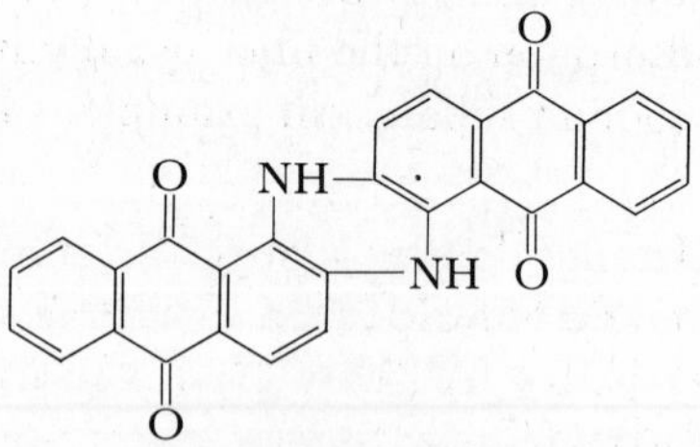

Vat Blue 4
(Indanthrene Blue R)

Sulfur dyes

Sulfur dyes are applied in much the same way as vat dyes. They contain disulfide linkages, which on reduction give thiol groups that permit solution in alkali. After being adsorbed on the fiber, the thiol groups are reoxidized to the insoluble disulfide.

$$DS\text{-}SD \underset{\text{Oxidation}}{\overset{\text{Reduction}}{\rightleftarrows}} 2\ DSH \overset{2\ Na_2S}{\rightleftarrows} 2\ DSNa + 2\ NaSH$$

Insoluble   Soluble

Sulfur dyes are used only on cotton because they are applied from a sodium sulfide solution, which attacks protein and ester fibers. **Sulfur Black 1,** the cheapest dye, is made from 2,4-dinitrophenol.

Direct dyes are not suitable for synthetic fibers such as cellulose acetate (p. 193), or for the polyester or polyamide fibers (p. 238), because the lack of hydroxyl or amino groups makes the fiber still less adsorbing than cellulose. Vat dyeing cannot be used because the alkaline solutions bring about partial hydrolysis of the ester or amide groups and deluster and weaken the fiber. Dyeing can be brought about, however, by colloidal aqueous dispersions of dyes that lack sulfonic acid groups and are soluble in the organic polymer. Such dyes are called **disperse dyes.** The colors must *Disperse dyes* be very finely divided to increase the rate of solution in water, because the dyeing mechanism appears to involve the removal by the fiber of the small amount of dye that is dissolved in the water. **Disperse Yellow 3** (*Celliton Fast Yellow G*) is an example of a widely-used disperse dye for cellulose acetate.

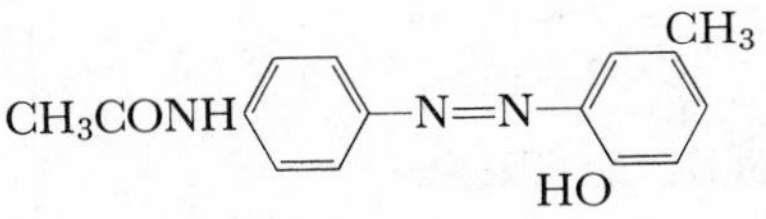

Disperse Yellow 3
(Celliton Fast Yellow G)

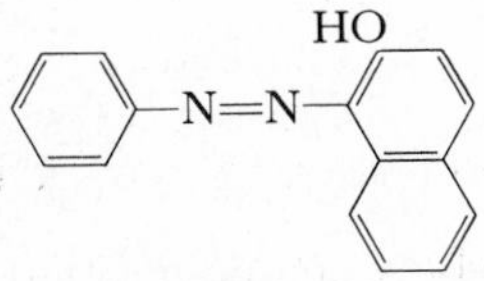

Solvent Yellow 14
(Oil Orange, Sudan I)

Many colored compounds that lack sulfonic acid groups are soluble in organic solvents and are used to dye gasoline, plastics, fats, oils and waxes, spirit printing inks, and stains. **Solvent Yellow 14** (*Oil Orange, Sudan I*) is representative of **oil-soluble colors.**

COLOR OF FLOWERS

Most of the red and blue colors of flowers are due to phenolic *Flower colors* oxygen heterocycles. They occur in the plants as glucosides known as **anthocyanins,** the aglycone being called an **anthocyanidin.** The anthocyanidins derived from natural anthocyanins belong to three groups. All have hydroxyl groups in the 3, 5, and 7 positions. **Pelargonidin chloride** (scarlet pelargonium, orange dahlia) contains an additional hydroxyl group in the 4' position; **cyanidin chloride** (red rose, blue cornflower, red dahlia, black cherry, plum) has two hydroxyl groups in the 3' and 4' positions; **delphinidin chloride** (delphinium, violet pansy, purple grape) contains three hydroxyl groups in the 3', 4', and 5' positions.

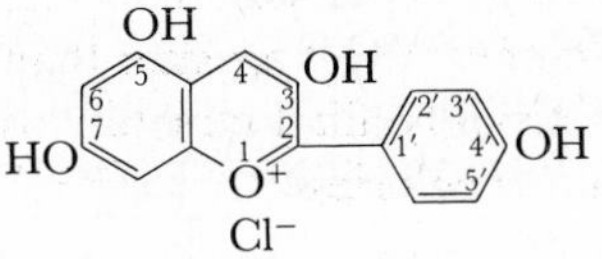

Pelargonidin chloride

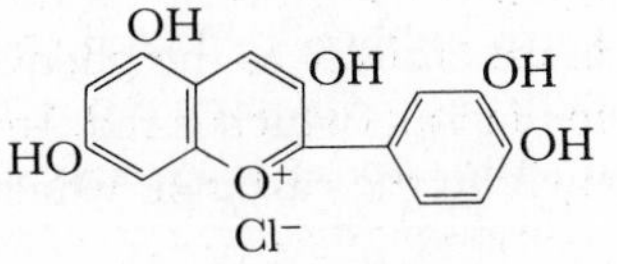

Cyanidin chloride

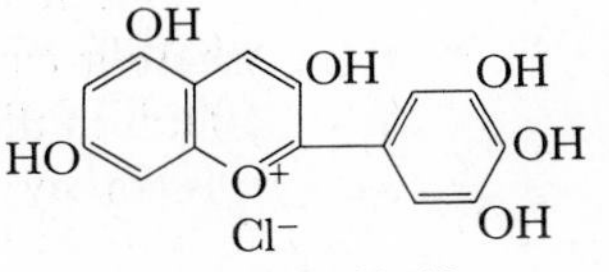

Delphinidin chloride

The color of the anthocyanins, which usually are 3,5-diglucosides, depends not only on their components but also on whether the anthocyanin

is complexed with a metallic atom. Thus the rose is red because the anthocyanin is not present as a coordination complex. The cornflower is blue
because the pigment is present as a complex with ferric or aluminum ion.

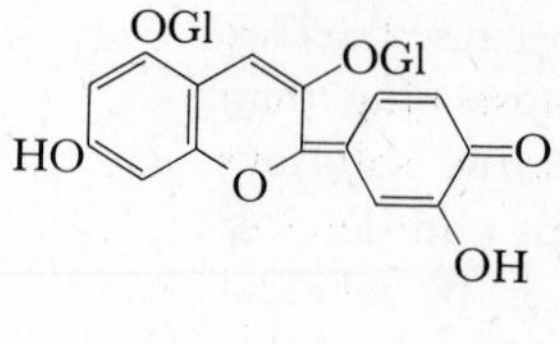

Red rose pigment

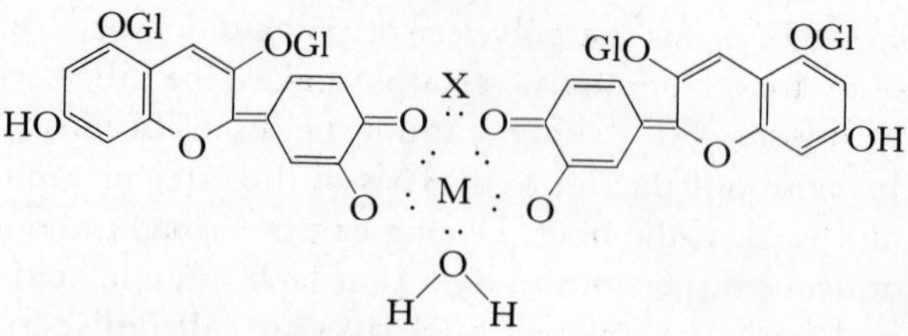

Blue cornflower pigment
M = Fe^{III} or Al^{III}, X = some negative ion

Oxygen in both the 3' and 4' positions is necessary for complex formation. Flowers that contain only pelargonidin as the anthocyanidin cannot
have blue varieties.

INDICATOR ACTION

Acid-base indicators

Many compounds have different colors at different hydrogen ion concentrations. These color changes occur because the compounds themselves
are acids or bases that enter into proton transfer reactions, and because
the undissociated acid or the free base has a different color than the ionized
salt. The hydrogen ion concentration at which the color change takes place
depends on the strength of the compound as an acid or as a base.

Methyl Orange in solutions that are more basic than pH 4.4 exists
almost entirely as the yellow negative ion. In solutions more acidic than
pH 3.1, it combines almost completely with a proton and forms the red
dipolar ion.

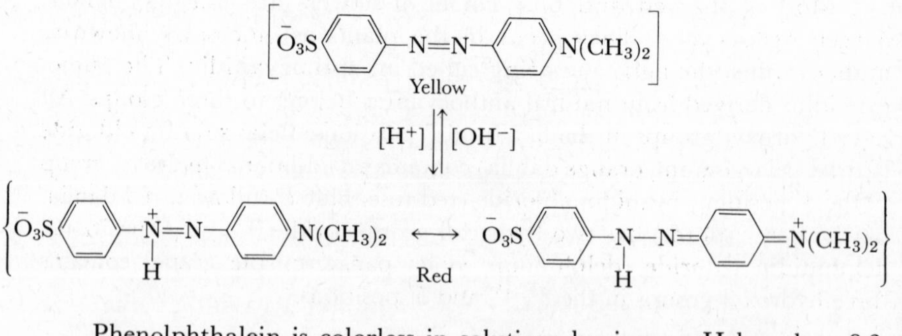

Phenolphthalein is colorless in solutions having a pH less than 8.3,
where it exists almost entirely as the phenolic lactone. At pH greater than
10 it is in the form of a salt, which is red. In very strongly alkaline solutions
it is converted slowly to the carbinol, which again is colorless.

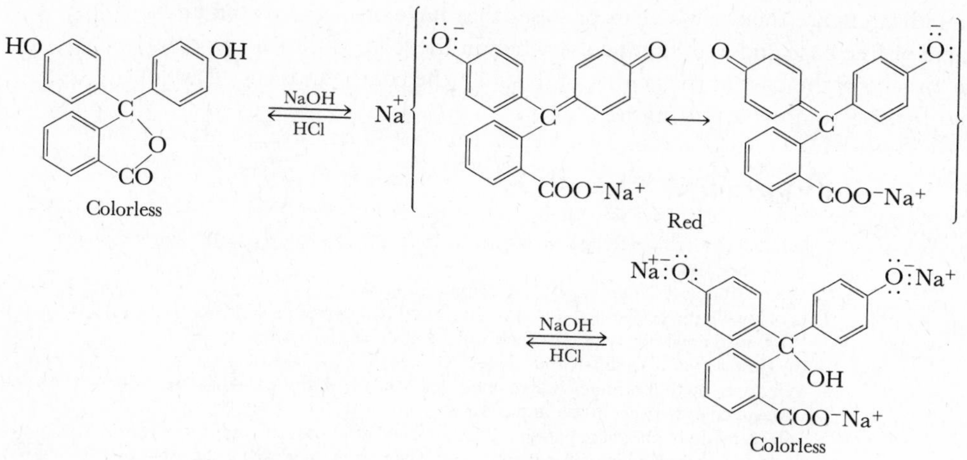

HO — OH ... C, O, CO — Colorless

$\xrightarrow[\text{HCl}]{\text{NaOH}}$

Red

$\xrightarrow[\text{HCl}]{\text{NaOH}}$

Colorless

SUMMARY

1. Dyes are colored substances that can be fixed to a material and are fast to washing and to light.

2. Direct dyes are those applicable by direct application of a solution of a dye in water. Protein fibers can be dyed readily by simple dyes having basic or acidic groups. Cellulosic fibers require dyes of higher molecular weight because adsorption on a hydroxylic surface is not so strong as on a surface containing amino and carboxyl groups.

3. Disperse dyes are those that are applied from a colloidal emulsion to synthetic fibers. They dissolve in the polymeric substance from which the fiber is spun.

4. Mordant dyes are those that form chelate complexes with hydroxides of iron, aluminum, or chromium. The hydroxides are precipitated within the fibers and then dyed; or it is possible to dye with a direct dye and then immerse in a mordanting solution to increase the fastness, as in after-chroming.

5. The azo dyes compose one of the largest classes of commercial dyes. They are made by diazotizing a primary aromatic amine and coupling with an aromatic amine or a phenol. The diazotized monoamines when coupled with monohydroxy compounds give monoazo dyes. It is possible, using polyamines and aminophenols, to prepare dyes having two, three, or four azo groups, giving rise to diazo, trisazo and tetra-kisazo dyes.

6. Vat dyes are water-insoluble colored compounds that can be rendered soluble in alkali by reduction. After dyeing the cloth in the reduced bath, exposure to air or to an oxidizing solution oxidizes the dye to the insoluble form, precipitating the dye on the fiber. Indigo was one of the first of the vat dyes, but the most important are the anthraquinone vats.

7. Sulfur dyes are water-insoluble compounds that are rendered soluble in alkali by the production of thiol groups. Oxidation on the fiber precipitates an insoluble disulfide.

8. Most of the red and blue coloring matters of flowers are derivatives of phenolic oxygen heterocycles.

9. Acid-base indicators are themselves acids or bases that have one color as the undissociated acid or free base and a different color when in the form of the salt. Depending on the basicity of the base or the acidity of the acid, the compounds change color
at different hydrogen-ion concentrations.

EXERCISES

1. What is the characteristic structural feature of: (a) azo dyes; (b) anthraquinone dyes;
   (c) anthocyanidins?
2. What structural feature is necessary in mordant dyes?
3. (a) How do direct dyes for cotton differ from direct dyes for silk or wool?
   (b) How do dyes for synthetic fibers differ from those for natural fibers?
   (c) How do vat dyes differ from direct dyes?
4. Why does methyl orange change color between pH 3 and pH 4, whereas phenolphthalein
   changes color between pH 9 and pH 10?
5. Why is methyl orange used as an indicator when estimating an amine by titrating with standard acid, whereas phenolphthalein is used when estimating carboxylic acids by titrating with
   standard base?

CHAPTER 18

COMPLEX
NATURAL PRODUCTS

Many products of animal or vegetable origin are rather complex compounds. One of the triumphs of organic chemistry has been the elucidation of their structure and in many instances their total synthesis. Frequently these compounds have marked physiological action or play an important role in biological processes.

TERPENES

The term *terpene* (Gr. *terebinthos,* turpentine tree) originally was applied to ten-carbon hydrocarbons present in the exudations of pine trees and in the volatile oils of citrus fruit rind and of other plants. It soon became evident, however, that compounds containing 15, 20, 30, and 40 carbon atoms also are closely related to the terpenes. The one common characteristic of all of these compounds is that their carbon skeletons are evenly divisible into iso-C_5 units (frequently referred to as *isoprene* or *isopentane units*). The term *terpene* in its broadest sense now includes all such compounds, whether hydrocarbons or not. Terpene in the limited sense still refers to compounds containing two iso-C_5 units. Hence the broad class of terpenes is divided into hemiterpenes, C_5; terpenes, C_{10}; sesquiterpenes, C_{15}; diterpenes, C_{20}; triterpenes, C_{30}; tetraterpenes, C_{40}; and polyterpenes, C_{5x}.

Citronellal from oil of citronella, **limonene** from lemon oil, **menthol** from Japanese peppermint oil, and **pinene** from turpentine are typical terpenes. In order to simplify the writing of structural formulas of cyclic terpenes, the convention is adopted that carbon and hydrogen atoms are not indicated but only the bonds between the carbon atoms. Hence in these formulas a carbon atom is present at each intersection of two or more lines and at the end of each line. Double bonds and elements other than carbon and hydrogen are shown. It is understood that each carbon atom is attached to a sufficient number of hydrogen atoms to satisfy the remaining valences. Dotted lines indicate the division into iso-C_5 units.

Sources of terpenes

Classification

Terpenes

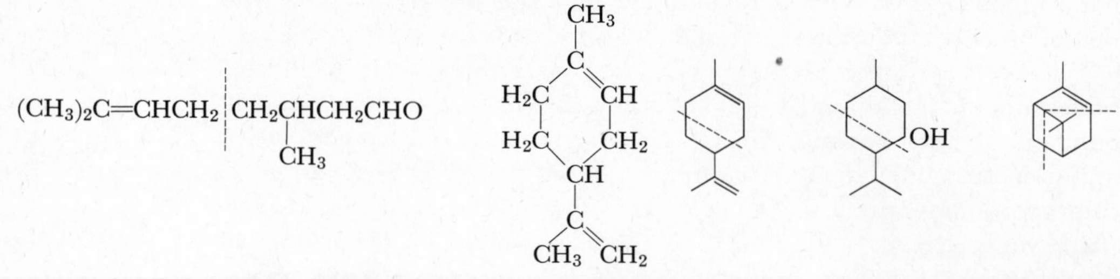

$(CH_3)_2C{=}CHCH_2 \mid CH_2CHCH_2CHO$
$\mid$
CH_3

$$
\begin{array}{c}
CH_3 \\
C \\
H_2C \quad CH \\
H_2C \quad CH_2 \\
CH \\
C \\
CH_3 \ \ CH_2
\end{array}
$$

| Citronellal | Limonene | Menthol | α-Pinene |

Sesquiterpenes;
azulenes

The **azulenes** are sesquiterpenes that are of interest because they have a seven-membered ring fused to a five-membered ring and on dehydrogenation give blue oils. These blue compounds have a completely conjugated system of five double bonds, which gives them some of the characteristics of aromatic compounds. A typical example is **vetivone** from vetiver oil.

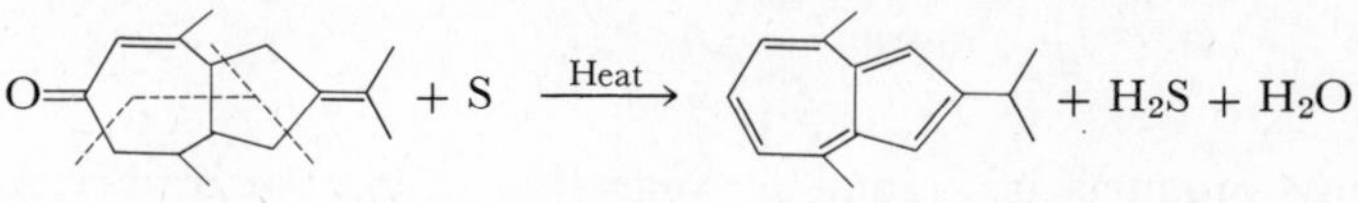

O= ... + S →(Heat) ... + H₂S + H₂O

| Vetivone | Vetivazulene |

Diterpenes;
phytol

Phytol, $C_{20}H_{39}OH$, an acyclic diterpene, constitutes about one-third of the chlorophyll molecule (p. 226), from which it is obtained by saponification.

$(CH_3)_2CHCH_2CH_2 \mid (CH_2CHCH_2CH_2)_2\ CHC{=}CHCH_2OH$
$\mid$ $\mid$
CH_3 CH_3

Phytol

Vitamins A_1 and A_2

Vitamin A_1 is the fat-soluble vitamin necessary for the growth of rats; it plays a part in the resistance of the animal organism to infection and is required for the production of visual purple, a pigment necessary for sight. It is a monocyclic diterpene. Before commercial production of the acetate by synthesis, which began in 1950, the chief sources were the cod, halibut, and soupfin shark liver oils, which vary greatly in potency. **Vitamin A_2** from the liver oil of fresh-water fish has an additional double bond in the ring in conjugation with the other double bonds. **Visual purple** (*rhodopsin*) is a protein complex, the prosthetic group of which is **retinene₁**, the aldehyde corresponding to vitamin A_1. **Retinene₂** is the aldehyde corresponding to vitamin A_2.

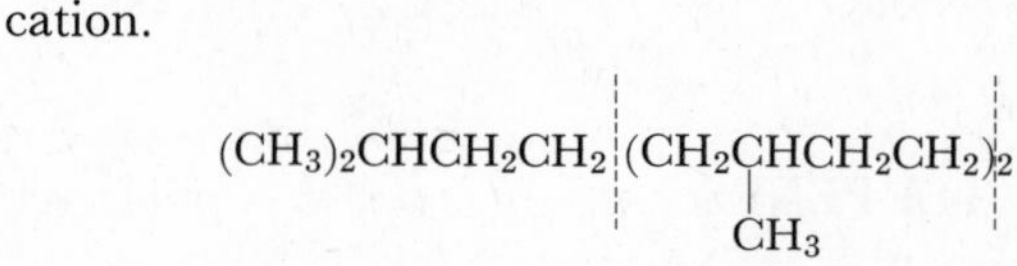

CH=CHC=CHCH=CHC=CHCH₂OH
CH₃ CH₃

Vitamin A₁

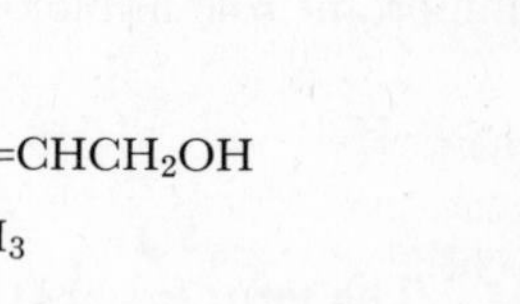

HOOC

Abietic acid

Rosin; abietic
acid

The most important diterpene commercially is the tricyclic **abietic acid,** $C_{20}H_{30}O_2$. It is the chief component of rosin or colophony, the resin obtained from various species of pine (L. *abies,* fir). Abietic acid is an origi-

nal component of the tree secretions, and is formed also by the isomerization of other acids during the distillation of the turpentine.

Rosin is an important article of commerce. Production in the United
States amounts to around 1 billion pounds per year. It is the most abundant and cheapest organic acid. The crude sodium salt is used to size paper
and to increase the lathering property of laundry soap. The sodium salt of
disproportionated rosin is used as an emulsifier in the production of synthetic rubber (p. 237). Rosin is used also as a component of varnish, but
its glyceryl ester, known as *ester gum,* is superior for this purpose. Uses of
lesser importance are too numerous to mention.

Triterpenes

Although hydrocarbons usually have not been considered to play an
important part in animal metabolism, **squalene,** $C_{30}H_{50}$, makes up as high
as 90 per cent of the liver oil of certain species of sharks of the family
Squalidae. It is an acyclic triterpene whose reactions can be explained by
assuming that it consists of two sesquiterpene chains joined end to end.

Squalene   HO   Lanosterol

It now is known that squalene is an intermediate in the biological synthesis
of cholesterol (p. 218) and probably is present in all animals. Numerous
tetracyclic triterpenes are known, the most important of which is **lanosterol,**
$C_{30}H_{50}O$, which occurs along with other triterpenes and with the steroid
cholesterol in wool grease (*lanolin*), and is an intermediate in the biological
conversion of squalene to cholesterol (p. 219).

Tetraterpenes

Most members of the large group of compounds known as *carotenoids*
may be classed as tetraterpenes. They constitute the yellow to red fat-soluble
pigments of plants. Usually several pigments occur together. Because of the
small amounts present and the close similarities in structure, isolation and
purification by the usual crystallization procedures have been difficult.
Rapid progress in the chemistry of the carotenoids began with the use of
chromatographic adsorption on alumina, magnesia, or calcium carbonate.
It was in the separation of carotenoids that this technique first was highly
developed.

Lycopene, $C_{40}H_{56}$, is the red pigment in the ripe fruit of the tomato
(*Lycopersicum esculentum*) and of the watermelon (*Cucumis citrullus*). Its carbon
skeleton is that of two phytyl chains joined end to end.

$$\left[(CH_3)_2C{=}CHCH_2CH_2C{=}CHCH{=}CHC{=}CHCH{=}CHC{=}CHCH{=}\right]_2$$
$$CH_3CH_3CH_3$$

Lycopene

Carotenes

The tetraterpenes that have been of greatest interest are the **carotenes,**
because they are converted by the animal organism into vitamin A_1. The

name *carotene* was given to the yellow pigment of the carrot (*Daucus carota*) from which it first was isolated in 1831. The correct molecular formula, $C_{40}H_{56}$, was not established until 1907.

The application of the methods of chromatographic adsorption has shown that the early carotene is a mixture of isomers. Six carotenes have been identified so far and have been named α-, β-, γ-, δ-, ϵ-, and ζ-*carotene*. Of these the most important is **β-carotene.**

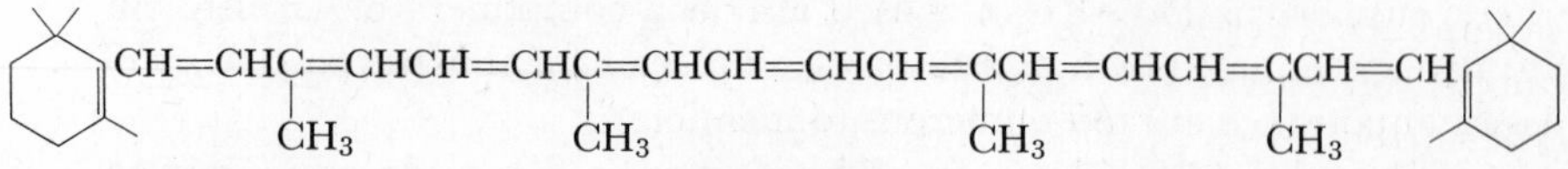

$$CH=CHC=CHCH=CHC=CHCH=CHCH=CHCH=CCH=CHCH=CCH=CH$$
$$CH_3 \qquad CH_3 \qquad CH_3 \qquad CH_3$$

β-Carotene

If β-carotene could react by oxidation and reduction at the center of the molecule in such a way that scission takes place and the two central carbon atoms become primary alcohol groups, two molecules of vitamin A_1 would result. The intestines and liver of the animal organism have the power to bring this about, and β-carotene has vitamin A activity. The commercial synthesis of β-carotene has made available a yellow coloring matter for foods that can replace the carcinogenic (cancer-producing) azo dyes.

Yellow pigments of leaves

Leaves contain, in addition to the carotenes, yellow pigments known as **xanthophylls** (leaf yellow) or **xanthins,** which contain oxygen. It is these pigments, along with the carotenes, that are responsible for the autumn color of leaves, because they persist after the destruction of the green chlorophyll. A typical example is **lutein** (leaf xanthophyll), which is present in green and yellow leaves, in yellow flowers, and in egg yolk.

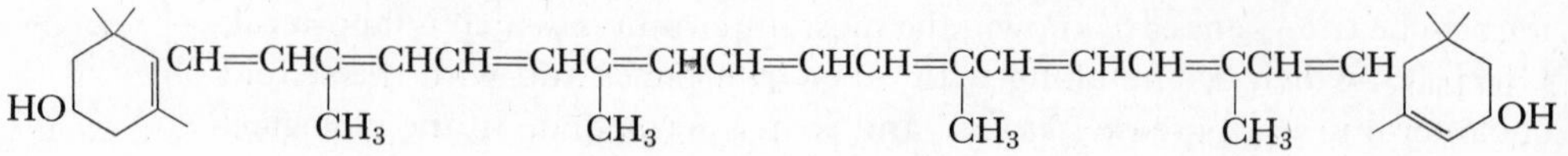

$$HO \quad CH=CHC=CHCH=CHC=CHCH=CHCH=CCH=CHCH=CCH=CH \quad OH$$
$$CH_3 \qquad CH_3 \qquad CH_3 \qquad CH_3$$

Lutein

Yellow to red tetraterpenes containing oxygen also are the pigments in other plant organs such as ripe pepper pods and yew berries.

Polyterpenes

Rubber, gutta percha, and balata are polyterpenes. Their structure and properties are discussed on page 236.

STEROIDS

Steroids may be defined as those compounds that contain a ring system like that present in cholesterol.

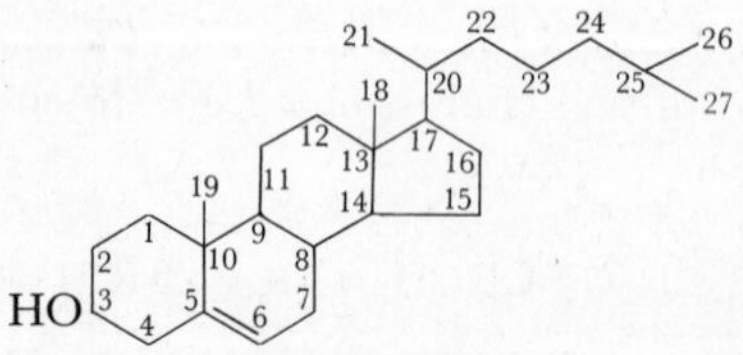

Cholesterol

To this group belong the sterols, the bile acids, the cardiac aglycones, the sex hormones, the adrenal steroids, the toad poisons, and the steroid sapogenins. In view of the complexity of the chemistry and the large number of compounds in the group, the formulas of only a few representatives of the various subgroups are given.

Cholesterol, $C_{27}H_{46}O$, is present in the blood of animals and hence in all parts of the body. It is concentrated in the spinal cord, the brain, skin secretions, and gallstones. It was isolated first from gallstones by Conradi in 1775 and was named cholesterine (Gr. *chole,* bile; *stereos,* solid) in 1816 by Chevreul (p. 119), who showed that, unlike the fats, it was not saponifiable. Berthelot (p. 66) recognized that it was an alcohol in 1859, but the correct molecular formula was not proposed until 1888 by Reinitzer. The currently accepted structure was not arrived at until 1932 after over eighty years of active chemical investigation. With eight asymmetric carbon atoms, 256 active isomers are possible. Not only has the configuration of each asymmetric carbon atom been established, but the last steps in the total synthesis of cholesterol having the exact configuration of the natural product were completed in 1951. It also has been established by means of isotopically labeled compounds that cholesterol is synthesized by the animal organism from acetate ion, and that squalene and lanosterol (p. 217) are intermediates in the synthesis.

Sterols

Ergosterol, $C_{28}H_{44}O$, was isolated first from ergot but is obtained more readily from yeast. Irradiation by ultraviolet light transforms it into a number of products, one of which is the antirachitic vitamin **calciferol** or **vitamin D_2.**

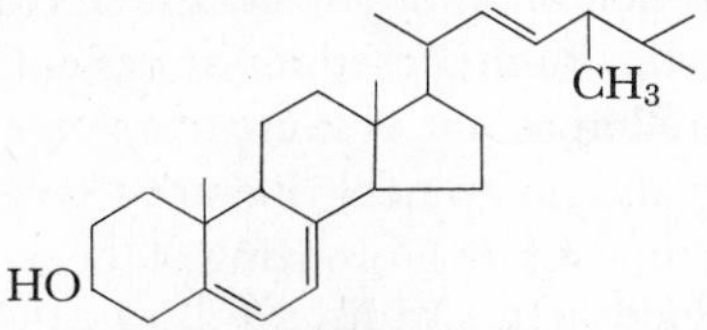

Ergosterol 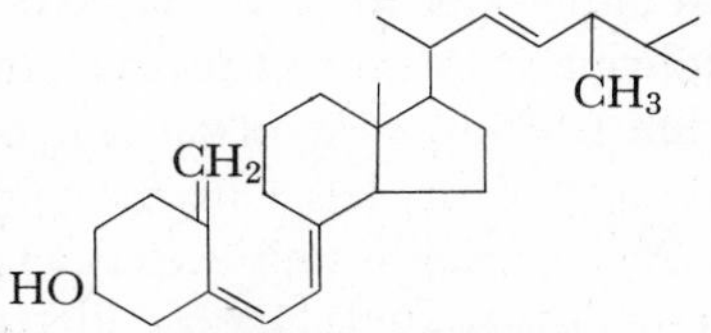   Calciferol (vitamin D_2)

The sex hormones are substances responsible for the sex characteristics and the sexual processes of the animal organism. They are formed in the testes and ovaries, which are stimulated by other hormones, the gonado-tropic hormones secreted by the anterior lobe of the pituitary gland. **Testosterone** is secreted by the testes and controls the development of the genital tract, accessory male organs, and secondary male characteristics such as the comb and wattles of a rooster. **Estradiol** is produced in the ovaries, probably in the ripening follicles.

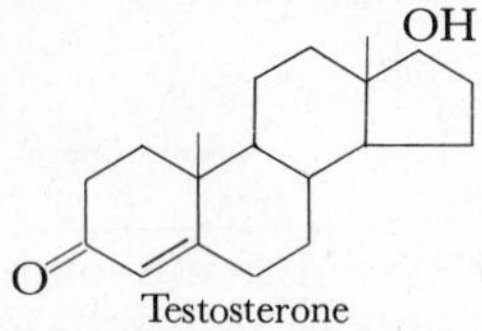

Sex hormones

Testosterone 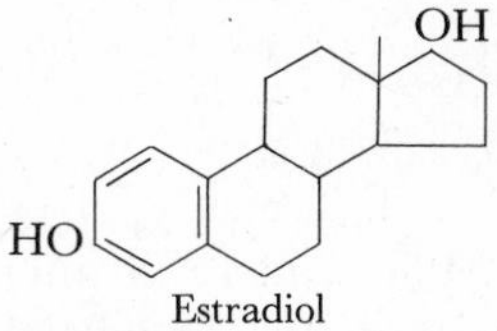   Estradiol

It controls the development of female characteristics and initiates the first phase in the menstrual cycle, namely the proliferation of cells in the uterus. The estrogenic effect is not very specific and a synthetic compound, **stil-bestrol** (*diethylstilbestrol*), is used more commonly than natural estradiol to alleviate trouble arising from a deficiency of the hormone and to arrest prostatic cancer.

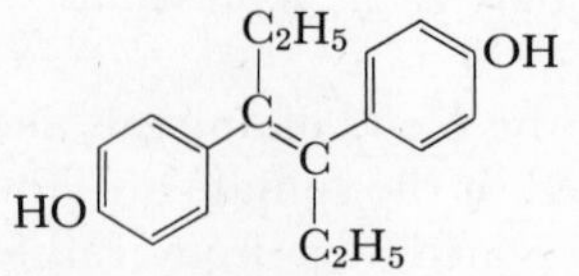

Stilbestrol

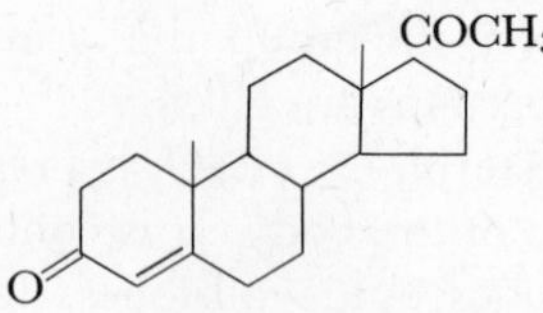

Progesterone

Progesterone is secreted by the corpus luteum (yellow body) formed after the expulsion of the ovum. This hormone prepares the bed of the uterus for the implantation of the fertilized ovum and suppresses further ovulation. It is used clinically to prevent abortion. Certain related compounds such as **Norlutin** and **Enovid** are more effective in suppressing ovulation and are used as oral contraceptives.

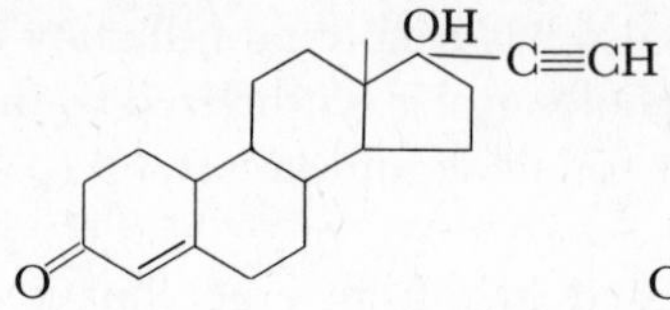

Norlutin

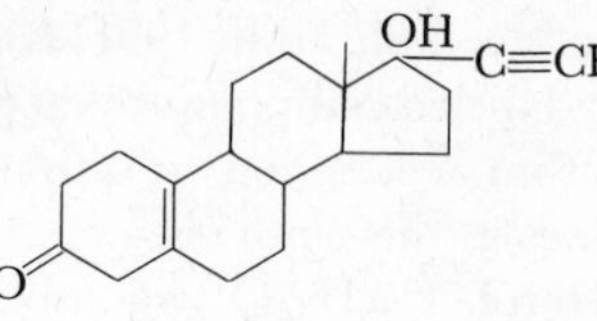

Enovid

Adrenal hormones

The adrenals are two small glands, one above each kidney, that have two important functions, namely the secretion of epinephrine and norepinephrine (p. 135) and the secretion of cortin. Both secretions are essential to life, but the secretion of cortin is the more important because it is secreted only by the adrenals, whereas epinephrine and norepinephrine are secreted by other organs as well. A deficiency of cortin leads to a bronzing of the skin, muscular weakness, and an increase in blood urea (Addison's disease). An excess in children produces precocious sex development.

Cortin activity resides in the steroidal fraction present in the adrenal cortex. Forty-one different compounds of the androstane and pregnane series have been isolated from this fraction and their structure identified. Eight of these have cortin activity. The structures of two of the compounds are indicated.

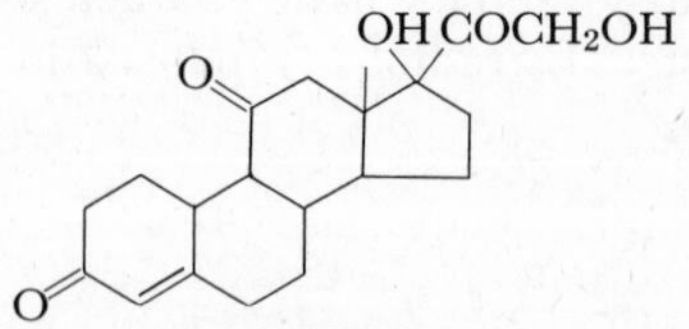

Cortisone

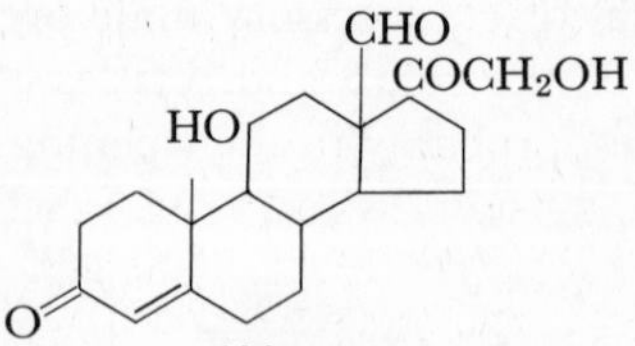

Aldosterone

Since 1948 considerable interest has centered on the component called **cortisone** because of its beneficial effects in the treatment of various maladies, especially rheumatoid arthritis. Numerous modifications in the structure of cortisone have been made with the object of enhancing its desirable properties or reducing undesirable action. Some of the more effective compounds contain a double bond at the 1,2 position, halogen at the 9 position, or a methyl group at the 2 position.

ALKALOIDS

The term *alkaloid* means *like an alkali,* and alkaloids usually are defined as basic nitrogenous plant products having a marked physiological action when administered to animals. Some compounds, however, are included under the term that do not conform to this definition. For example piperine, the alkaloid of pepper, is not basic and has practically no physiological activity. On the other hand some compounds such as caffeine (p. 227) definitely are alkaloids but are so innocuous that they frequently are not considered as such. Furthermore, some compounds either are so closely related in structure to the alkaloids or have such similar physiological action that it is natural to think of them along with the alkaloids, even though they do not come within the usual definition. Thus epinephrine and ephedrine (p. 135) are closely related, but only ephedrine is a plant product; opium and hashish (marijuana) are both habit-forming drugs having similar action, yet the active principle of the latter is not basic and does not contain nitrogen (p. 224).

Coniine is α-*n*-propylpiperidine, the simplest of the alkaloids. It is present in all parts of the poison hemlock (*Conium masculatium;* Gr. *konas,* to whirl around).

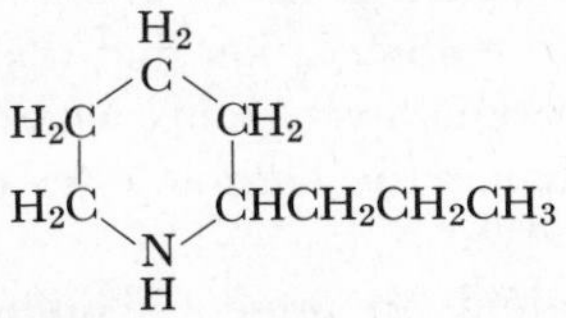

Coniine 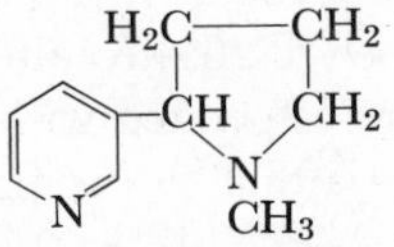 · Nicotine

At least ten alkaloids are present in tobacco (*Nicotiana tabacum*). About three fourths of the total alkaloids is **nicotine.** It is highly toxic to animals, but in small amounts it causes an initial and transient stimulation followed by depression. It is used extensively as a contact insecticide.

Piperine is the alkaloid of black pepper (*Piper nigrum*). The piperine content varies from 5 to 9 per cent.

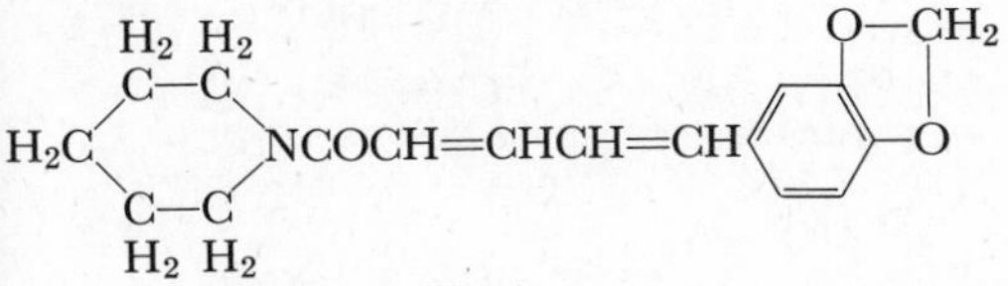

Piperine 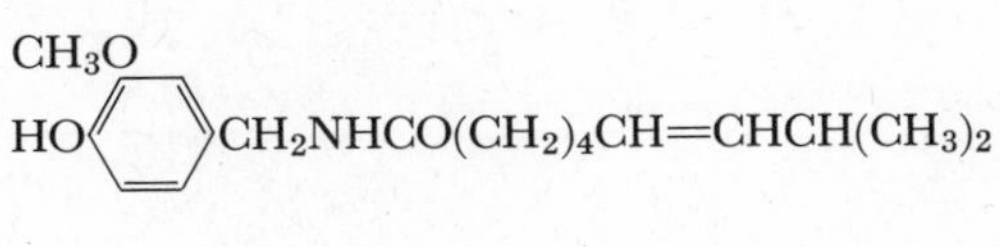 Capsaicin

Capsaicin is the pungent principle of tabasco (*Capsicum* species), cayenne or red pepper (*Capsicum fastigatum*), and paprika (*Capsicum annuum*), the relative pungencies being proportional to the capsaicin content.

Numerous alkaloids have a **tropane ring system,** in which two methylene groups bridge the 2,6 positions of a piperidine ring. **(−)-Hyoscyamine** is the chief alkaloid of many plants of the family *Solanaceae,* especially henbane (*Hyoscyamus niger*), belladonna (*Atropa belladona*), and the deadly nightshade (*Datura stramonium*). It is racemized readily to **atropine,** which

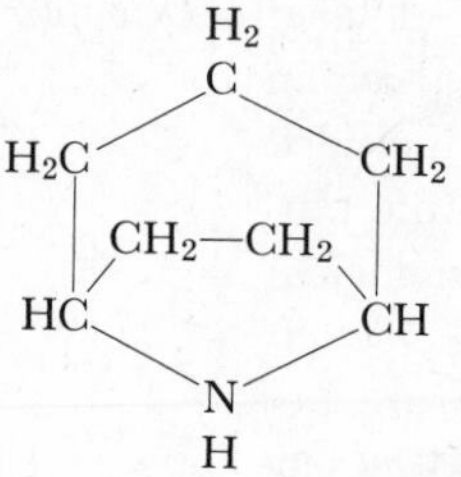

$$CH_2OH$$

Tropane

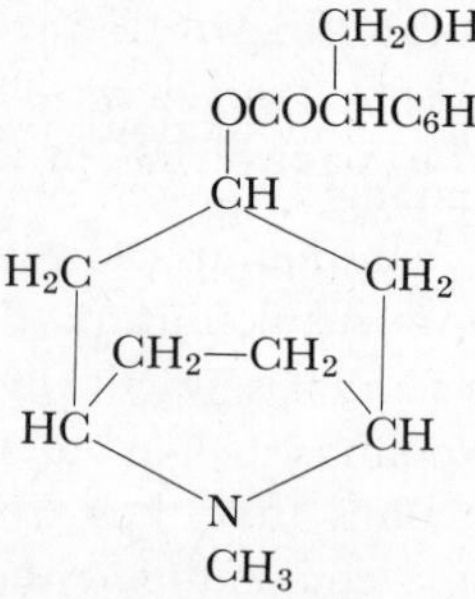

(−)-Hyoscyamine
and atropine

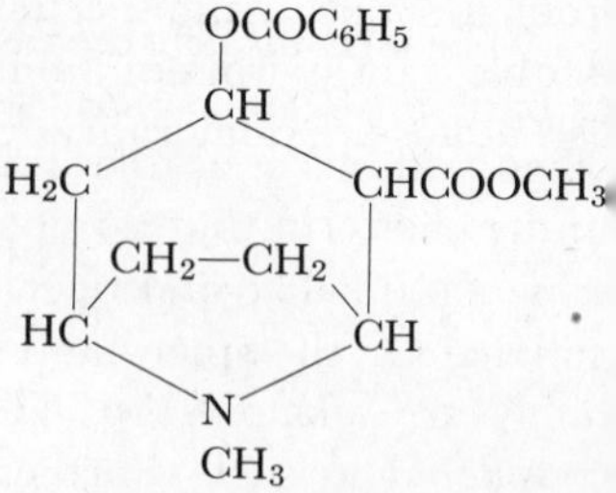

Cocaine

probably does not occur naturally in more than traces. **Cocaine** is the chief alkaloid in the leaves of the Peruvian bush, *Erythroxylum coca*.

All of the alkaloids of this group are characterized by their mydriatic action. Atropine causes dilation of the pupil of the eye at a dilution of 1 in 130,000 parts of water. Cocaine is noted particularly for its stimulating action on the central nervous system, permitting great physical endurance, and for its local anesthetic action. Before the dangers of addiction were understood, it was self-administered widely in Europe and was a component of many patent medicines. The development of the local anesthetics of the procaine type (p. 205) resulted from the observation that the toxic effects of cocaine are associated with the carbomethoxy group, whereas the anesthetic action is due to the portion that is the benzoic ester of an amino alcohol.

Opium alkaloids

At least twenty-four different alkaloids are present in **opium** (Gr. *opion*, poppy juice), the dried latex of the species of poppy (*Papaver somniferum*) that is indigenous to Asia Minor. These alkaloids fall chiefly into two groups, the benzylisoquinoline group and the phenanthrene group. In the former are **papaverine, narcotine,** and **laudanine,** and in the latter **morphine, codeine,** and **thebaine.**

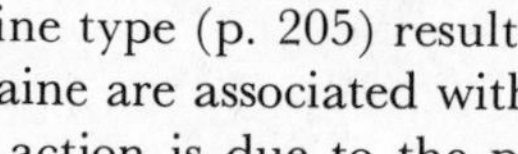

Papaverine

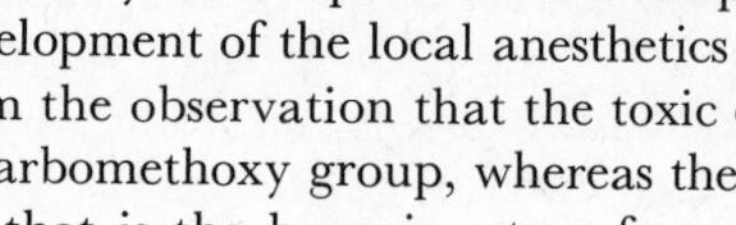

Morphine

One of the hydroxyl groups of morphine is phenolic and can be methylated readily. The resulting methyl ether is identical with natural **codeine.** **Thebaine** is the dimethyl derivative. Acetylation of morphine gives the diacetate, **heroine,** which does not occur in opium.

Arrow poisons of the Amazon region

The material known as **curare** is used as an arrow poison by the South American aborigines. In 1935 a crystalline active alkaloid was isolated from tube curare and called **d-tubocurarine chloride.** Later the same alkaoid was isolated from a sample of curare known to have been prepared from a single plant species, *Chondodendron tomentosum*. This alkaloid is a double tetrahydroisoquinoline related to papaverine, in which both nitrogen atoms are quaternary.

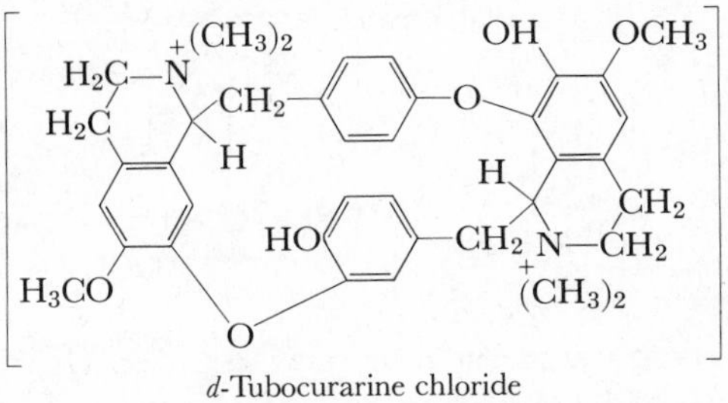

d-Tubocurarine chloride

The paralytic or curariform activity is general for quaternary ammonium salts (p. 132).

Another important group of alkaloids is that derived from **cinchona bark.** The name commonly is thought to be derived from that of Countess Anna del Chinchon, wife of the Spanish Viceroy to Peru, who was cured of malaria by treatment with it in 1638. It has been suggested also that the name was derived from the Inca word *kinia* meaning *bark*. *Antimalarials*

The bark probably reached Europe about 1632, and its use was widespread by 1640. The genus *Cinchona* was established by Linnaeus in 1742, and the tree known as *Cinchona officinalis*, which is native to the high eastern slopes of the Andes, was described by him in 1753. The alkaloids **quinine** and **cinchonine** were not isolated until 1820 by Pelletier and Caventou. By about 1860 the near extinction of the native trees caused such a rise in price of the drug that attempts were made to cultivate cinchona elsewhere. It was grown successfully in India, Ceylon, and Java. Today more than 90 per cent of the quinine produced comes from plantations in Java. The total alkaloid content of the bark of the cultivated trees is 6 per cent, of which 70 per cent is quinine. The last phase of a total synthesis of quinine was completed successfully in 1944.

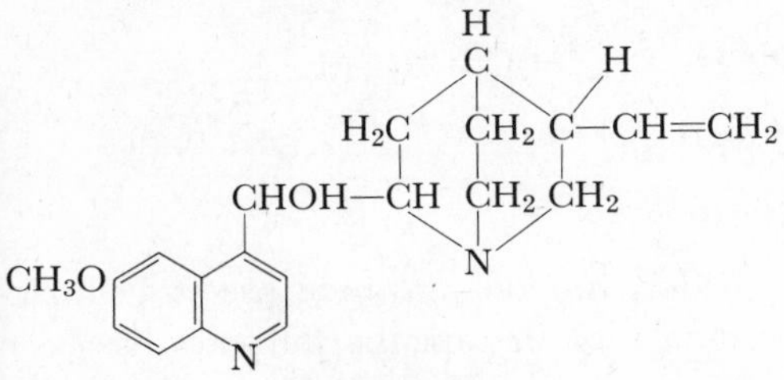

Quinine

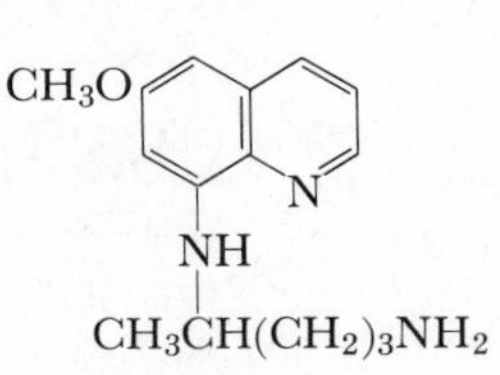

Primaquine

The chief value of quinine lies in its specific action in the treatment of malaria. It has been replaced for this purpose by synthetic compounds, of which **primaquine** is now the preferred drug.

The **ergot alkaloids** are derived from ergot, a fungus that grows on rye and other cereals. They are responsible for a disease known as *ergotism* that was prevalent in the Middle Ages. All are amides of **lysergic acid.** *Psychogenic compound*

Ergonovine, which is the amide of 2-amino-1-propanol, is used medicinally to induce uterine contractions at childbirth. The administration of the synthetic **diethylamide** produces a psychosis resembling schizophrenia.

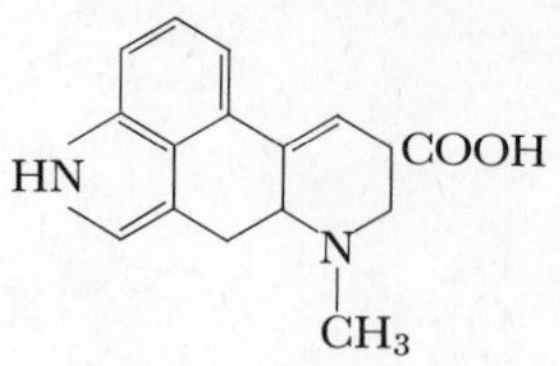

Lysergic acid

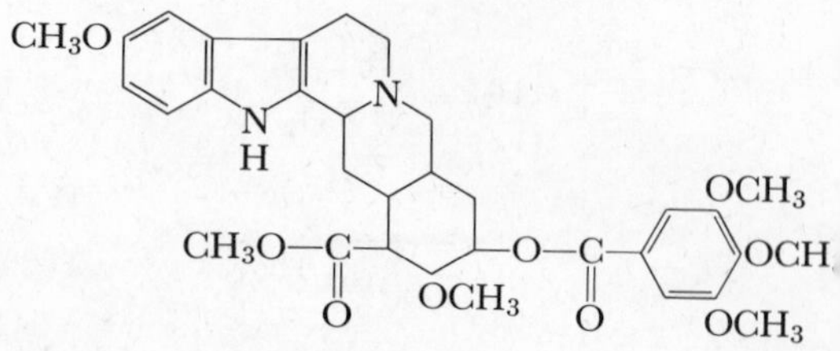

Reserpine (Serpasil)

Tranquilizing alkaloid

Rauwolfia serpentina (Indian snake root) is a shrub that grows in the hot moist regions of India. Extracts of the root have been used as a remedy for fever, snake bite, and dysentery. In recent times it has been used to lower blood pressuue and to treat some types of insanity. The active alkaloid was isolated in a pure state in 1952 and named **reserpine** or **Serpasil.** Since then it has been used extensively in the treatment of hypertension and as a general sedative. Violent schizophrenics are calmed without being put to sleep. Thus they become amenable to psychiatric treatment, and frequently the necessity for hospitalization is avoided.

NONALKALOIDAL HETEROCYCLIC COMPOUNDS

Many biologically important compounds other than alkaloids contain heterocyclic rings. Frequently several hetero atoms are present. The germ oil of seeds, especially wheat germ oil, contains substances designated as *Vitamins E* *vitamin E* that are necessary for the growth and normal reproduction of the rat. At least four compounds are present that have this activity and they have been called the *tocopherols* (Gr. *tokos,* childbirth; *pherein,* to bear). The most active is **α-tocopherol,** which contains a benzopyran ring system (p. 83).

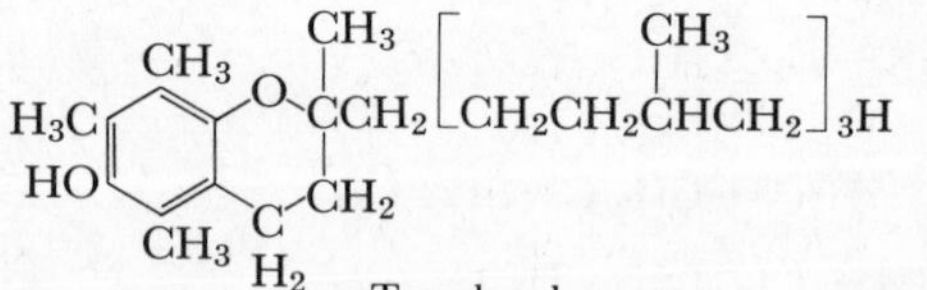

α-Tocopherol

The tocopherols are distributed widely in food, and their use as a supplement to the diet of man and animals for therapeutic purposes has been controversial. The tocopherols have a marked antioxidant action and decrease the rate at which rancidity develops in foods containing fats (p. 122).

Marijuana components

The resin from the flowering tops of hemp (*Cannabis sativa*) has been used since antiquity for its physiological effects. The resin is known as *hashish* or *bhang* and the dried tops as *marijuana.* The active components are believed to be isomeric **tetrahydrocannabinols,** one of which has been synthesized.

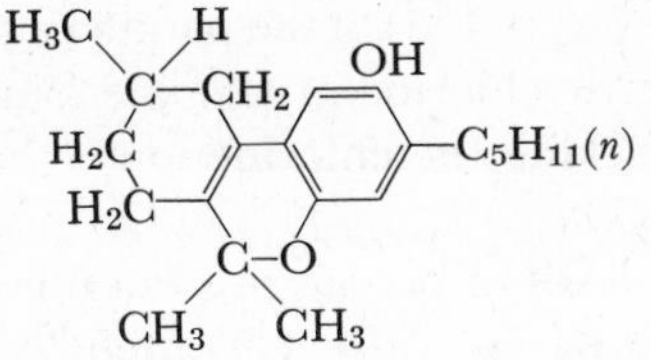

Tetrahydrocannabinol

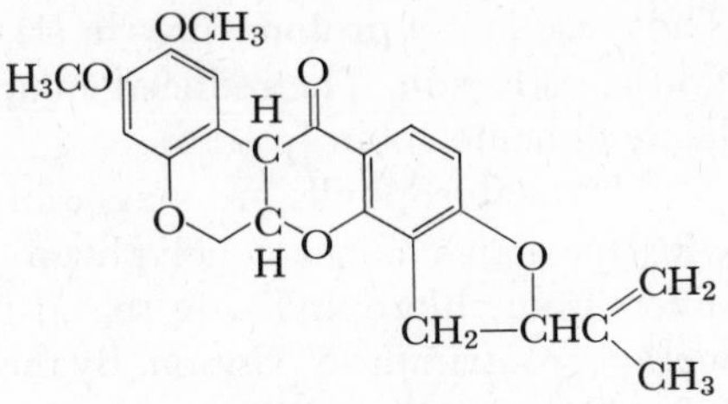

Rotenone

Rotenone an insecticide

Rotenone contains two dihydropyran rings and a dihydrofuran ring (p. 83). It is one of the active components of several plants that are used as insecticides. They are highly toxic to fish also but are relatively harmless to human beings. Hence they are safe to use on plants bearing food. Rotenone and related compounds have been identified in sixty-seven species of plants, but the chief commercial sources are the roots of *Derris elliptica* (tuba) cultivated in Malaya and the East Indies, and of *Lonchocarpus nicou* (timbo or cube) grown in South America.

Alkylated pyrrole nuclei form the building units for many biologically important pigments, for example those of bile and blood, and the green coloring matter of plants. These pigments have a fundamental structure known as the **porphin nucleus** (I), which contains a flat 16-membered ring. The **porphyrins** derived from natural pigments (Gr. *porphyra*, purple) have substituents in the eight β positions of the pyrrole nuclei. The natural

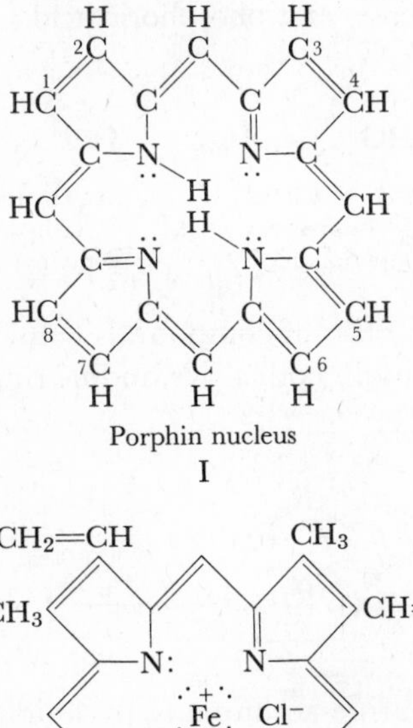

Pyrrole nuclei make up porphin nucleus

Porphin nucleus

I

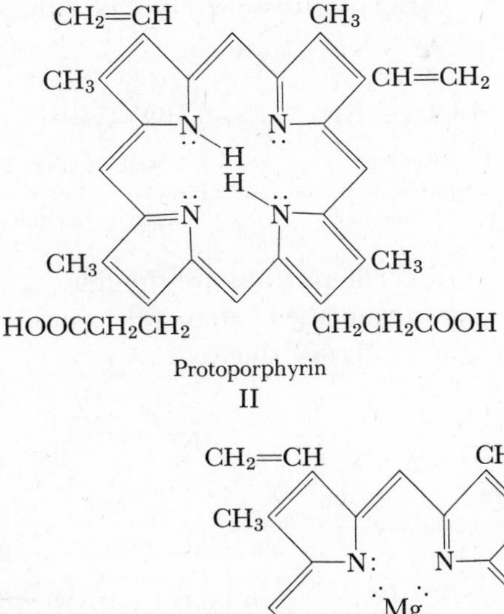

Protoporphyrin

II

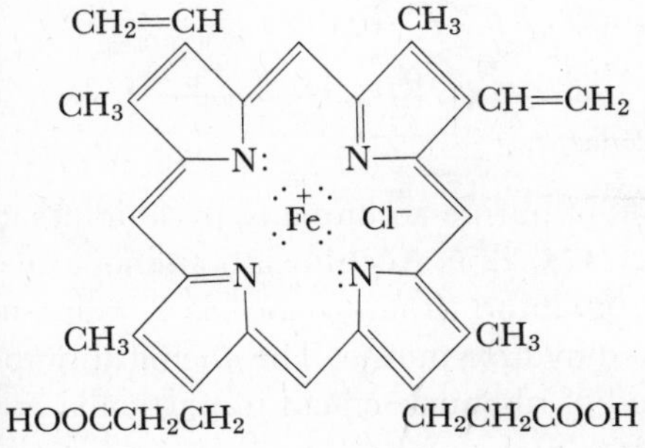

Hemin

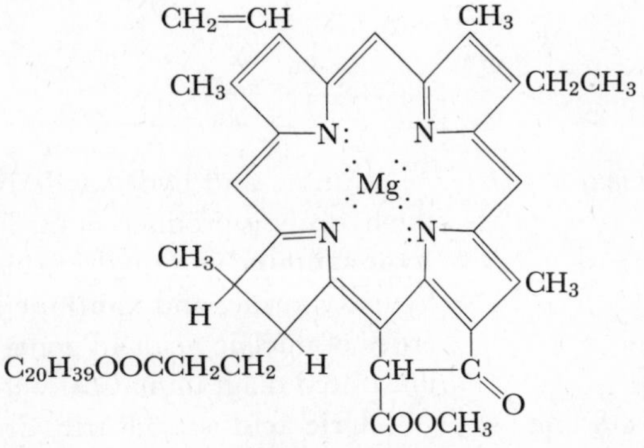

Chlorophyll a

pigments themselves are metal chelate complexes (p. 133) of the porphyrins. Thus reaction of **protoporphyrin** (II) with ferric chloride in alkaline solution gives **hemin.** The reduced compound lacking the chloride ion is the **heme** of hemoglobin (p. 196).

The **chlorophylls** are magnesium complexes of porphyrins esterified with the long-chain alcohol phytol, $C_{20}H_{39}OH$ (p. 216). Chlorophyll *b* differs from chlorophyll *a* in that it has an aldehyde group replacing the methyl group in the 3 position. By the use of isotopically labelled molecules it has been shown that the porphyrin nucleus of both heme and chlorophyll is synthesized biologically from glycine and acetic acid and that the steps of the synthesis by the red blood cell and by the chloroplast of the plant are identical. The total synthesis of racemic chlorophyll in the laboratory was reported in 1960.

Six-membered rings with two or more hetero atoms

Three six-membered ring systems containing two nitrogen atoms are known, namely the 1,2-diazines or pyridazines, the 1,3-diazines or pyrimidines, and the 1,4-diazines or pyrazines.

1,2-Diazine or pyridazine

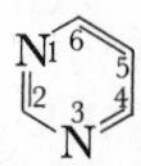

1,3-Diazine or pyrimidine

1,4-Diazine or pyrazine

Pyrimidines from nucleoproteins

Compounds containing the **pyrimidine** ring are present in all living cells. Hydrolysis of nucleic acids obtained from nucleoproteins (p. 196) yields the pyrimidines **cytosine, 5-methylcytosine, uracil,** and **thymine,** along with purines, D-ribose (p. 178) or 2-deoxy-D-ribose, and phosphoric acid.

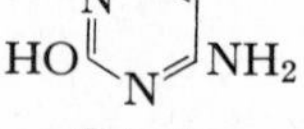

Cytosine
(2-hydroxy-4-amino-pyrimidine)

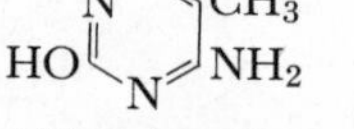

5-Methylcytosine
(2-hydroxy-4-amino-5-methylpyrimidine)

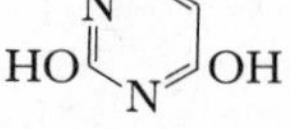

Uracil
(2,4-dihydroxy-pyrimidine)

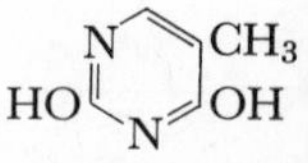

Thymine
(2,4-dihydroxy-5-methylpyrimidine)

Purine has condensed pyrimidine and imidazole rings

The **purines** are the most important class of compounds containing two condensed heterocyclic rings. They contain both a pyrimidine ring and an imidazole ring.

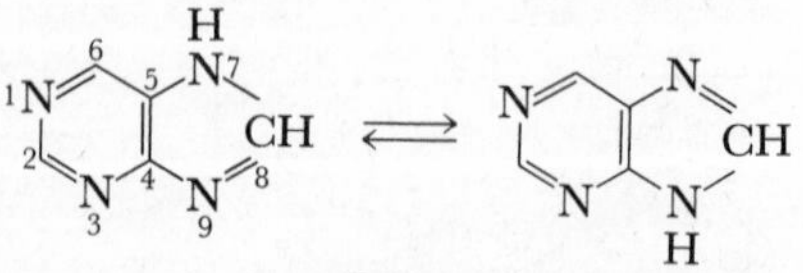

Purine

Present in nucleic acids

Amino and hydroxy derivatives of purine accompany pyrimidines in the hydrolysis products of nucleic acids (p. 227). **Adenine** is 6-aminopurine, **hypoxanthine** is 6-hydroxypurine, **guanine** (from guano) is 2-amino-6-hydroxypurine, and **xanthine** is 2,6-dihydroxypurine. The chemical properties of nucleic acids in general and of ribonucleic acid in particular are illustrated diagrammatically in Figure 30.

Present in uric acid

Uric acid is 2,6,8-trihydroxypurine. It is present in blood and urine and can cause the formation of urinary calculi, from which it first was isolated by Scheele in 1776. Crystals of the monosodium salt deposited in the

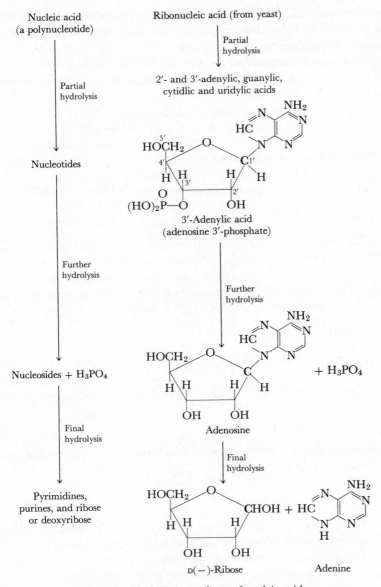

Figure 30.   Hydrolytic products of nucleic acids.

joints cause the painful condition known as gout. Although uric acid is eliminated only in small amounts by mammals, it is the chief product of nitrogen metabolism by caterpillars, birds, and reptiles. Guano, which contains about 25 per cent uric acid, is one of the best sources.

Uric acid

Caffeine

Caffeine is an alkaloid (p. 221), but it is considered here because it has a purine nucleus. It is chiefly responsible for the stimulating action of coffee, tea, cola drinks, and maté.

The natural **penicillins,** the first antibiotics used in medicine, contain the thiazole ring system. They are produced chiefly from the mold *Penicillium chrysogenum.*

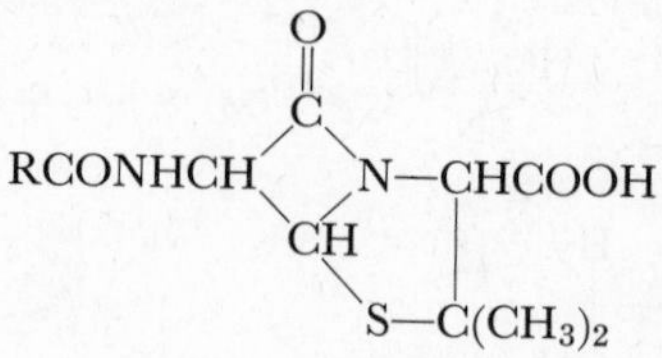

PENICILLIN	R
G or II	$C_6H_5CH_2-$
X or III	$p\text{-}HOC_6H_4CH_2-$
F or I	$CH_3CH_2CH=CHCH_2-$
Dihydro F	$CH_3(CH_2)_4-$
Flavicidin	$CH_3CH=CH(CH_2)_2-$
K or IV	$CH_3(CH_2)_6-$
V	$C_6H_5OCH_2-$

Natural Penicillins

Vitamin B and cocarboxylase

Thiamine (*vitamin B_1, aneurin*) contains a pyrimidine nucleus joined through a methylene group to a thiazole nucleus. Its absence from the diet causes the deficiency diseases known as beriberi in man and polyneuritis in birds. The pyrophosphate is **cocarboxylase,** which is necessary for the enzymic decarboxylation of pyruvic acid (p. 173).

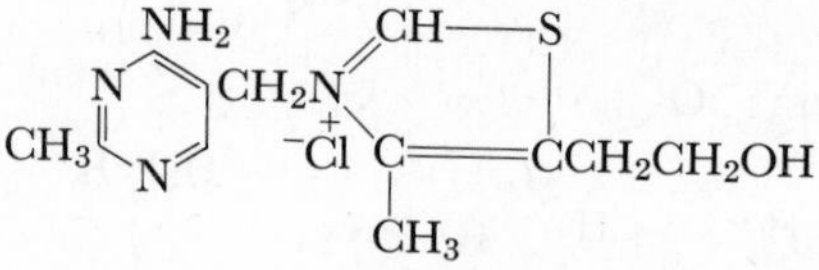

Thiamine
(vitamin B_1, aneurin)

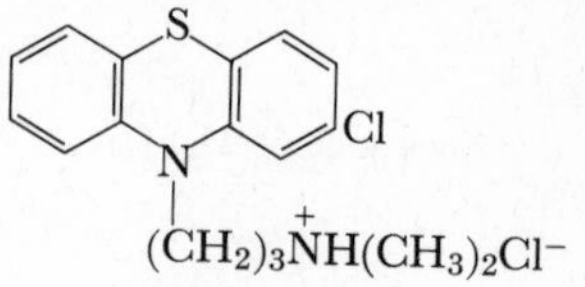

Chlorpromazine

Chlorpromazine is a synthetic sulfur-nitrogen heterocyclic compound used as a tranquilizing drug.

SUMMARY

1. Terpenes form a class of natural products whose carbon skeletons are divisible into iso-C_5 units. The class is divided into the terpenes proper, the sesquiterpenes, the diterpenes, the triterpenes, the tetraterpenes and the polyterpenes, depending on whether the compounds have 10, 15, 20, 30, 40, or a very large number of carbon atoms respectively.

2. Terpenes may be acyclic or alicyclic. They comprise odorous liquids and solids, vitamins, pigments, and natural rubber.

3. Steroids all contain the same alicyclic ring system known as the steroid nucleus. Sterols, bile acids, cardiac aglycones, sex hormones, and adrenal hormones belong to this group.

4. Alkaloids are basic nitrogenous plant products that produce a marked physiological reaction in animals. Some of the more important alkaloids are nicotine, atropine, cocaine, morphine, curare, quinine, and reserpine.

5. Numerous five- and six-membered rings contain more than one hetero atom. The more common ones are the pyrimidine ring, the purine ring, and the thiazole ring, which are present in nucleic acids, enzymes, and numerous important drugs.

EXERCISES

1. Write structural formulas showing all of the atoms in: (a) menthol; (b) α-pinene; (c) abietic acid; (d) cholesteroi.
2. (a) How many asymmetric carbon atoms are present in the cortisone molecule?
   (b) How many stereoisomers of cortisone are possible?
3. Piperine contains an amide linkage. Write an equation for the alkaline hydrolysis of piperine. What is the name of the heterocyclic product of hydrolysis?
4. Indicate by dotted lines the portion of the cocaine molecule that is believed to be responsible for its local anesthetic action and compare it with the structure of procaine (Novocain).
5. What portion of the tocopherol molecule has the same carbon skeleton as the phytol molecule?

CHAPTER 19

POLYMERS AND POLYMERIZATION. SYNTHETIC PLASTICS, RESINS, AND FIBERS

POLYMERS AND POLYMERIZATION

Polymers are compounds of high molecular weight (macromolecules) that are composed of a large number of units of low molecular weight joined by covalent bonds. In the molecules of **linear polymers,** the units of low molecular weight are bonded end-to-end in a long chain, and no chemical bonds, or practically none, exist between the chains. These chains may be without protruding groups, or they may be branched, that is, have protruding groups or side chains.

Linear polymers may be unbranched or branched

Cellulose (p. 192) and silk (p. 200) are natural linear polymers of high tensile strength. The chains can approach each other closely enough and the molecular weights are high enough ($>1,000,000$) that the van der Waals forces between molecules are sufficiently strong to prevent molecules from slipping past each other even at elevated temperatures. Hence they do not soften when heated unless the temperature is high enough to break covalent bonds and cause decomposition of the molecule.

On the other hand, linear polymers of lower molecular weight (10,000–300,000), such as those prepared by synthesis, soften when heated, because the thermal agitation is sufficient to overcome the van der Waals forces and to allow molecules to slip past each other. The hot plastic then may be extruded through fine holes to form fibers, or it may be molded into desired shapes. Cooling causes solidification. Such polymers are said to be **thermoplastic.** If the van der Waals forces are not too great, these polymers may be soluble in organic solvents. The solutions then may be used to produce fibers, sheets, or protective coatings of the polymer. Acetylation of the hydroxyl groups of cellulose reduces the van der Waals forces by preventing proton bonding between chains and by introducing some protruding groups that keep the molecular chains further apart. Hence some of the cellulose acetates are thermoplastic and soluble in organic solvents.

Thermoplastic polymers

In fibers that have been extruded through fine holes (p. 201), either *Fiber formation*
from a melt or from solution, the molecules are not aligned very well. When
such fibers are placed under tension, they may stretch to as much as three
or four times their original length, and the fiber becomes correspondingly
thinner in diameter. In the stretching process the molecules become more
aligned and are brought closer together, thus increasing the van der Waals
forces and the strength of the fiber. All synthetic fibers are stretched at some
point in the manufacturing process.

It should be noted that all types of van der Waals forces, namely London
forces (p. 21), hydrogen bonding (p. 61), and dipole association (p. 94),
contribute to the attractive forces between macromolecules as well as
between small molecules. Hence different types of thermoplastic polymers
must be of different molecular weights to achieve the same mechanical *Molecular weights vary*
strength. Thus if polar groups or groups capable of forming proton bonds
are present, molecular weights of the order of 20,000 may suffice to give a
useful material, whereas a molecular weight ten to fifteen times larger may
be necessary to give a saturated hydrocarbon polymer similar properties.
The amylopectin of starch (p. 192) consists of highly branched molecules of very high molecular weight. Hence the van der Waals forces act
between a large number of relatively short chains, and there is no tendency
for the molecules to become aligned and form fibers.

In the types of molecules discussed thus far, no chemical bonds, or
practically none, exist between the long chains. If many bonds tie the different chains together at numerous points, the polymer becomes one large
three-dimensional unit which is infusible and insoluble. Such bonds usually
are called *cross links*, and the polymer is said to be highly *cross-linked*. Thermoplastic polymers that, when heated, undergo secondary reactions to
give a highly cross-linked product are said to be **thermosetting.** If only a *Thermosetting polymers*
few cross links are formed, the product usually is elastic, and the process is *and vulcanization*
called **vulcanization.**

Synthetic polymers frequently are called synthetic plastics or synthetic
resins. These terms are almost synonymous, although usually *resin* is used
for a compound readily soluble in organic solvents that can be used as the
film-forming substance in a protective coating, whereas *plastic* is applied to
a material that can be molded into some useful object. Frequently the same
polymer may be used as a resin, or as a plastic, or even as a synthetic fiber.

The process of converting compounds of low molecular weight into
polymers is called *polymerization*. The compounds of low molecular weight
from which polymers are formed are called *monomers*. Two types of poly- *Polymers made*
merization are recognized, namely, addition polymerization and condensa- *from monomers*
tion polymerization. In **addition polymerization,** unsaturated or cyclic
molecules are caused to add to each other without the elimination of any *Polymerization by*
portion of the monomer. In **condensation polymerization** a chemical reac- *addition or by condensation*
tion takes place between the monomeric molecules during which some small
molecule, such as water, is eliminated. Sometimes polymers are formed both
by addition and by condensation, either separately or simultaneously.

In either addition or condensation polymerization it is essential that
the reaction be functionally capable of proceeding indefinitely; that is, each

time two molecules react, the product must contain a functional group capable of reacting with another molecule of monomer. In addition polymerization, the monomer need have only one functional group, but in condensation polymerization the monomer must have at least two functional groups.

Steps of addition polymerizations

Addition polymerization usually must be catalyzed by an acid, by a base, or by free radicals. All addition polymerizations go through three stages, namely, *initiation, propagation,* and *termination.* In the **initiation of the reaction,** the catalyst molecules attack the monomers to give intermediates that, during the **propagation stage,** are capable of attacking other molecules of monomer with lengthening of the chain. In the **termination step** further reaction of a chain is blocked by elimination of a group from the reacting end of the chain or by addition of a group to the end of the chain.

Acid-catalyzed polymerizations

These steps may be illustrated by the acid-catalyzed polymerization of olefins.

(1) Initiation: $CH_2{=}CH + HB \longrightarrow CH_3{-}\overset{+}{C}H + B^-$
                    $|$ $|$
                    R   R
                    I   II

(2) Propagation: $CH_3{-}\overset{+}{C}H + CH_2{=}CH \longrightarrow CH_3{-}CH{-}CH_2{-}\overset{+}{C}H \xrightarrow{xCH_2{=}CHR}$
                     $|$ $|$ $|$ $|$
                     R   R   R   R
                                            III

                               $CH_3{-}CH{-}(CH_2{-}CH{-})_x CH_2{-}\overset{+}{C}H$
                                      $|$ $|$ $|$
                                      R   R   R
                                            IV

(3) Termination: $CH_3{-}CH{-}(CH_2{-}CH{-})_x CH_2{-}\overset{+}{C}H + B^- \longrightarrow$
                     $|$ $|$ $|$
                     R   R   R

                               $CH_3{-}CH{-}(CH_2{-}CH{-})_x CH{=}CH + HB$
                                      $|$ $|$ $|$
                                      R   R   R
                                           V

Initially a molecule of unsaturated monomer (I) is attacked by a molecule of acid, and a proton is transferred to the unsaturated molecule according to the Markovnikov rule (p. 33). The intermediate carbonium ion (II) attacks a second molecule to give a dimeric ion (III). The dimeric ion and subsequent carbonium ions repeat the process, giving rise to the polymeric carbonium ion (IV). Eventually, when most of the monomer has been consumed, the polymeric ion collides with a base, which removes a proton and gives the unsaturated polymeric molecule (V).

Polymerizations catalyzed by free radicals

Addition polymerizations catalyzed by free radicals follow a course similar to acid- or base-catalyzed polymerizations. The free radicals used as catalysts are derived from organic or inorganic peroxides or other organic compounds that decompose readily into free radicals. A large number of compounds are available for this purpose, and one is chosen that has the right solubility characteristics and that gives the desired catalytic activity at the optimum temperature for the particular reaction. Thus benzoyl peroxide decomposes fairly rapidly at $80°$ into benzoyl radicals, which undergo further decomposition into free phenyl radicals.

$$C_6H_5\overset{\|}{\underset{O}{C}}-O-O-\overset{\|}{\underset{O}{C}}C_6H_5 \longrightarrow 2\ C_6H_5\overset{\|}{\underset{O}{C}}-O\cdot \longrightarrow 2\ C_6H_5\cdot + 2\ CO_2$$

Azobisisobutyronitrile at $70°$ yields cyanoisopropyl radicals.

$$(CH_3)_2\underset{CN}{C}-N{=}N-\underset{CN}{C}(CH_3)_2 \longrightarrow 2\ (CH_3)_2\underset{CN}{C}\cdot + N_2$$

Any of the free radicals may be represented by the symbol $Z\cdot$. The course of the polymerization then may be indicated by the three steps of initiation, propagation, and termination.

Mechanism of free-radical polymerizations

(1) Initiation: $Z\cdot + CH_2{=}\underset{X}{CH} \longrightarrow Z-CH_2-\underset{X}{CH}\cdot$

(2) Propagation: $Z-CH_2-\underset{X}{CH}\cdot + CH_2{=}\underset{X}{CH} \longrightarrow Z-CH_2-\underset{X}{CH}-CH_2-\underset{X}{CH}\cdot \xrightarrow{xCH_2{=}CHX}$

$$Z-CH_2-\underset{X}{CH}-(CH_2-\underset{X}{CH}-)_x CH_2{=}\underset{X}{CH}\cdot$$

Because the double bond is polarized by the substituent group, X, and because the group X has a greater blocking effect than hydrogen, polymerization proceeds for the most part in a regular "head to tail" fashion.

(3) Termination: $Z-CH_2-\underset{X}{CH}-(CH_2-\underset{X}{CH}-)_x CH_2-\underset{X}{CH}\cdot + \cdot W \longrightarrow$

$$Z-CH_2-\underset{X}{CH}-(CH_2-\underset{X}{CH}-)_x CH_2-\underset{X}{CH}-W$$

where $\cdot W$ is any other radical with which the intermediate may happen to collide in the proper way. The result is a saturated molecule, and because any two radicals may couple and stop the chain, one obtains a mixture of molecules of different molecular weights. Incidentally it will be noted that the catalyst becomes an integral part of the final polymer. If two or more monomers undergo addition polymerization with each other, the process is called **copolymerization,** and the product is called a **copolymer.**

Copolymerization and copolymers

One other point should be mentioned. The polymerization of unsymmetrically substituted monomers leads to the production of asymmetric carbon atoms. Each time a monomer adds to a chain, it gives rise to a new asymmetric carbon atom, which may have either of two configurations. In recent years catalysts have been discovered that produce polymers that consist of an equimolecular mixture of chains of opposite configurations but in which all of the carbon atoms in a given chain have the same configuration. Such polymers are said to be **isotactic** (Gr. *isos,* equal; *taktika,* arrangement). If the configurations are random within a chain, the polymer is said to be **atactic.**

Isotactic polymers

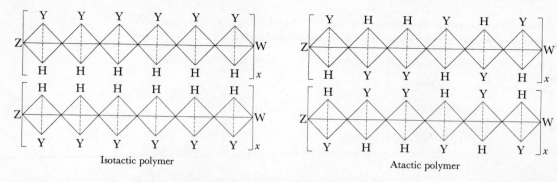

Isotactic polymer   Atactic polymer

The molecules of isotactic polymers are more regularly oriented than those of atactic polymers, and the isotactic polymer may be a useful plastic or fiber, whereas the atactic form is a useless gum. It should be noted that, because there is an equal probability of forming a particular configuration for a chain and for its mirror image, even isotactic polymers are optically inactive (p. 163) unless the catalyst itself is optically active (p. 165).

Some of the more important addition polymers, together with the formula of the monomer and the repeating unit in the polymer, are listed in Table 13. Polymers from substituted ethylenes that contain the vinyl group, $CH_2=CH-$, frequently are called **vinyl plastics.**

TABLE 13.   ADDITION POLYMERS

NAME	FORMULA OF MONOMER	TYPE OF CATALYST	REPEATING UNIT	PRINCIPAL USE
Polyethylene, Polythene	$CH_2=CH_2$	radical	$-CH_2-CH_2-$	molded articles, sheet, pipe
Polypropylene	$CH_2=CHCH_3$	stereo-selective	$-CH_2-CH-$ $\quad\quad\;\; CH_3$	molded articles, fiber
Polyisobutylene, Vistanex	$CH_2=C(CH_3)_2$	acid	$\quad\quad\;\; CH_3$ $-CH_2-C-$ $\quad\quad\;\; CH_3$	motor oil thickener
Poly(tetrafluoroethylene), Teflon[a]	$F_2C=CF_2$	radical	$-CF_2-CF_2-$	molded articles
Poly(chlorotrifluoroethylene), Kel-F, or Fluorothene	$F_2C=CFCl$	radical	$-CF_2-CFCl-$	molded articles
Poly(vinyl chloride)[b]	$CH_2=CHCl$	radical	$-CH_2-CHCl-$	plasticized sheet
Poly(vinyl acetate)[c]	$CH_2=CHOCOCH_3$	radical	$-CH_2-CH-$ $\quad\quad\;\; OCOCH_3$	adhesives, protective coatings
Poly(vinyl alcohol)[d]	. . . .	. . . .	$-CH_2-CHOH-$	coatings for paper and textiles

TABLE 13.   ADDITION POLYMERS (*Continued*)

NAME	FORMULA OF MONOMER	TYPE OF CATALYST	REPEATING UNIT	PRINCIPAL USE
Poly(vinyl butyral), Butex[e]	. . . .	. . . .	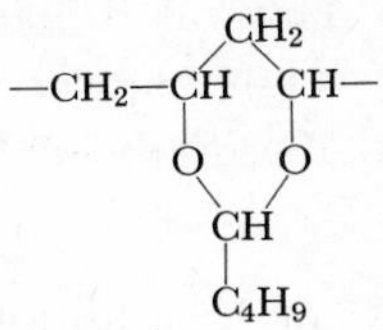 $-CH_2-CH\ \ CH-$ with CH_2 bridge, O, O, CH, C_4H_9	safety glass laminate
Poly(vinylidene chloride), Saran[f]	$CH_2{=}CCl_2$	radical	$-CH_2-CCl_2-$	fiber, film, pipe
Poly(vinyl methyl ether)	$CH_2{=}CHOCH_3$	radical	$-CH_2-CH-$ OCH_3	resin
Poly(vinyl cyanide), polyacrylonitrile, Orlon, Acrilan[g]	$CH_2{=}CHCN$	radical	$-CH_2-CH-$ CN	fiber
Polystyrene,[h] Styron, Lustron	$CH_2{=}CHC_6H_5$	radical	$-CH_2-CH-$ C_6H_5	molded articles, rigid foams
Poly(methyl methacrylate), Lucite, Crystallite, Plexiglas, Perspex	$CH_2{=}C-COOCH_3$ CH_3	radical	CH_3 $-CH_2-C-$ $COOCH_3$	transparent sheets, protective coatings
Poly(vinyl pyrrolidone), Periston	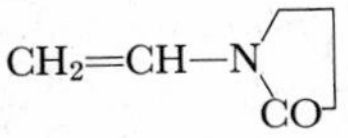 $CH_2{=}CH-N$ (ring) CO	radical	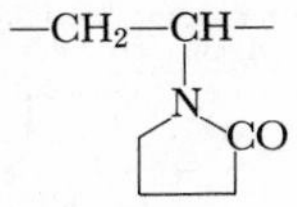 $-CH_2-CH-$ N (ring) CO	hair sprays
Polyformaldehyde, Delrin	$H_2C{=}O$	acid (trace of water)	$-O-CH_2-$[i]	molded articles
Poly(ethylene oxide), poly(ethylene glycol), Carbowax	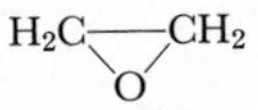 H_2C-CH_2 O	acid	$-OCH_2CH_2-$	water-soluble waxes
Polycaprolactam, nylon 6	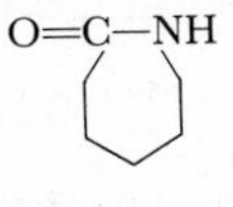 $O{=}C-NH$ (ring)	base	$-CO(CH_2)_5NH-$	fiber
Polypyrrolidone, nylon 4	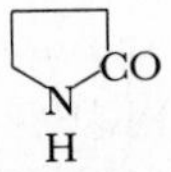 (ring) CO N H	base	$-CO(CH_2)_3NH-$	molded articles

[a] Teflon 100 is a copolymer with hexafluoropropylene.

[b] Brittle resin converted into useful products by plasticizers. *Vinylite* is copolymer with vinyl acetate.

[c] *Vinylite* is copolymer with vinyl chloride

[d] Made by saponification of poly(vinyl acetate); monomer unknown

[e] Made by condensation of poly(vinyl alcohol) with *n*-butyraldehyde

[f] Sarans are copolymers with small amounts of vinyl chloride or acrylonitrile

[g] Usually copolymerized with small amounts of other monomers; *Verel* is a copolymer with 40 per cent of vinyl chloride and *Dynel* is copolymer with about 60 per cent of vinyl chloride.

[h] Polystyrenes containing sulfonic acid groups are *cation exchange-resins;* those containing basic groups are *anion exchange-resins.*

[i] Depolymerization is prevented, probably by acetylation of the terminal hydroxyl groups.

1,3-DIENE ADDITION POLYMERS

1,3-Diene molecules undergo 1,4 addition (p. 35) with each other or copolymerization with other unsaturated molecules to give linear polymers. Natural rubber and most synthetic rubbers are polymers of 1,3-dienes. Thus **natural rubber,** the coagulated latex from the rubber tree, *Hevea braziliensis,* has the formula $(-CH_2CH=CCH_2-)_x$, which could result from
$$| \atop CH_3$$
the 1,4 addition of isoprene molecules, $CH_2=CHC=CH_2$. Although natu-
$$| \atop CH_3$$
ral rubber is not formed in this way by the plant, isoprene can be polymerized to a product almost identical with natural rubber. Being linear polymers with short branches, these products are thermoplastic. However,

because double bonds are present, they can react with sulfur, which ties the chains together with disulfide linkages. This process is known as **vulcanization.** If only a few cross links are present, the molecules can be aligned and elongated to a considerable extent by stretching but cannot slip past one another. When the tension is removed, thermal agitation returns the molecules to their original random orientation (Fig. 31), thus accounting for the elastic properties. If a large number of cross links are formed, the product is a rigid solid, which is called **hard rubber** or **ebonite.**

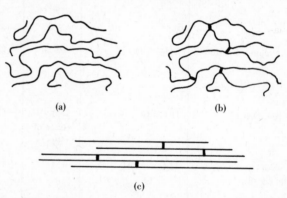

(a)   (b)

(c)

Figure 31.   Rubber molecules: (a) unvulcanized; (b) vulcanized but unstretched; (c) vulcanized and stretched.

Gutta-percha and **balata** are natural products that have the same constitution as rubber but are tough and hornlike. They differ from rubber only in that the double bonds have the *trans* configuration, whereas those in rubber have the *cis* configuration.

$$\left[\begin{array}{cc} -CH_2 & CH_2- \\ & C=C \\ CH_3 & H \end{array} \right]_x \qquad \left[\begin{array}{cc} -CH_2 & H \\ & C=C \\ CH_3 & CH_2- \end{array} \right]_x$$

Rubber   Gutta-percha or balata

The difficulty with most synthetic rubbers has been that they are hard to work and generate excessive heat when flexed rapidly (as in an automobile tire) because they have chiefly the *trans* configuration. The development of stereoselective catalysts has led to the production of *cis*-polyisoprene and *cis*-polybutadiene which have characteristics more closely resembling those of natural rubber.

Natural rubber has cis configuration, synthetics mostly trans

Although the term *synthetic rubber* is in common use, none is identical with natural rubber, even though *cis*-polyisoprene (NR) comes very close. However, many different synthetic products are made, each having its own characteristics, which frequently are superior to natural rubber for a particular purpose. Table 14 lists the more common synthetic rubbers available in 1961. SBR is the type produced in largest amount.

Stereoselective catalysts give cis synthetics

TABLE 14.   SYNTHETIC RUBBERS

TYPE	MONOMERS	REPEATING UNIT
cis-Butadiene	1,3-butadiene	$-CH_2CH=CHCH_2-$
NR	isoprene	$-CH_2CH=CCH_2-$ with CH_3
CR (neoprene)	2-chloro-1,3,- butadiene (chloroprene)	$-CH_2CH=CCH_2-$ with Cl
SBR (GRS, Buna-S)	styrene, 1,3- butadiene	$-CH_2CH(CH_2CH=CHCH_2)_6-$ 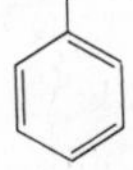 (phenyl)
NBR (GRN, Buna-N)	acrylonitrile, 1,3-butadiene	$-CH_2CHCH_2CH=CHCH_2-$ with CN
IIR (Butyl)	isobutylene, isoprene	$-CH_2CHCH_2CH_2CH=CHCH_2-$ with CH_3 and CH_3

CONDENSATION POLYMERS

Condensation polymers are those formed by a chemical reaction between two functional groups during which some small molecule, such as water or hydrogen chloride, is eliminated. For polymeric molecules to result, the monomers must be polyfunctional, that is, have two or more reactive groups. At each step of the reaction, the product still is polyfunctional, and the reaction can be repeated. Usually two different monomers, one of which contains one type of function and the other another type, react with each other, but different functions capable of reacting with each other may be present in the same molecule.

Union of monomers with loss of small molecule yields condensation polymers

If both monomers contain only two reactive functions, only a linear polymer can result. If one or both of the monomers contains three or more functional groups, cross linking can take place to yield an insoluble, infusible resin. Table 15 lists some of the more important condensation polymers.

Three or more functions in monomer permits cross linking

TABLE 15. CONDENSATION POLYMERS

NAME	MONOMERS	TYPE OF LINKAGE	REPEATING UNIT	CHIEF USE
Nylon 66	adipic acid and hexamethylene diamine	amide	$-CO(CH_2)_4CONH(CH_2)_6NH-$	fiber, molded articles
Dacron, terylene, cronar, mylar	terephthalic acid and ethylene glycol	ester	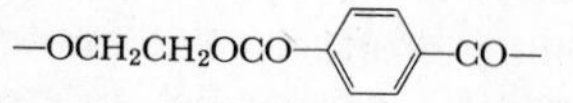 $-OCH_2CH_2OCO-$⟨benzene ring⟩$-CO-$	fiber, film
Glyptal	glycerol and phthalic anhydride	ester	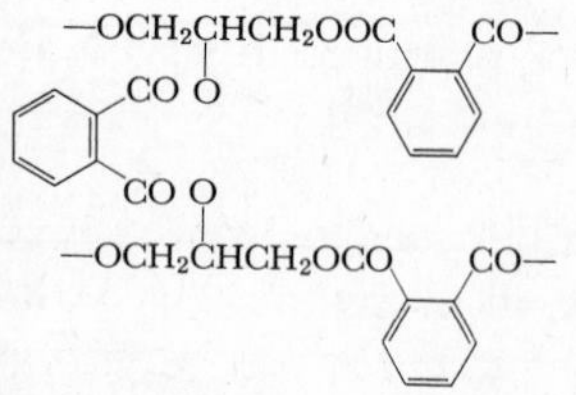 $-OCH_2CHCH_2OOC-$⟨ring⟩$-CO-$ with CO O / CO O and $-OCH_2CHCH_2OCO-$⟨ring⟩$-CO-$	protective coatings
Polycarbonates	bisphenol-A and phosgene, $(COCl_2)$	ester	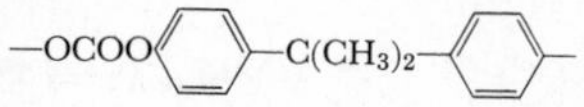 $-OCOO$⟨ring⟩$-C(CH_3)_2-$⟨ring⟩	molded articles
Epoxy resins (epoxies)	bisphenol-A and epichlorohydrin, 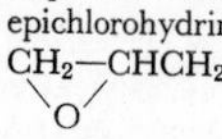 CH_2-CHCH_2Cl with O	ether	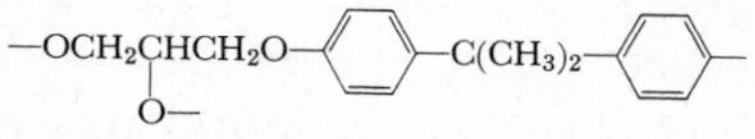 $-OCH_2CHCH_2O-$⟨ring⟩$-C(CH_3)_2-$⟨ring⟩ with $O-$	protective coatings and potting resins
Urethan rubbers and rigid foams	adipic acid, ethylene glycol, and tolylene di-isocyanate or	ester and amide	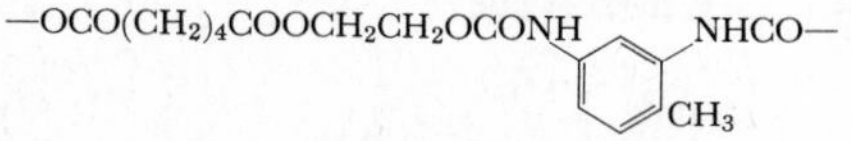 $-OCO(CH_2)_4COOCH_2CH_2OCONH-$⟨ring⟩$-NHCO-$ with CH_3	foamed rubbers and rigid foams
	poly(propylene glycol) and tolylene diisocyanate	ether, ester, and amide	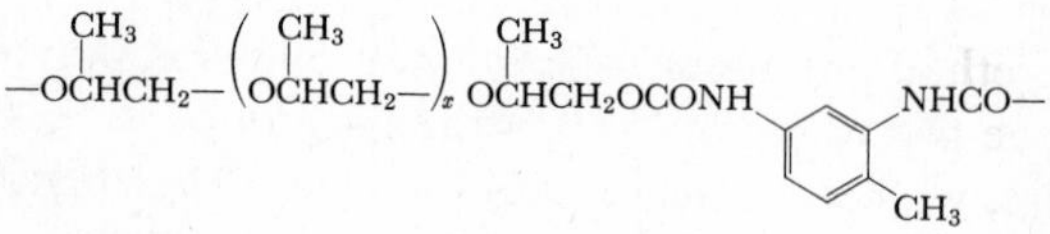 $-OCHCH_2-(OCHCH_2-)_x OCHCH_2OCONH-$⟨ring⟩$-NHCO-$ with CH_3 groups and CH_3	
Polysulfide rubbers (Thiokols)	ethylene chloride and sodium poly-sulfide	polysulfide	$-CH_2CH_2S_4-$	gaskets
Silicones	aryl or alkyl dichloro- or trichlorosilanes	silicon-oxygen	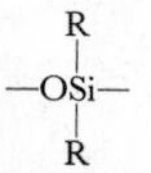 $-OSi-$ with R above and R below	oils, resins, rubbers
Phenol-form-aldehyde	phenol and formaldehyde	carbon-carbon	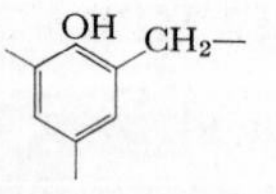 ⟨ring with OH⟩CH_2-	molded articles laminating resins, adhesives
Urea-form-aldehyde	urea and formaldehyde	carbon-nitrogen, amide	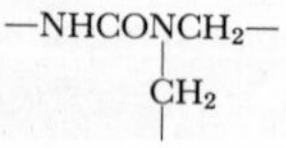 $-NHCONCH_2-$ with CH_2	molded articles laminating adhesives
Melamine-formaldehyde	melamine and formaldehyde	carbon-nitrogen	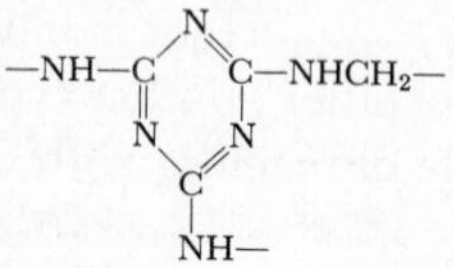 $-NH-C$⟨triazine ring with N⟩$C-NHCH_2-$ with $NH-$	dinner ware

Special consideration may be given to a few of these polymers. The glyptal resins are **baking enamels**, i.e., thermosetting polymers. The first-stage resin is essentially a linear polymer containing free hydroxyl and carboxyl groups, which is soluble in organic solvents. When a film of this polymer is heated (*baked*), the esterification is completed, which cross links the chains and gives a solid film. Glyptal is only one member of a large class of protective coatings known as **alkyd resins.** In addition to phthalic anhydride and glycerol, other dibasic acids such as isophthalic, maleic, adipic, and succinic acids, and other polyhydric alcohols such as pentaerythritol may be used to modify the properties of the resin. If acids from drying oils are incorporated, polymerization of the unsaturated acids also occurs during the baking process.

Alkyd resins as protective coatings

The **polyester resins** result from an alkyd resin, usually prepared from maleic anhydride, adipic acid and propylene glycol, dissolved in 30 per cent of its weight of styrene. Just prior to use, a peroxide catalyst and a cobalt or manganese promoter is added. Copolymerization of the maleic units with the styrene then takes place at room temperature or above to give a solid product. Polyester resins are used as a binding agent for glass fiber in the manufacture of boat hulls, automobile fenders, and fishing rods. The liquid also may be cast or used as a potting agent for small parts.

Polyester, epoxy, and urethan polymers

The **epoxy resins** are sold as essentially linear polymers of relatively low molecular weight with an excess of oxide rings at the ends of the chains. Addition of an amine or a dibasic acid catalyzes cross linking and tying together of the ends of the chains to give the final product of high molecular weight.

The **urethan polymers** are formed by allowing polyesters of adipic acid and ethylene glycol having end hydroxyl groups to react with an arylene diisocyanate, which ties the ends of the chains together.

$$-CH_2OH + O{=}C{=}N{-}Ar{-}N{=}C{=}O + HOCH_2{-} \longrightarrow$$
$$-CH_2OCONHArNHCOOCH_2{-}$$

If water is added simultaneously, the intermediate carbamic acid loses carbon dioxide, which converts the mass to a foam. The resulting amino groups still can react with isocyanate groups to permit tying the ends together.

$$-CH_2OH + O{=}C{=}N{-}Ar{-}N{=}C{=}O + H_2O \longrightarrow$$
$$-CH_2OCONHArNHCOOH \longrightarrow -CH_2OCONHArNH_2 + CO_2$$
$$-CH_2OCONHArNH_2 + O{=}C{=}N{-}Ar{-}N{=}C{=}O + HOCH_2{-} \longrightarrow$$
$$-CH_2OCONHArNHCONHArNHCOOCH_2{-}$$

The **silicones** are formed by the hydrolysis of alkyl or aryl dichloro- or trichlorosilanes. If dichlorosilanes are used, only linear polymers are formed, which are liquids.

Silicones are heat-resistant

$$R_2SiCl_2 + H_2O \longrightarrow HO{-}Si(R_2){-}Cl$$
$$x\,HO{-}Si(R_2){-}Cl + H_2O \longrightarrow HO{-}[Si(R_2){-}O{-}]_xH + x\,HCl$$

If trichlorosilanes are present, cross linking and solidification takes place. The silicones are characterized by their stability at relatively high temperatures.

Phenol-, urea-, and melamine-formaldehyde polymers are thermosetting plastics

The **phenol-formaldehyde, urea-formaldehyde,** and **melamine-form-aldehyde resins** are thermosetting. The first-stage resins are linear polymers that still contain open *ortho* or *para* positions in the benzene ring or groups that can react with more formaldehyde. They can be mixed with fillers and pigments and an additional amount of paraformaldehyde or a reaction product of formaldehyde and ammonia known as hexamethylenetetramine, $(CH_2)_6N_4$. When the mixture is heated, it first flows and then sets to a rigid solid as cross linking of the chains takes place.

SUMMARY

1. Polymers are very large molecules that may be considered as being made up of many small units of low molecular weight. Polymeric molecules frequently are referred to as macro-molecules.

2. Proteins, starch, cellulose, and rubber are the most important of the naturally occurring polymers. The units in proteins are amino acid residues, $-NH-CHR-CO-$; in starch and cellulose they are glucose residues, $-CH(CHOH)_2CH-O-$; and

$$HOCH_2CH\text{————}O$$

in rubber they are isoprene residues, $-CH_2-CH=C-CH_2-$.
$$\underset{CH_3}{|}$$

3. Synthetic polymers may be made by a process called polymerization. Polymerization may take place by addition of monomers to each other without the formation of any other compound to give addition polymers, or by condensation of monomers in which some small molecule such as water is eliminated to give condensation polymers. Occasionally polymers result from both addition and condensation.

4. Polymers that can be molded into useful objects, spun into threads, or used as the vehicle for protective coatings are called synthetic plastics and resins. The synthetic plastics may be thermoplastic (flow when subjected to heat and pressure and solidify on cooling) or thermosetting (flow when subjected to heat and pressure but then undergo a secondary reaction that ties the chains together by cross links which cause the plastic to set to an insoluble, infusible product).

5. Linear polymers of sufficiently high molecular weight (above 10,000) without protruding groups frequently can be drawn into threads to give useful synthetic fibers. Examples are the nylons, which are polyamides, the glycol terephthalates such as Dacron, and the acrylic fibers such as Orlon and Acrilan.

6. If groups protrude from the sides of the chains, thus preventing sufficiently close alignment of the molecules to give a fiber, the product may have rubber-like properties. Examples are natural rubber, SBR, and butyl rubber. If the chains are linked together at a few points, a process called vulcanization, the mass can be elongated, but the chains cannot slip past one another. When the tension is released, thermal agitation brings the mass to its original condition. The cross linking thus confers elastic properties on the product.

7. Highly cross-linked polymers are infusible and insoluble in organic solvents. They may be hard and tough or hard and brittle.

8. Highly cross-linked polymers that contain sulfonic acid groups are cation-exchange resins, and those that contain quaternary ammonium groups are anion-exchange resins.

EXERCISES

1. Describe the three main types of attractive forces between molecules that are grouped together under the term van der Waals forces.
2. Write equations showing: (a) the steps in the conversion of styrene into polystyrene; (b) of poly(vinyl acetate) to poly(vinyl alcohol) by saponification; (c) of poly(vinyl alcohol) to poly(vinyl butyral) by reaction with n-butyraldehyde.
3. Write equations for: (a) the acid hydrolysis of nylon 66; (b) the saponification of Dacron.
4. Which of the common synthetic rubbers are : (a) homopolymers; (b) copolymers?
5. Which of the addition polymers in Table 13 would be expected to react fairly readily with: (a) aqueous or alcoholic mineral acids; (b) aqueous or alcoholic sodium hydroxide? Support your answers by giving equations for the reactions expected to take place.
6. Which of the condensation polymers listed in Table 15 contain: (a) ester linkages; (b) amide linkages; (c) ether linkages; (d) elements other than carbon, hydrogen, oxygen, and nitrogen?

INDEX

Don S. Pate
136 E. Bennett